EIGHT COUSINS

LOUISA MAY ALCOTT (1832–1888) was born in Pennsylvania and grew up in Boston and Concord, Massachusetts. Her father, Bronson Alcott, was a prominent educator, philosopher, and author, whose ideas, however, were not widely popular. While Louisa and her three sisters were growing up, Bronson Alcott's utopian community and the school based on his radical educational theories, were failing.

By her mid-teens, Louisa had to find a way to supplement the family income. She wrote and sold stories to magazines. She penned melodramatic plots for cheap paperback novels. In 1863, she published the widely acclaimed *Hospital Sketches*, based on her experiences as a Union nurse in the Civil War. Louisa May Alcott is best known for *Little Women*, her novel about the March family, which was published in 1868 with great success.

Eight Cousins (1875) and its sequel, *Rose in Bloom* (1876), show the same richness of imagination and attention to detail as *Little Women*. They have the same ability to move readers to laughter and tears. In *Eight Cousins*, when Rose

Campbell is orphaned, she is sent to the "Aunt Hill" to live with her six aunts and—even worse—seven rowdy boy cousins. Rose's guardian, the idealist Uncle Alec, may be partly modeled on Bronson Alcott. *Rose in Bloom* tells the story of Rose as a young adult, discovering the wider world—and falling in love.

Louisa May Alcott took an active part in the women's suffrage and temperance movements. She died in 1888, two days after the death of her father.

Other Puffin Classics by Louisa May Alcott

EIGHT COUSINS
OR
THE AUNT HILL

LOUISA MAY ALCOTT

PUFFIN

PUFFIN BOOKS

Published by Penguin Group

Penguin Young Readers Group, 345 Hudson Street, New York, New York 10014, U.S.A.

Penguin Books Ltd, 80 Strand, London WC2R ORL, England

Penguin Books Australia Ltd, 250 Camberwell Road, Camberwell, Victoria 3124, Australia

Penguin Books Canada Ltd, 10 Alcorn Avenue, Toronto, Ontario, Canada M4V 3B2

Penguin Books (N.Z.) Ltd, 182-190 Wairau Road, Auckland 10, New Zealand

First published by Roberts Brothers, 1875
Published in Puffin Books, 1989
Reissued in Puffin Books, 1995
Reissued in Puffin Books, a division of Penguin Young Readers Group, 2004

28 29 30

THE LIBRARY OF CONGRESS HAS CATALOGED THE EARLIER PUFFIN EDITION
UNDER CATALOG CARD NUMBER 89-61293

This edition ISBN: 0-14-037456-6

Printed in the United States of America

To

The many boys & girls
whose letters it has been
impossible to answer,
this book is dedicated
as a peace offering
by their friend

L. M. Alcott

PREFACE

The Author is quite aware of the defects of this little story, many of which were unavoidable, as it first appeared serially. But, as Uncle Alec's experiment was intended to amuse the young folks, rather than suggest educational improvements for the consideration of the elders, she trusts that these short-comings will be overlooked by the friends of the EIGHT COUSINS, and she will try to make amends in a second volume, which shall attempt to show THE ROSE IN BLOOM.

—L. M. A.

CONTENTS

CONTENTS

1
Two Girls

Rose sat all alone in the big best parlor, with her little handkerchief laid ready to catch the first tear, for she was thinking of her troubles, and a shower was expected. She had retired to this room as a good place in which to be miserable; for it was dark and still, full of ancient furniture, sombre curtains, and hung all round with portraits of solemn old gentlemen in wigs, severe-nosed ladies in top-heavy caps, and staring children in little bob-tailed coats or short-waisted frocks. It *was* an excellent place for woe; and the fitful spring rain that pattered on the window-pane seemed to sob, "Cry away: I'm with you."

Rose really did have some cause to be sad; for she had no mother, and had lately lost her father also, which left her no home but this with her great aunts. She had been with them only a week, and though the dear old ladies had tried their best to make her happy, they had not succeeded very well, for she was unlike any child they had ever seen, and they felt very much as if they had the care of a low-spirited butterfly.

They had given her the freedom of the house,

and for a day or two she had amused herself roaming all over it, for it was a capital old mansion, and was full of all manner of odd nooks, charming rooms, and mysterious passages. Windows broke out in unexpected places, little balconies overhung the garden most romantically, and there was a long upper hall full of curiosities from all parts of the world; for the Campbells had been sea-captains for generations.

Aunt Plenty had even allowed Rose to rummage in her great china closet,—a spicy retreat, rich in all the "goodies" that children love; but Rose seemed to care little for these toothsome temptations; and when that hope failed, Aunt Plenty gave up in despair.

Gentle Aunt Peace had tried all sorts of pretty needle-work, and planned a doll's wardrobe that would have won the heart of even an older child. But Rose took little interest in pink satin hats and tiny hose, though she sewed dutifully till her aunt caught her wiping tears away with the train of a wedding-dress, and that discovery put an end to the sewing society.

Then both old ladies put their heads together and picked out the model child of the neighborhood to come and play with their niece. But Annabel Bliss was the worst failure of all, for Rose could not bear the sight of her, and said she was so like a wax doll she longed to give her a pinch and see if she would squeak. So prim little Annabel was sent home, and the exhausted aunties left Rose to her own devices for a day or two.

Bad weather and a cold kept her in-doors, and she spent most of her time in the library where her father's books were stored. Here she read a great deal, cried a little, and dreamed many of the innocent bright dreams in which imaginative children find such comfort and delight. This suited her better than any thing else, but it was not good for her, and she grew pale, heavy-eyed, and listless, though Aunt Plenty gave her iron enough to make a cooking-stove, and Aunt Peace petted her like a poodle.

Seeing this, the poor aunties racked their brains for a new amusement, and determined to venture a bold stroke, though not very hopeful of its success. They said nothing to Rose about their plan for this Saturday afternoon, but let her alone till the time came for the grand surprise, little dreaming that the odd child would find pleasure for herself in a most unexpected quarter.

Before she had time to squeeze out a single tear a sound broke the stillness, making her prick up her ears. It was only the soft twitter of a bird, but it seemed to be a peculiarly gifted bird, for while she listened the soft twitter changed to a lively whistle, then a trill, a coo, a chirp, and ended in a musical mixture of all the notes, as if the bird burst out laughing. Rose laughed also, and, forgetting her woes, jumped up, saying eagerly,—

"It is a mocking-bird. Where is it?"

Running down the long hall, she peeped out at both doors, but saw nothing feathered except a draggle-tailed chicken under a burdock leaf. She listened again, and the sound seemed to be in the house. Away she went, much excited by the chase, and following the changeful song it led her to the china-closet door.

"In there? How funny!" she said. But when she entered, not a bird appeared except the everlastingly kissing swallows on the Canton china that lined the shelves. All of a sudden Rose's face brightened, and, softly opening the slide, she peered into the kitchen. But the music had stopped, and all she saw was a girl in a blue apron scrubbing the hearth. Rose stared about her for a minute, and then asked abruptly,—

"Did you hear that mocking-bird?"

"I should call it a phebe-bird," answered the girl, looking up with a twinkle in her black eyes.

"Where did it go?"

"It is here still."

"Where?"

"In my throat. Do you want to hear it?"

"Oh, yes! I'll come in." And Rose crept through the slide to the wide shelf on the other side, being too hurried and puzzled to go round by the door.

The girl wiped her hands, crossed her feet on the little island of carpet where she was stranded in a sea of soap-suds, and then, sure enough, out of her slender throat came the swallow's twitter, the robin's whistle, the blue-jay's call, the thrush's song, the wood-dove's coo, and many another familiar note, all ending as before with the musical ecstasy of a bobolink singing and swinging among the meadow grass on a bright June day.

Rose was so astonished that she nearly fell off her perch, and when the little concert was over clapped her hands delightedly.

"Oh, it was lovely! Who taught you?"

"The birds," answered the girl, with a smile, as she fell to work again.

"It is very wonderful! I can sing, but nothing half so fine as that. What is your name, please?"

"Phebe Moore."

"I've heard of phebe-birds; but I don't believe the real ones could do that," laughed Rose, adding, as she watched with interest the scattering of dabs of soft soap over the bricks, "May I stay and see you work? It is very lonely in the parlor."

"Yes, indeed, if you want to," answered Phebe, wringing out her cloth in a capable sort of way that impressed Rose very much.

"It must be fun to swash the water round and dig out the soap. I'd love to do it, only aunt wouldn't like it, I suppose," said Rose, quite taken with the new employment.

"You'd soon get tired, so you'd better keep tidy and look on."

"I suppose you help your mother a good deal?"

"I haven't got any folks."

"Why, where do you live, then?"

"I'm going to live here, I hope. Debby wants

some one to help round, and I've come to try for a week."

"I hope you *will* stay, for it is very dull," said Rose, who had taken a sudden fancy to this girl, who sung like a bird and worked like a woman.

"Hope I shall; for I'm fifteen now, and old enough to earn my own living. You have come to stay a spell, haven't you?" asked Phebe, looking up at her guest and wondering how life *could* be dull to a girl who wore a silk frock, a daintily frilled apron, a pretty locket, and had her hair tied up with a velvet snood.

"Yes, I shall stay till my uncle comes. He is my guardian now, and I don't know what he will do with me. Have you a guardian?"

"My sakes, no! I was left on the poor-house steps a little mite of a baby, and Miss Rogers took a liking to me, so I've been there ever since. But she is dead now, and I take care of myself."

"How interesting! It is like Arabella Montgomery in the 'Gypsy's Child.' Did you ever read that sweet story?" asked Rose, who was fond of tales of foundlings, and had read many.

"I don't have any books to read, and all the spare time I get I run off into the woods; that rests me better than stories," answered Phebe, as she finished one job and began on another.

Rose watched her as she got out a great pan of beans to look over, and wondered how it would seem to have life all work and no play. Presently

Phebe seemed to think it was her turn to ask questions, and said, wistfully,—

"You've had lots of schooling, I suppose?"

"Oh, dear me, yes! I've been at boarding-school nearly a year, and I'm almost dead with lessons. The more I got, the more Miss Power gave me, and I was so miserable I 'most cried my eyes out. Papa never gave me hard things to do, and he always taught me so pleasantly I loved to study. Oh, we were *so* happy and so fond of one another! But now he is gone, and I am left all alone."

The tear that would not come when Rose sat waiting for it came now of its own accord,—two of them in fact,—and rolled down her cheeks, telling the tale of love and sorrow better than any words could do it.

For a minute there was no sound in the kitchen but the little daughter's sobbing and the sympathetic patter of the rain. Phebe stopped rattling her beans from one pan to the other, and her eyes were full of pity as they rested on the curly head bent down on Rose's knee, for she saw that the heart under the pretty locket ached with its loss, and the dainty apron was used to dry sadder tears than any she had ever shed.

Somehow, she felt more contented with her brown calico gown and blue-checked pinafore; envy changed to compassion; and if she had dared she would have gone and hugged her afflicted guest.

Fearing that might not be considered proper, she said, in her cheery voice,—

"I'm sure you ain't all alone with such a lot of folks belonging to you, and all so rich and clever. You'll be petted to pieces, Debby says, because you are the only girl in the family."

Phebe's last words made Rose smile in spite of her tears, and she looked out from behind her apron with an April face, saying in a tone of comic distress,—

"That's one of my troubles! I've got six aunts, and they all want me, and I don't know any of them very well. Papa named this place the Aunt-hill, and now I see why."

Phebe laughed with her as she said encouragingly,—

"Every one calls it so, and it's a real good name, for all the Mrs. Campbells live handy by, and keep coming up to see the old ladies."

"I could stand the aunts, but there are dozens of cousins, dreadful boys all of them, and I detest boys! Some of them came to see me last Wednesday, but I was lying down, and when auntie came to call me I went under the quilt and pretended to be asleep. I shall *have* to see them some time, but I do dread it so." And Rose gave a shudder, for, having lived alone with her invalid father, she knew nothing of boys, and considered them a species of wild animal.

"Oh! I guess you'll like 'em. I've seen 'em flying round when they come over from the Point, sometimes in their boats and sometimes on horse-back. If you like boats and horses, you'll enjoy yourself first-rate."

"But I don't! I'm afraid of horses, and boats make me ill, and I *hate* boys!" And poor Rose wrung her hands at the awful prospect before her. One of these horrors alone she could have borne, but all together were too much for her, and she began to think of a speedy return to the detested school.

Phebe laughed at her woe till the beans danced in the pan, but tried to comfort her by suggesting a means of relief.

"Perhaps your uncle will take you away where there ain't any boys. Debby says he is a real kind man, and always brings heaps of nice things when he comes."

"Yes, but you see that is another trouble, for I don't know Uncle Alec at all. He hardly ever came to see us, though he sent me pretty things very often. Now I belong to him, and shall have to mind him, till I am eighteen. I may not like him a bit, and I fret about it all the time."

"Well, I wouldn't borrow trouble, but have a real good time. I'm sure I should think I was in clover if I had folks and money, and nothing to do but enjoy myself," began Phebe, but got no fur-ther, for a sudden rush and rumble outside made them both jump.

"It's thunder," said Phebe.

"It's a circus!" cried Rose, who from her elevated

perch had caught glimpses of a gay cart of some sort and several ponies with flying manes and tails.

The sound died away, and the girls were about to continue their confidences when old Debby appeared, looking rather cross and sleepy after her nap.

"You are wanted in the parlor, Miss Rose."

"Has anybody come?"

"Little girls shouldn't ask questions, but do as they are bid," was all Debby would answer.

"I do hope it isn't Aunt Myra; she always scares me out of my wits asking how my cough is, and groaning over me as if I was going to die," said Rose, preparing to retire the way she came, for the slide, being cut for the admission of bouncing Christmas turkeys and puddings, was plenty large enough for a slender girl.

"Guess you'll wish it *was* Aunt Myra when you see who has come. Don't never let me catch you coming into my kitchen that way again, or I'll shut you up in the big biler," growled Debby, who thought it her duty to snub children on all occasions.

THE CLAN

Rose scrambled into the china-closet as rapidly as possible, and there refreshed herself by making faces at Debby, while she settled her plumage and screwed up her courage. Then she crept softly down the hall and peeped into the parlor. No one appeared, and all was so still she felt sure the company was upstairs. So she skipped boldly through the half-open folding-doors, to behold on the other side a sight that nearly took her breath away.

Seven boys stood in a row,—all ages, all sizes, all yellow-haired and blue-eyed, all in full Scotch costume, and all smiling, nodding, and saying as with one voice, "How are you, cousin?"

Rose gave a little gasp and looked wildly about her as if ready to fly, for fear magnified the seven and the room seemed full of boys. Before she could run, however, the tallest lad stepped out of the line, saying pleasantly,—

"Don't be frightened. This is the clan come to welcome you; and I'm the chief, Archie, at your service."

He held out his hand as he spoke, and Rose timidly put her own into a brown paw, which closed over the white morsel and held it as the chief continued his introductions.

"We came in full rig, for we always turn out in style on grand occasions. Hope you like it. Now I'll tell you who these chaps are, and then we shall be all right. This big one is Prince Charlie, Aunt Clara's boy. She has but one, so he is an extra good one. This old fellow is Mac, the bookworm, called Worm for short. This sweet creature is Steve the Dandy. Look at his gloves and topknot, if you please. They are Aunt Jane's lads, and a precious pair you'd better believe. These are the Brats, my brothers, Geordie and Will, and Jamie the Baby. Now, my men, step out and show your manners."

At this command, to Rose's great dismay, six more hands were offered, and it was evident that she was expected to shake them *all*. It was a trying moment to the bashful child; but, remembering that they were her kinsmen come to welcome her, she tried her best to return the greeting cordially.

This impressive ceremony being over, the clan broke ranks, and both rooms instantly appeared to be pervaded with boys. Rose hastily retired to the shelter of a big chair and sat there watching the invaders and wondering when her aunt would come and rescue her.

As if bound to do their duty manfully, yet rather oppressed by it, each lad paused beside her chair in his wanderings, made a brief remark, received a still briefer answer, and then sheered off with a relieved expression.

Archie came first, and, leaning over the chair-back, observed in a paternal tone,—

"I'm glad you've come, cousin, and I hope you'll find the Aunt-hill pretty jolly."

"I think I shall."

Mac shook his hair out of his eyes, stumbled over a stool, and asked abruptly,—

"Did you bring any books with you?"

"Four boxes full. They are in the library."

Mac vanished from the room, and Steve, striking an attitude which displayed his costume effectively, said with an affable smile,—

"We were sorry not to see you last Wednesday. I hope your cold is better."

"Yes, thank you." And a smile began to dimple about Rose's mouth as she remembered her retreat under the bed-cover.

Feeling that he had been received with distinguished marks of attention, Steve strolled away with his top-knot higher than ever, and Prince Charlie pranced across the room, saying in a free and easy tone,—

"Mamma sent her love and hopes you will be well enough to come over for a day next week. It must be desperately dull here for a little thing like you."

"I'm thirteen and a half, though I *do* look small," cried Rose, forgetting her shyness in indignation at this insult to her newly acquired teens.

"Beg pardon, ma'am; never should have guessed it." And Charlie went off with a laugh, glad to have struck a spark out of his meek cousin.

Geordie and Will came together, two sturdy eleven and twelve year olders, and, fixing their round blue eyes on Rose, fired off a question apiece as if it was a shooting match and she the target.

"Did you bring your monkey?"

"No; he is dead."

"Are you going to have a boat?"

"I hope not."

Here the two, with a right-about-face movement, abruptly marched away, and little Jamie demanded with childish frankness,—

"Did you bring me any thing nice?"

"Yes, lots of candy," answered Rose, whereupon Jamie ascended into her lap with a sounding kiss and the announcement that he liked her very much.

This proceeding rather startled Rose, for the other lads looked and laughed, and in her confusion she said hastily to the young usurper,—

"Did you see the circus go by?"

"When? Where?" cried all the boys in great excitement at once.

"Just before you came. At least I thought it was a circus, for I saw a red and black sort of cart and ever so many little ponies, and—"

She got no farther, for a general shout made her pause suddenly, as Archie explained the joke by saying in the middle of his laugh,—

"It was our new dog-cart and the Shetland ponies. You'll never hear the last of your circus, cousin."

"But there were so many, and they went so fast, and the cart was so very red," began Rose, trying to explain her mistake.

"Come and see them all!" cried the Prince. And before she knew what was happening she was borne away to the barn and tumultuously introduced to three shaggy ponies and the gay new dog-cart.

She had never visited these regions before, and had her doubts as to the propriety of her being there now, but when she suggested that "Auntie might not like it," there was a general cry of,—

"She told us to amuse you, and we can do it ever so much better out here than poking round in the house."

"I'm afraid I shall get cold without my sacque," began Rose, who wanted to stay, but felt rather out of her element.

"No, you won't! We'll fix you," cried the lads, as one clapped his cap on her head, another tied a rough jacket round her neck by the sleeves, a third nearly smothered her in a carriage blanket, and a fourth threw open the door of the old barouche that stood there, saying with a flourish,—

"Step in, ma'am, and make yourself comfortable while we show you some fun."

So Rose sat in state enjoying herself very much, for the lads proceeded to dance a Highland Fling with a spirit and skill that made her clap her hands and laugh as she had not done for weeks.

"How is that, my lassie?" asked the Prince, coming

up all flushed and breathless when the ballet was over.

"It was splendid! I never went to the theatre but once, and the dancing was not half so pretty as this. What clever boys you must be!" said Rose, smiling upon her kinsmen like a little queen upon her subjects.

"Ah, we're a fine lot, and that is only the beginning of our larks. We haven't got the pipes here or we'd

'Sing for you, play for you
A dulcy melody.' "

answered Charlie, looking much elated at her praise.

"I did not know we were Scotch; papa never said any thing about it, or seemed to care about Scotland, except to have me sing the old ballads," said Rose, beginning to feel as if she had left America behind her somewhere.

"Neither did we till lately. We've been reading Scott's novels, and all of a sudden we remembered that our grandfather was a Scotchman. So we hunted up the old stories, got a bagpipe, put on our plaids, and went in, heart and soul, for the glory of the clan. We've been at it some time now, and it's great fun. Our people like it, and I think we are a pretty canny set."

Archie said this from the other coach-step, where he had perched, while the rest climbed up before and behind to join in the chat as they rested.

"I'm Fitzjames and he's Roderick Dhu, and we'll give you the broadsword combat some day. It's a great thing, you'd better believe," added the Prince.

"Yes, and you should hear Steve play the pipes. He makes 'em skirl like a good one," cried Will from the box, eager to air the accomplishments of his race.

"Mac's the fellow to hunt up the old stories and tell us how to dress right, and pick out rousing bits for us to speak and sing," put in Geordie, saying a good word for the absent Worm.

"And what do you and Will do?" asked Rose of Jamie, who sat beside her as if bound to keep her in sight till the promised gift had been handed over.

"Oh, I'm the little foot-page, and do errands, and Will and Geordie are the troops when we march, and the stags when we hunt, and the traitors when we want to cut any heads off."

"They are very obliging, I'm sure," said Rose, whereat the "utility men" beamed with modest pride, and resolved to enact Wallace and Montrose as soon as possible for their cousin's special benefit.

"Let's have a game of tag," cried the Prince, swinging himself up to a beam with a sounding slap on Stevie's shoulder.

Regardless of his gloves, Dandy tore after him,

and the rest swarmed in every direction as if bent on breaking their necks and dislocating their joints as rapidly as possible.

It was a new and astonishing spectacle to Rose, fresh from a prim boarding-school, and she watched the active lads with breathless interest, thinking their antics far superior to those of Mops, the dear departed monkey.

Will had just covered himself with glory by pitching off of a high loft head first and coming up all right, when Phebe appeared with a cloak, hood, and rubbers, also a message from Aunt Plenty that "Miss Rose was to come in directly."

"All right; we'll bring her!" answered Archie, issuing some mysterious order, which was so promptly obeyed that, before Rose could get out of the carriage, the boys had caught hold of the pole and rattled her out of the barn, round the oval and up to the front door with a cheer that brought two caps to an upper window, and caused Debby to cry aloud from the back porch,—

"Them harum-scarum boys will certainly be the death of that delicate little creter!"

But the "delicate little creter" seemed all the better for her trip, and ran up the steps looking rosy, gay, and dishevelled, to be received with lamentation by Aunt Plenty, who begged her to go and lie down at once.

"Oh, please don't! We have come to tea with our cousin, and we'll be as good as gold if you'll let us stay, auntie," clamored the boys, who not only approved of "our cousin," but had no mind to lose their tea, for Aunt Plenty's name but feebly expressed her bountiful nature.

"Well, dears, you can; only be quiet, and let Rose go and take her iron and be made tidy, and then we will see what we can find for supper," said the old lady as she trotted away, followed by a volley of directions for the approaching feast.

"Marmalade for me, auntie."

"Plenty of plum-cake, please."

"Tell Debby to trot out the baked pears."

"I'm your man for lemon-pie, ma'am."

"Do have fritters; Rose will like 'em."

"She'd rather have tarts, *I* know."

When Rose came down, fifteen minutes later, with every curl smoothed and her most beruffled apron on, she found the boys loafing about the long hall, and paused on the half-way landing to take an observation, for till now she had not really examined her new-found cousins.

There was a strong family resemblance among them, though some of the yellow heads were darker than others, some of the cheeks brown instead of rosy, and the ages varied all the way from sixteen-year-old Archie to Jamie, who was ten years younger. None of them were especially comely but the Prince, yet all were hearty, happy-looking lads, and Rose decided that boys were not as dreadful as she had expected to find them.

They were all so characteristically employed that she could not help smiling as she looked. Archie and Charlie, evidently great cronies, were pacing up and down, shoulder to shoulder, whistling "Bonnie Dundee;" Mac was reading in a corner, with his book close to his near-sighted eyes; Dandy was arranging his hair before the oval glass in the hat-stand; Geordie and Will investigating the internal economy of the moon-faced clock; and Jamie lay kicking up his heels on the mat at the foot of the stairs, bent on demanding his sweeties the instant Rose appeared.

She guessed his intention, and forestalled his demand by dropping a handful of sugar-plums down upon him.

At his cry of rapture the other lads looked up and smiled involuntarily, for the little kinswoman standing there above was a winsome sight with her shy, soft eyes, bright hair, and laughing face. The black frock reminded them of her loss, and filled the boyish hearts with a kindly desire to be good to "our cousin," who had no longer any home but this.

"There she is, as fine as you please," cried Steve, kissing his hand to her.

"Come on, Missy; tea is ready," added the Prince encouragingly.

"*I* shall take her in." And Archie offered his arm with great dignity, an honor that made Rose turn as red as a cherry and long to run upstairs again.

It was a merry supper, and the two elder boys added much to the fun by tormenting the rest with dark hints of some interesting event which was about to occur. Something uncommonly fine they declared it was, but enveloped in the deepest mystery for the present.

"Did I ever see it?" asked Jamie.

"Not to remember it; but Mac and Steve have, and liked it immensely," answered Archie, thereby causing the two mentioned to neglect Debby's delectable fritters for several minutes, while they cudgelled their brains.

"Who will have it first?" asked Will, with his mouth full of marmalade.

"Aunt Plenty, I guess."

"When will she have it?" demanded Geordie, bouncing in his seat with impatience.

"Sometime on Monday."

"Heart alive! what is the boy talking about?" cried the old lady from behind the tall urn, which left little to be seen but the topmost bow of her cap.

"Doesn't auntie know?" asked a chorus of voices.

"No; and that's the best of the joke, for she is desperately fond of it."

"What color is it?" asked Rose, joining in the fun.

"Blue and brown."

"Is it good to eat?" asked Jamie.

"Some people think so, but I shouldn't like to try it," answered Charlie, laughing so he spilt his tea.

"Who does it belong to?" put in Steve.

Archie and the Prince stared at one another

rather blankly for a minute, then Archie answered with a twinkle of the eye that made Charlie explode again,—

"To Grandfather Campbell."

This was a poser, and they gave up the puzzle, though Jamie confided to Rose that he did not think he could live till Monday without knowing what this remarkable thing was.

Soon after tea the clan departed, singing "All the blue bonnets are over the border" at the tops of their voices.

"Well, dear, how do you like your cousins?" asked Aunt Plenty, as the last pony frisked round the corner and the din died away.

"Pretty well, ma'am; but I like Phebe better." An answer which caused Aunt Plenty to hold up her hands in despair and trot away to tell sister Peace that she never *should* understand that child, and it was a mercy Alec was coming soon to take the responsibility off their hands.

Fatigued by the unusual exertions of the afternoon, Rose curled herself up in the sofa corner to rest and think about the great mystery, little guessing that she was to know it first of all.

Right in the middle of her meditations, she fell asleep and dreamed she was at home again in her own little bed. She seemed to wake and see her father bending over her; to hear him say, "My little Rose;" to answer, "Yes, papa;" and then to feel him take her in his arms and kiss her tenderly. So sweet, so real was the dream, that she started up with a cry of joy to find herself in the arms of a brown, bearded man, who held her close, and whispered in a voice so like her father's that she clung to him involuntarily,—

"This is my little girl, and I am Uncle Alec."

3

UNCLES

When Rose woke next morning, she was not sure whether she had dreamed what occurred the night before, or it had actually happened. So she hopped up and dressed, although it was an hour earlier than she usually rose, for she could not sleep any more, being possessed with a strong desire to slip down and see if the big portmanteau and packing-cases were really in the hall. She seemed to remember tumbling over them when she went to bed, for the aunts had sent her off very punctually, because they wanted their pet nephew all to themselves.

The sun was shining, and Rose opened her window to let in the soft May air fresh from the sea. As she leaned over her little balcony, watching an early bird get the worm, and wondering how she should like Uncle Alec, she saw a man leap the garden wall and come whistling up the path. At first she thought it was some trespasser, but a second look showed her that it was her uncle returning from an early dip into the sea. She had hardly dared to look at him the night before, because whenever she tried to do so she always found a pair of keen blue eyes looking at her. Now she could take a good stare at him as he lingered along, looking about him as if glad to see the old place again.

A brown, breezy man, in a blue jacket, with no hat on the curly head which he shook now and then like a water-dog; broad-shouldered, alert in his motions, and with a general air of strength and stability about him which pleased Rose, though she could not explain the feeling of comfort it gave her. She had just said to herself, with a sense of relief, "I guess I *shall* like him, though he looks as if he made people mind," when he lifted his eyes to examine the budding horse-chestnut overhead, and saw the eager face peering down at him. He waved his hand to her, nodded, and called out in a bluff, cheery voice,—

"You are on deck early, little niece."

"I got up to see if you had really come, uncle."

"Did you? Well, come down here and make sure of it."

"I'm not allowed to go out before breakfast, sir."

"Oh, indeed!" with a shrug. "Then I'll come aboard and salute," he added; and, to Rose's great amazement, Uncle Alec went up one of the pillars of the back piazza hand over hand, stepped across the roof, and swung himself into her balcony, saying, as he landed on the wide balustrade: "Have you any doubts about me now, ma'am?"

Rose was so taken aback, she could only answer with a smile as she went to meet him.

"How does my girl do this morning?" he asked,

taking the little cold hand she gave him in both his big warm ones.

"Pretty well, thank you, sir."

"Ah, but it should be *very well*. Why isn't it?"

"I always wake up with a headache, and feel tired."

"Don't you sleep well?"

"I lie awake a long time, and then I dream, and my sleep does not seem to rest me much."

"What do you do all day?"

"Oh, I read, and sew a little, and take naps, and sit with auntie."

"No running about out of doors, or house-work, or riding, hey?"

"Aunt Plenty says I'm not strong enough for much exercise. I drive out with her sometimes, but I don't care for it."

"I'm not surprised at that," said Uncle Alec, half to himself, adding, in his quick way: "Who have you had to play with?"

"No one but Annabel Bliss, and she was *such* a goose I couldn't bear her. The boys came yesterday, and seemed rather nice; but, of course, I couldn't play with them."

"Why not?"

"I'm too old to play with boys."

"Not a bit of it: that's just what you need, for you've been molly-coddled too much. They are good lads, and you'll be mixed up with them more or less for years to come, so you may as well be friends and playmates at once. I will look you up some girls also, if I can find a sensible one who is not spoilt by her nonsensical education."

"Phebe is sensible, I'm sure, and I like her, though I only saw her yesterday," cried Rose, waking up suddenly.

"And who is Phebe, if you please?"

Rose eagerly told all she knew, and Uncle Alec listened, with an odd smile lurking about his mouth, though his eyes were quite sober as he watched the face before him.

"I'm glad to see that you are not aristocratic in your tastes, but I don't quite make out why you like this young lady from the poor-house."

"You may laugh at me, but I do. I can't tell why, only she seems so happy and busy, and sings so beautifully, and is strong enough to scrub and sweep, and hasn't any troubles to plague her," said Rose, making a funny jumble of reasons in her efforts to explain.

"How do you know that?"

"Oh, I was telling her about mine, and asked if she had any, and she said, 'No, only I'd like to go to school, and I mean to some day.'"

"So she doesn't call desertion, poverty, and hard work, troubles? She's a brave little girl, and I shall be proud to know her." And Uncle Alec gave an approving nod, that made Rose wish she had been the one to earn it.

"But what are these troubles of yours, child?" he asked, after a minute of silence.

"Please don't ask me, uncle."

"Can't you tell them to me as well as to Phebe?"

Something in his tone made Rose feel that it would be better to speak out and be done with it, so she answered, with sudden color and averted eyes,—

"The greatest one was losing dear papa."

As she said that, Uncle Alec's arm came gently round her, and he drew her to him, saying, in the voice so like papa's,—

"That *is* a trouble which I cannot cure, my child; but I shall try to make you feel it less. What else, dear?"

"I am so tired and poorly all the time, I can't do any thing I want to, and it makes me cross," sighed Rose, rubbing the aching head like a fretful child.

"That we *can* cure and we *will*," said her uncle, with a decided nod that made the curls bob on his head, so that Rose saw the gray ones underneath the brown.

"Aunt Myra says I have no constitution, and never shall be strong," observed Rose, in a pensive tone, as if it was rather a nice thing to be an invalid.

"Aunt Myra is a—ahem!—an excellent woman, but it is her hobby to believe that every one is tottering on the brink of the grave; and, upon my life, I believe she is offended if people don't fall into it! We will show her how to make constitutions and turn pale-faced little ghosts into rosy, hearty girls. That's my business, you know," he added, more quietly, for his sudden outburst had rather startled Rose.

"I had forgotten you were a doctor. I'm glad of it, for I do want to be well, only I hope you won't give me much medicine, for I've taken quarts already, and it does me no good."

As she spoke, Rose pointed to a little table just inside the window, on which appeared a regiment of bottles.

"Ah, ha! Now we'll see what mischief these blessed women have been at." And, making a long arm, Dr. Alec set the bottles on the wide railing before him, examined each carefully, smiled over some, frowned over others, and said, as he put down the last: "Now I'll show you the best way to take these messes." And, as quick as a flash, he sent one after another smashing down into the posy-beds below.

"But Aunt Plenty won't like it; and Aunt Myra will be angry, for she sent most of them!" cried Rose, half frightened and half pleased at such energetic measures.

"You are my patient now, and I'll take the responsibility. My way of giving physic is evidently the best, for you look better already," he said, laughing so infectiously that Rose followed suit, saying saucily,—

"If I don't like your medicines any better than those, I shall throw them into the garden, and then what will you do?"

"When I prescribe such rubbish, I'll give you leave to pitch it overboard as soon as you like. Now what is the next trouble?"

"I hoped you would forget to ask."

"But how can I help you if I don't know them? Come, let us have No. 3."

"It is very wrong, I suppose, but I do sometimes wish I had not *quite* so many aunts. They are all very good to me, and I want to please them; but they are so different, I feel sort of pulled to pieces among them," said Rose, trying to express the emotions of a stray chicken with six hens all clucking over it at once.

Uncle Alec threw back his head and laughed like a boy, for he could entirely understand how the good ladies had each put in her oar and tried to paddle her own way, to the great disturbance of the waters and the entire bewilderment of poor Rose.

"I intend to try a course of uncles now, and see how that suits your constitution. I'm going to have you all to myself, and no one is to give a word of advice unless I ask it. There is no other way to keep order aboard, and I am captain of this little craft, for a time at least. What comes next?"

But Rose stuck there, and grew so red, her uncle guessed what that trouble was.

"I don't think I *can* tell this one. It wouldn't be polite, and I feel pretty sure that it isn't going to be a trouble any more."

As she blushed and stammered over these words, Dr. Alec turned his eyes away to the distant sea, and said so seriously, so tenderly, that she felt every word and long remembered them,—

"My child, I don't expect you to love and trust me all at once, but I do want you to believe that I shall give my whole heart to this new duty; and if I make mistakes, as I probably shall, no one will grieve over them more bitterly than I. It is my fault that I am a stranger to you, when I want to be your best friend. That is one of my mistakes, and I never repented it more deeply than I do now. Your father and I had a trouble once, and I thought I never could forgive him; so I kept away for years. Thank God, we made it all up the last time I saw him, and he told me then, that if he was forced to leave her he should bequeath his little girl to me as a token of his love. I can't fill his place, but I shall try to be a father to her; and if she learns to love me half as well as she did the good one she has lost, I shall be a proud and happy man. Will she believe this and try?"

Something in Uncle Alec's face touched Rose to the heart, and when he held out his hand with that anxious, troubled look in his eyes, she was moved to put up her innocent lips and seal the contract with a confiding kiss. The strong arm held her close a minute, and she felt the broad chest heave once as if with a great sigh of relief; but not a word was spoken till a tap at the door made both start.

Rose popped her head through the window to say "come in," while Dr. Alec hastily rubbed the sleeve of his jacket across his eyes and began to whistle again.

Phebe appeared with a cup of coffee.

"Debby told me to bring this and help you get up," she said, opening her black eyes wide, as if she wondered how on earth "the sailor man" got there.

"I'm all dressed, so I don't need any help. I hope that is good and strong," added Rose, eying the steaming cup with an eager look.

But she did not get it, for a brown hand took possession of it as her uncle said quickly,—

"Hold hard, my lass, and let me overhaul that dose before you take it. Do you drink all this strong coffee every morning, Rose?"

"Yes, sir, and I like it. Auntie says it 'tones' me up, and I always feel better after it."

"This accounts for the sleepless nights, the flutter your heart gets into at the least start, and this is why that cheek of yours is pale yellow instead of rosy red. No more coffee for you, my dear, and by and by you'll see that I am right. Any new milk downstairs, Phebe?"

"Yes, sir, plenty,—right in from the barn."

"That's the drink for my patient. Go bring me a pitcherful, and another cup; I want a draught myself. This won't hurt the honeysuckles, for they have no nerves to speak of." And, to Rose's great discomfort, the coffee went after the medicine.

Dr. Alec saw the injured look she put on, but took no notice, and presently banished it by saying pleasantly,—

"I've got a capital little cup among my traps, and I'll give it to you to drink your milk in, as it is made of wood that is supposed to improve whatever is put into it,—something like a quassia cup. That reminds me; one of the boxes Phebe wanted to lug upstairs last night is for you. Knowing that I was coming home to find a ready-made daughter, I picked up all sorts of odd and pretty trifles along the way, hoping she would be able to find something she liked among them all. Early to-morrow we'll have a grand rummage. Here's our milk! I propose the health of Miss Rose Campbell—and drink it with all my heart."

It was impossible for Rose to pout with the prospect of a delightful boxful of gifts dancing before her eyes; so, in spite of herself, she smiled as she drank her own health, and found that fresh milk was not a hard dose to take.

"Now I must be off, before I am caught again with my wig in a toss," said Dr. Alec, preparing to descend the way he came.

"Do you always go in and out like a cat, uncle?" asked Rose, much amused at his odd ways.

"I used to sneak out of my window when I was a boy, so I need not disturb the aunts, and now I rather like it, for it's the shortest road, and it keeps me limber when I have no rigging to climb. Good-by till breakfast." And away he went down the water-spout, over the roof, and vanished among the budding honeysuckles below.

"Ain't he a funny guardeen?" exclaimed Phebe, as she went off with the cups.

"He is a very kind one, I think," answered Rose,

following, to prowl round the big boxes and try to guess which was hers.

When her uncle appeared at sound of the bell, he found her surveying with an anxious face a new dish that smoked upon the table.

"Got a fresh trouble, Rosy?" he asked, stroking her smooth head.

"Uncle, *are* you going to make me eat oatmeal?" asked Rose, in a tragic tone.

"Don't you like it?"

"I de-test it!" answered Rose, with all the emphasis which a turned-up nose, a shudder, and a groan could give to the three words.

"You are not a true Scotchwoman, if you don't like the 'parritch.' It's a pity, for I made it myself, and thought we'd have such a good time with all that cream to float it in. Well, never mind." And he sat down with a disappointed air.

Rose had made up her mind to be obstinate about it, because she did heartily "detest" the dish; but as Uncle Alec did not attempt to make her obey, she suddenly changed her mind and thought she would.

"I'll try to eat it to please you, uncle; but people are always saying how wholesome it is, and that makes me hate it," she said, half ashamed at her silly excuse.

"I do want you to like it, because I wish my girl to be as well and strong as Jessie's boys, who are brought up on this in the good old fashion. No hot bread and fried stuff for them, and they are the biggest and bonniest lads of the lot. Bless you, auntie, and good morning!"

Dr. Alec turned to greet the old lady, and, with a firm resolve to eat or die in the attempt, Rose sat down.

In five minutes she forgot what she was eating, so interested was she in the chat that went on. It amused her very much to hear Aunt Plenty call her forty-year-old nephew "my dear boy;" and Uncle Alec was so full of lively gossip about all creation in general, and the Aunt-hill in particular, that the detested porridge vanished without a murmur.

"You will go to church with us, I hope, Alec, if you are not too tired," said the old lady, when breakfast was over.

"I came all the way from Calcutta for that express purpose, ma'am. Only I must send the sisters word of my arrival, for they don't expect me till tomorrow, you know, and there will be a row in church if those boys see me without warning."

"I'll send Ben up the hill, and you can step over to Myra's yourself; it will please her, and you will have plenty of time."

Dr. Alec was off at once, and they saw no more of him till the old barouche was at the door, and Aunt Plenty just rustling downstairs in her Sunday best, with Rose like a little black shadow behind her.

Away they drove in state, and all the way Uncle

Alec's hat was more off his head than on, for every one they met smiled and bowed, and gave him as blithe a greeting as the day permitted.

It was evident that the warning had been a wise one, for, in spite of time and place, the lads were in such a ferment that their elders sat in momentary dread of an unseemly outbreak somewhere. It was simply impossible to keep those fourteen eyes off Uncle Alec, and the dreadful things that were done during sermon-time will hardly be believed.

Rose dared not look up after a while, for these bad boys vented their emotions upon her till she was ready to laugh and cry with mingled amusement and vexation. Charlie winked rapturously at her behind his mother's fan; Mac openly pointed to the tall figure beside her; Jamie stared fixedly over the back of his pew, till Rose thought his round eyes would drop out of his head; George fell over a stool and dropped three books in his excitement; Will drew sailors and Chinamen on his clean cuffs, and displayed them, to Rose's great tribulation; Steve nearly upset the whole party by burning his nose with salts, as he pretended to be overcome by his joy; even dignified Archie disgraced himself by writing in his hymn-book, "Isn't he *blue* and *brown?*" and passing it politely to Rose.

Her only salvation was trying to fix her attention upon Uncle Mac,—a portly, placid gentleman, who seemed entirely unconscious of the iniquities of the clan, and dozed peacefully in his pew corner. This was the only uncle Rose had met for

years, for Uncle Jem and Uncle Steve, the hus-
bands of Aunt Jessie and Aunt Clara, were at sea,
and Aunt Myra was a widow. Uncle Mac was a
merchant, very rich and busy, and as quiet as a
mouse at home, for he was in such a minority
among the women folk he dared not open his lips,
and let his wife rule undisturbed.

Rose liked the big, kindly, silent man who came
to her when papa died, was always sending her
splendid boxes of goodies at school, and often invited her into his great warehouse, full of teas and
spices, wines and all sorts of foreign fruits, there to
eat and carry away whatever she liked. She had secretly regretted that he was not to be her guardian;
but since she had seen Uncle Alec she felt better
about it, for she did not particularly admire Aunt
Jane.

When church was over, Dr. Alec got into the
porch as quickly as possible, and there the young
bears had a hug all round, while the sisters shook
hands and welcomed him with bright faces and
glad hearts. Rose was nearly crushed flat behind a
door in that dangerous passage from pew to porch;
but Uncle Mac rescued her, and put her into the
carriage for safe keeping.

"Now, girls, I want you all to come and dine
with Alec; Mac also, of course. But I cannot ask
the boys, for we did not expect this dear fellow till
to-morrow, you know, so I made no preparations.
Send the lads home, and let them wait till Monday, for really I was shocked at their behavior

in church," said Aunt Plenty, as she followed Rose.

In any other place the defrauded boys would have set up a howl; as it was, they growled and protested till Dr. Alec settled the matter by saying,—

"Never mind, old chaps, I'll make it up to you to-morrow, if you sheer off quietly; if you don't, not a blessed thing shall you have out of my big boxes."

AUNTS

All dinner-time Rose felt that she was going to be talked about, and afterward she was sure of it, for Aunt Plenty whispered to her as they went into the parlor,—

"Run up and sit awhile with Sister Peace, my dear. She likes to have you read while she rests, and we are going to be busy."

Rose obeyed, and the quiet rooms above were so like a church that she soon composed her ruffled feelings, and was unconsciously a little minister of happiness to the sweet old lady, who for years had sat there patiently waiting to be set free from pain.

Rose knew the sad romance of her life, and it gave a certain tender charm to this great-aunt of hers, whom she already loved. When Peace was twenty, she was about to be married; all was done, the wedding-dress lay ready, the flowers were waiting to be put on, the happy hour at hand, when word came that the lover was dead. They thought that gentle Peace would die too; but she bore it bravely, put away her bridal gear, took up her life afresh, and lived on,—a beautiful, meek woman, with hair as white as snow and cheeks that never bloomed again. She wore no black, but soft, pale colors, as if always ready for the marriage that had never come.

For thirty years she had lived on, fading slowly, but cheerful, busy, and full of interest in all that went on in the family; especially the joys and sorrows of the young girls growing up about her, and to them she was adviser, confidante, and friend in all their tender trials and delights. A truly beautiful old maiden, with her silvery hair, tranquil face, and an atmosphere of repose about her that soothed whoever came to her!

Aunt Plenty was utterly dissimilar, being a stout, brisk old lady, with a sharp eye, a lively tongue, and a face like a winter-apple. Always trotting, chatting, and bustling, she was a regular Martha, cumbered with the cares of this world and quite happy in them.

Rose was right; and while she softly read psalms to Aunt Peace, the other ladies were talking about her little self in the frankest manner.

"Well, Alec, how do you like your ward?" began Aunt Jane, as they all settled down, and Uncle Mac deposited himself in a corner to finish his doze.

"I should like her better if I could have begun at the beginning, and so got a fair start. Poor George led such a solitary life that the child has suffered in many ways, and since he died she has been going on worse than ever, judging from the state I find her in."

"My dear boy, we did what we thought best while waiting for you to wind up your affairs and get home. I always told George he was wrong to bring her up as he did; but he never took my advice, and now here we are with this poor dear child upon our hands. I, for one, freely confess that I don't know what to do with her any more than if she was one of those strange, outlandish birds you used to bring home from foreign parts." And Aunt Plenty gave a perplexed shake of the head which caused great commotion among the stiff loops of purple ribbon that bristled all over her cap like crocus buds.

"If *my* advice had been taken, she would have remained at the excellent school where I placed her. But our aunt thought best to remove her because she complained, and she has been dawdling about ever since she came. A most ruinous state of things for a morbid, spoilt girl like Rose," said Mrs. Jane, severely.

She had never forgiven the old ladies for yielding to Rose's pathetic petition that she might wait her guardian's arrival before beginning another term at the school, which was a regular Blimber hot-bed, and turned out many a feminine Toots.

"*I* never thought it the proper school for a child in good circumstances,—an heiress, in fact, as Rose is. It is all very well for girls who are to get their own living by teaching, and that sort of thing; but all *she* needs is a year or two at a fashionable finishing-school, so that at eighteen she can come out with *éclat*," put in Aunt Clara, who had been a beauty and a belle, and was still a handsome woman.

"Dear, dear! how short-sighted you all are to be discussing education and plans for the future, when this unhappy child is so plainly marked for the tomb," sighed Aunt Myra, with a lugubrious sniff and a solemn wag of the funereal bonnet, which she refused to remove, being afflicted with a chronic catarrh.

"Now, it is my opinion that the dear thing only wants freedom, rest, and care. There is a look in her eyes that goes to my heart, for it shows that she feels the need of what none of us can give her—a mother," said Aunt Jessie, with tears in her own bright eyes at the thought of her boys being left, as Rose was, to the care of others.

Uncle Alec, who had listened silently as each spoke, turned quickly toward the last sister, and said, with a decided nod of approval,—

"You've got it, Jessie; and, with you to help me, I hope to make the child feel that she is not quite fatherless and motherless."

"I'll do my best, Alec; and I think you *will* need me, for, wise as you are, you cannot understand a tender, timid little creature like Rose as a woman can," said Mrs. Jessie, smiling back at him with a heart full of motherly good-will.

"I cannot help feeling that *I*, who have had a daughter of my own, can best bring up a girl; and I am *very* much surprised that George did not intrust her to me," observed Aunt Myra, with an air of melancholy importance, for she was the only one who had given a daughter to the family, and she felt that she had distinguished herself, though ill-natured people said that she had dosed her darling to death.

"I never blamed him in the least, when I remember the perilous experiments you tried with poor Carrie," began Mrs. Jane, in her hard voice.

"Jane Campbell, I will *not* hear a word! My sainted Caroline is a sacred subject," cried Aunt Myra, rising as if to leave the room.

Dr. Alec detained her, feeling that he must define his position at once, and maintain it manfully if he hoped to have any success in his new undertaking.

"Now, my dear souls, don't let us quarrel and make Rose a bone of contention,—though, upon my word, she *is* almost a bone, poor little lass! You have had her among you for a year, and done what you liked. I cannot say that your success is great, but that is owing to too many fingers in the pie. Now, I intend to try my way for a year, and if at the end of it she is not in better trim than now, I'll give up the case, and hand her over to some one else. That's fair, I think."

"She will not be here a year hence, poor darling, so no one need dread future responsibility," said Aunt Myra, folding her black gloves as if all ready for the funeral.

"By Jupiter, Myra, you are enough to damp the

ardor of a saint!" cried Dr. Alec, with a sudden spark in his eyes. "Your croaking will worry that child out of her wits, for she is an imaginative puss, and will fret and fancy untold horrors. You have put it into her head that she has no constitution, and she rather likes the idea. If she had not had a pretty good one, she *would* have been 'marked for the tomb' by this time, at the rate you have been going on with her. I will not have any interference,—please understand that; so just wash your hands of her, and let me manage till I want help, then I'll ask for it."

"Hear, hear!" came from the corner where Uncle Mac was apparently wrapt in slumber.

"You were appointed guardian, so we can do nothing. But I predict that the girl will be spoilt, utterly spoilt," answered Mrs. Jane, grimly.

"Thank you, sister. I have an idea that if a woman can bring up two boys as perfectly as you do yours, a man, if he devotes his whole mind to it, may at least attempt as much with one girl," replied Dr. Alec, with a humorous look that tickled the others immensely, for it was a well-known fact in the family that Jane's boys were more indulged than all the other lads put together.

"*I* am quite easy, for I really do think that Alec will improve the child's health; and by the time his year is out, it will be quite soon enough for her to go to Madame Roccabella's and be finished off," said Aunt Clara, settling her rings, and thinking, with languid satisfaction, of the time when she could bring out a pretty and accomplished niece.

"I suppose you will stay here in the old place, unless you think of marrying, and it's high time you did," put in Mrs. Jane, much nettled at her brother's last hit.

"No, thank you. Come and have a cigar, Mac," said Dr. Alec, abruptly.

"Don't marry; women enough in the family already," muttered Uncle Mac; and then the gentlemen hastily fled.

"Aunt Peace would like to see you all, she says," was the message Rose brought before the ladies could begin again.

"Hectic, hectic!—dear me, dear me!" murmured Aunt Myra, as the shadow of her gloomy bonnet fell upon Rose, and the stiff tips of a black glove touched the cheek where the color deepened under so many eyes.

"I am glad these pretty curls are natural; they will be invaluable by and by," said Aunt Clara, taking an observation with her head on one side.

"Now that your uncle has come, I no longer expect you to review the studies of the past year. I trust your time will not be *entirely* wasted in frivolous sports, however," added Aunt Jane, sailing out of the room with the air of a martyr.

Aunt Jessie said not a word, but kissed her little niece, with a look of tender sympathy that made Rose cling to her a minute, and follow her with grateful eyes as the door closed behind her.

After everybody had gone home, Dr. Alec paced

up and down the lower hall in the twilight for an hour, thinking so intently that sometimes he frowned, sometimes he smiled, and more than once he stood still in a brown study. All of a sudden he said, half aloud, as if he had made up his mind,—

"I might as well begin at once, and give the child something new to think about, for Myra's dismals and Jane's lectures have made her as blue as a little indigo bag."

Diving into one of the trunks that stood in a corner, he brought up, after a brisk rummage, a silken cushion, prettily embroidered, and a quaint cup of dark carved wood.

"This will do for a start," he said, as he plumped up the cushion and dusted the cup. "It won't do to begin too energetically, or Rose will be frightened. I must beguile her gently and pleasantly along till I've won her confidence, and then she will be ready for any thing."

Just then Phebe came out of the dining-room with a plate of brown bread, for Rose had been allowed no hot biscuit for tea.

"I'll relieve you of some of that," said Dr. Alec, and, helping himself to a generous slice, he retired to the study, leaving Phebe to wonder at his appetite.

She would have wondered still more if she had seen him making that brown bread into neat little pills, which he packed into an attractive ivory box, out of which he emptied his own bits of lovage.

"There! if they insist on medicine, I'll order these, and no harm will be done. I *will* have my own way, but I'll keep the peace, if possible, and confess the joke when my experiment has succeeded," he said to himself, looking very much like a mischievous boy, as he went off with his innocent prescriptions.

Rose was playing softly on the small organ that stood in the upper hall, so that Aunt Peace could enjoy it; and all the while he talked with the old ladies Uncle Alec was listening to the fitful music of the child, and thinking of another Rose who used to play for him.

As the clock struck eight, he called out,—

"Time for my girl to be abed, else she won't be up early, and I'm full of jolly plans for to-morrow. Come and see what I have found for you to begin upon."

Rose ran in and listened with bright, attentive face, while Dr. Alec said, impressively,—

"In my wanderings over the face of the earth, I have picked up some excellent remedies, and, as they are rather agreeable ones, I think you and I will try them. This is an herb-pillow, given to me by a wise old woman when I was ill in India. It is filled with saffron, poppies, and other soothing plants; so lay your little head on it to-night, sleep sweetly without a dream, and wake to-morrow without a pain."

"Shall I really? How nice it smells." And Rose willingly received the pretty pillow, and stood enjoying its faint, sweet odor, as she listened to the doctor's next remedy.

"This is the cup I told you of. Its virtue depends, they say, on the drinker filling it himself; so you must learn to milk. I'll teach you."

"I'm afraid I never can," said Rose; but she surveyed the cup with favor, for a funny little imp danced on the handle, as if all ready to take a header into the white sea below.

"Don't you think she ought to have something more strengthening than milk, Alec? I really shall feel anxious if she does not have a tonic of some sort," said Aunt Plenty, eying the new remedies suspiciously, for she had more faith in her old-fashioned doses than all the magic cups and poppy pillows of the East.

"Well, ma'am, I'm willing to give her a pill, if you think best. It is a very simple one, and very large quantities may be taken without harm. You know hasheesh is the extract of hemp? Well, this is a preparation of corn and rye, much used in old times, and I hope it will be again."

"Dear me, how singular!" said Aunt Plenty, bringing her spectacles to bear upon the pills, with a face so full of respectful interest that it was almost too much for Dr. Alec's gravity.

"Take one in the morning, and a good-night to you, my dear," he said, dismissing his patient with a hearty kiss.

Then, as she vanished, he put both hands into

his hair, exclaiming, with a comical mixture of anxiety and amusement,—

"When I think what I have undertaken, I declare to you, aunt, I feel like running away and not coming back till Rose is eighteen!"

A Belt and a Box

When Rose came out of her chamber, cup in hand, next morning, the first person she saw was Uncle Alec standing on the threshold of the room opposite, which he appeared to be examining with care. When he heard her step, he turned about and began to sing,—

"Where are you going, my pretty maid?"

"I'm going a-milking, sir, she said," answered Rose, waving the cup; and then they finished the verse together in fine style.

Before either spoke, a head, in a nightcap so large and beruffled that it looked like a cabbage, popped out of a room farther down the hall, and an astonished voice exclaimed,—

"What in the world are you about so early?"

"Clearing our pipes for the day, ma'am. Look here, auntie, can I have this room?" said Dr. Alec, making her a sailor's bow.

"Any room you like, except sister's."

"Thanks. And may I go rummaging round in the garrets and glory-holes to furnish it as I like?"

"My dear boy, you may turn the house upside down if you will only stay in it."

"That's a handsome offer, I'm sure. I'll stay, ma'am; here's my little anchor, so you will get more than you want of me this time."

"That's impossible! Put on your jacket, Rose. Don't tire her out with antics, Alec. Yes, sister, I'm coming!" and the cabbage vanished suddenly.

The first milking lesson was a droll one; but after several scares and many vain attempts, Rose at last managed to fill her cup, while Ben held Clover's tail so that it could not flap, and Dr. Alec kept her from turning to stare at the new milk-maid, who objected to both these proceedings very much.

"You look chilly in spite of all this laughing. Take a smart run round the garden and get up a glow," said the doctor, as they left the barn.

"I'm too old for running, uncle; Miss Power said it was not lady-like for girls in their teens," answered Rose primly.

"I take the liberty of differing from Madame Prunes and Prisms, and, as your physician, I *order* you to run. Off with you!" said Uncle Alec, with a look and a gesture that made Rose scurry away as fast as she could go.

Anxious to please him, she raced round the beds till she came back to the porch where he stood, and, dropping down upon the steps, she sat panting, with cheeks as rosy as the rigolette on her shoulders.

"Very well done, child; I see you have not lost the use of your limbs though you *are* in your teens.

That belt is too tight; unfasten it, then you can take a long breath without panting so."

"It isn't tight, sir; I can breathe perfectly well," began Rose, trying to compose herself.

Her uncle's only answer was to lift her up and unhook the new belt of which she was so proud. The moment the clasp was open the belt flew apart several inches, for it was impossible to restrain the involuntary sigh of relief that flatly contradicted her words.

"Why, I didn't know it was tight! it didn't feel so a bit. Of course it would open if I puff like this, but I never do, because I hardly ever run," explained Rose, rather discomfited by this discovery.

"I see you don't half fill your lungs, and so you can wear this absurd thing without feeling it. The idea of cramping a tender little waist in a stiff band of leather and steel just when it ought to be growing," said Dr. Alec, surveying the belt with great disfavor as he put the clasp forward several holes, to Rose's secret dismay, for she was proud of her slender figure and daily rejoiced that she wasn't as stout as Luly Miller, a former schoolmate, who vainly tried to repress her plumpness.

"It will fall off if it is so loose," she said anxiously, as she stood watching him pull her precious belt about.

"Not if you keep taking long breaths to hold it on. That is what I want you to do, and when you have filled this out we will go on enlarging it till your waist is more like that of Hebe, goddess of health, and less like that of a fashion-plate,—the ugliest thing imaginable."

"How it does look!" and Rose gave a glance of scorn at the loose belt hanging round her trim little waist. "It will be lost, and then I shall feel badly, for it cost ever so much, and is real steel and Russia leather. Just smell how nice."

"If it is lost I'll give you a better one. A soft silken sash is much fitter for a pretty child like you than a plated harness like this; and I've got no end of Italian scarfs and Turkish sashes among my traps. Ah! that makes you feel better, doesn't it?" and he pinched the cheek that had suddenly dimpled with a smile.

"It is very silly of me, but I can't help liking to know that"—here she stopped and blushed and held down her head, ashamed to add, "you think I am pretty."

Dr. Alec's eyes twinkled, but he said very soberly,—

"Rose, are you vain?"

"I'm afraid I am," answered a very meek voice from behind the veil of hair that hid the red face.

"That is a sad fault." And he sighed as if grieved at the confession.

"I know it is, and I try not to be; but people praise me, and I can't help liking it, for I really don't think I am repulsive."

The last word and the funny tone in which it was uttered were too much for Dr. Alec, and he laughed in spite of himself, to Rose's great relief.

"I quite agree with you; and in order that you may be still less repulsive, I want you to grow as fine a girl as Phebe."

"Phebe!" and Rose looked so amazed that her uncle nearly went off again.

"Yes, Phebe; for she has what you need,— health. If you dear little girls would only learn what real beauty is, and not pinch and starve and bleach yourselves out so, you'd save an immense deal of time and money and pain. A happy soul in a healthy body makes the best sort of beauty for man or woman. Do you understand that, my dear?"

"Yes, sir," answered Rose, much taken down by this comparison with the girl from the poor-house. It nettled her sadly, and she showed that it did by saying quickly,—

"I suppose you would like to have me sweep and scrub, and wear an old brown dress, and go round with my sleeves rolled up, as Phebe does?"

"I should very much, if you could work as well as she does, and show as strong a pair of arms as she can. I haven't seen a prettier picture for some time than she made of herself this morning, up to the elbows in suds, singing like a blackbird while she scrubbed on the back stoop."

"Well, I do think you are the queerest man that ever lived!" was all Rose could find to say after this display of bad taste.

"I haven't begun to show my oddities yet, so you must make up your mind to worse shocks than this," he said, with such a whimsical look that she was glad the sound of a bell prevented her showing more plainly what a blow her little vanities had already received.

"You will find your box all open up in auntie's parlor, and there you can amuse her and yourself by rummaging to your heart's content; I've got to be cruising round all the morning getting my room to rights," said Dr. Alec, as they rose from breakfast.

"Can't I help you, uncle?" asked Rose, quite burning to be useful.

"No, thank you. I'm going to borrow Phebe for a while, if Aunt Plenty can spare her."

"Anybody,—any thing, Alec. You will want me, I know, so I'll give orders about dinner and be all ready to lend a hand;" and the old lady bustled away full of interest and good-will.

"Uncle will find that *I* can do some things that Phebe can't; so now!" thought Rose, with a toss of the head as she flew to Aunt Peace and the long-desired box.

Every little girl can easily imagine what an extra good time she had diving into a sea of treasures and fishing up one pretty thing after another, till the air was full of the mingled odors of musk and sandal-wood, the room gay with bright colors, and Rose in a rapture of delight. She began to forgive Dr. Alec for the oatmeal diet when she saw a lovely ivory work-box; became resigned to the state of her belt when she found a pile of rainbow-colored sashes; and when she came to some distractingly pretty bottles of attar of rose, she felt that they almost atoned for the great sin of thinking Phebe the finer girl of the two.

Dr. Alec meanwhile had apparently taken Aunt Plenty at her word, and *was* turning the house upside down. A general revolution was evidently going on in the green-room, for the dark damask curtains were seen bundling away in Phebe's arms; the air-tight stove retiring to the cellar on Ben's shoulder; and the great bedstead going up garret in a fragmentary state, escorted by three bearers. Aunt Plenty was constantly on the trot among her store-rooms, camphor-chests, and linen-closets, looking as if the new order of things both amazed and amused her.

Half the peculiar performances of Dr. Alec cannot be revealed; but as Rose glanced up from her box now and then she caught glimpses of him striding by, bearing a bamboo chair, a pair of ancient andirons, a queer Japanese screen, a rug or two, and finally a large bathing-pan upon his head.

"What a curious room it will be," she said, as she sat resting and refreshing herself with "Lumps of Delight," all the way from Cairo.

"I fancy *you* will like it, deary," answered Aunt Peace, looking up with a smile from some pretty trifle she was making with blue silk and white muslin.

Rose did not see the smile, for just at that moment

her uncle paused at the door, and she sprang up to dance before him, saying, with a face full of childish happiness,—

"Look at me! look at me! I'm so splendid I don't know myself. I haven't put these things on right, I dare say, but I do like them *so* much!"

"You look as gay as a parrot in your fez and cabaja, and it does my heart good to see the little black shadow turned into a rainbow," said Uncle Alec, surveying the bright figure before him with great approbation.

He did not say it, but he thought she made a much prettier picture than Phebe at the wash-tub, for she had stuck a purple fez on her blonde head, tied several brilliant scarfs about her waist, and put on a truly gorgeous scarlet jacket with a golden sun embroidered on the back, a silver moon on the front, and stars of all sizes on the sleeves. A pair of Turkish slippers adorned her feet, and necklaces of amber, coral, and filigree hung about her neck, while one hand held a smelling-bottle, and the other the spicy box of oriental sweetmeats.

"I feel like a girl in the 'Arabian Nights,' and expect to find a magic carpet or a wonderful talisman somewhere. Only I don't see how I ever *can* thank you for all these lovely things," she said, stopping her dance, as if suddenly oppressed with gratitude.

"I'll tell you how,—by leaving off the black clothes, that never should have been kept so long on such a child, and wearing the gay ones I've brought. It will do your spirits good, and cheer up this sober old house. Won't it, auntie?"

"I think you are right, Alec, and it is fortunate that we have not begun on her spring clothes yet, for Myra thought she ought not to wear any thing brighter than violet, and she is too pale for that."

"You just let me direct Miss Hemming how to make some of these things. You will be surprised to see how much I know about piping hems and gathering arm-holes and shirring biases," began Dr. Alec, patting a pile of muslin, cloth, and silk with a knowing air.

Aunt Peace and Rose laughed so that he could not display his knowledge any farther till they stopped, when he said good-naturedly,—

"That will go a great way toward filling out the belt, so laugh away, Morgiana, and I'll go back to my work, or I never shall be done."

"I couldn't help it, 'shirred biases' were so very funny!" Rose said, as she turned to her box after the splendid laugh. "But really, auntie," she added soberly, "I feel as if I ought not to have so many nice things. I suppose it wouldn't do to give Phebe some of them? Uncle might not like it."

"He would not mind; but they are not suitable for Phebe. Some of the dresses you are done with would be more useful, if they can be made over to fit her," answered Aunt Peace in the prudent, moderate tone which is so trying to our feelings when we indulge in little fits of charitable enthusiasm.

"I'd rather give her new ones, for I think she is a

little bit proud and might not like old things. If she was my sister it would do, because sisters don't mind, but she isn't, and that makes it bad, you see. I know how I can manage beautifully; I'll adopt her!" and Rose looked quite radiant with this new idea.

"I'm afraid you could not do it legally till you are older, but you might see if she likes the plan, and at any rate you can be very kind to her, for in one sense we are all sisters, and should help one another."

The sweet old face looked at her so kindly that Rose was fired with a desire to settle the matter at once, and rushed away to the kitchen just as she was. Phebe was there, polishing up the antique andirons so busily that she started when a voice cried out: "Smell that, taste this, and look at me!"

Phebe sniffed attar of rose, crunched the "Lump of Delight" tucked into her mouth, and stared with all her eyes at little Morgiana prancing about the room like a brilliant paroquet.

"My stars, ain't you splendid!" was all she could say, holding up two dusty hands.

"I've got heaps of lovely things upstairs, and I'll show them all to you, and I'd go halves, only auntie thinks they wouldn't be useful, so I shall give you something else; and you won't mind, will you? because I want to adopt you as Arabella was in the story. Won't that be nice?"

"Why, Miss Rose, have you lost your wits?"

No wonder Phebe asked, for Rose talked very

fast, and looked so odd in her new costume, and was so eager she could not stop to explain. Seeing Phebe's bewilderment, she quieted down and said, with a pretty air of earnestness,—

"It isn't fair that I should have so much and you so little, and I want to be as good to you as if you were my sister, for Aunt Peace says we are all sisters really. I thought if I adopted you as much as I can now, it would be nicer. Will you let me, please?"

To Rose's great surprise, Phebe sat down on the floor and hid her face in her apron for a minute without answering a word.

"Oh dear, now she's offended, and I don't know what to do," thought Rose, much discouraged by this reception of her offer.

"Please, forgive me; I didn't mean to hurt your feelings, and hope you won't think—" she faltered presently, feeling that she must undo the mischief if possible.

But Phebe gave her another surprise, by dropping the apron and showing a face all smiles, in spite of tears in the eyes, as she put both arms round Rose and said, with a laugh and sob,—

"I think you are the dearest girl in the world, and I'll let you do any thing you like with me."

"Then you do like the plan? You didn't cry because I seemed to be kind of patronizing? I truly didn't mean to be," cried Rose, delighted.

"I guess I do like it! and cried because no one was ever so good to me before, and I couldn't help it. As for patronizing, you may walk on me if you want to, and I won't mind," said Phebe, in a burst of gratitude, for the words, "we are all sisters," went straight to her lonely heart and nestled there.

"Well, now, we can play I'm a good sprite out of the box, or, what is better, a fairy godmother come down the chimney, and you are Cinderella, and must say what you want," said Rose, trying to put the question delicately.

Phebe understood that, for she had a good deal of natural refinement, though she did come from the poor-house.

"I don't feel as if I wanted any thing now, Miss Rose, but to find some way of thanking you for all you've done," she said, rubbing off a tear that went rolling down the bridge of her nose in the most unromantic way.

"Why, I haven't done any thing but given you a bit of candy! Here, have some more, and eat 'em while you work, and think what I *can* do. I must go and clear up, so good-by, and don't forget I've adopted you."

"You've given me sweeter things than candy, and I'm not likely to forget it." And carefully wiping off the brick-dust, Phebe pressed the little hand Rose offered warmly in both her hard ones, while the black eyes followed the departing visitor with a grateful look that made them very soft and bright.

UNCLE ALEC'S ROOM

Soon after dinner, and before she had got acquainted with half her new possessions, Dr. Alec proposed a drive, to carry round the first instalment of gifts to the aunts and cousins. Rose was quite ready to go, being anxious to try a certain soft burnous from the box, which not only possessed a most engaging little hood, but had funny tassels bobbing in all directions.

The big carriage was full of parcels, and even Ben's seat was loaded with Indian war-clubs, a Chinese kite of immense size, and a pair of polished ox-horns from Africa. Uncle Alec, very blue as to his clothes, and very brown as to his face, sat bolt upright, surveying well-known places with interest, while Rose, feeling unusually elegant and comfortable, leaned back folded in her soft mantle, and played she was an Eastern princess making a royal progress among her subjects.

At three of the places their calls were brief, for Aunt Myra's catarrh was unusually bad; Aunt Clara had a room full of company; and Aunt Jane showed such a tendency to discuss the population, productions, and politics of Europe, Asia, and

Africa, that even Dr. Alec was dismayed, and got away as soon as possible.

"Now we will have a good time! I do hope the boys will be at home," said Rose, with a sigh of relief as they wound yet higher up the hill to Aunt Jessie's.

"I left this for the last call, so that we might find the lads just in from school. Yes, there is Jamie on the gate watching for us; now you'll see the clan gather; they are always swarming about together."

The instant Jamie saw the approaching guests he gave a shrill whistle, which was answered by echoes from meadow, house, and barn, as the cousins came running from all directions, shouting, "Hooray for Uncle Alec!" They went at the carriage like highwaymen, robbed it of every parcel, took the occupants prisoners, and marched them into the house with great exultation.

"Little Mum! little Mum! here they are with lots of goodies! Come down and see the fun right away! quick!" bawled Will and Geordie amidst a general ripping off of papers and a reckless cutting of strings that soon turned the tidy room into a chaos.

Down came Aunt Jessie with her pretty cap half on, but such a beaming face below it that one rather thought the fly-away head-gear an improvement than otherwise. She had hardly time to greet Rose and the doctor before the boys were about her, each clamoring for her to see his gift and rejoice over it with him, for "little Mum" went halves in every thing. The great horns skirmished about her as if to toss her to the ceiling; the war-clubs hurtled over her head as if to annihilate her; an amazing medley from the four quarters of the globe filled her lap, and seven excited boys all talked to her at once.

But she liked it; oh dear, yes! and sat smiling, admiring, and explaining, quite untroubled by the din, which made Rose cover up her ears and Dr. Alec threaten instant flight if the riot was not quelled. That threat produced a lull, and while the uncle received thanks in one corner, the aunt had some little confidences made to her in the other.

"Well, dear, and how are things going with you now? Better, I hope, than they were a week ago."

"Aunt Jessie, I think I'm going to be very happy, now uncle has come. He does the queerest things, but he is *so* good to me I can't help loving him;" and, nestling closer to little Mum, Rose told all that had happened, ending with a rapturous account of the splendid box.

"I am very glad, dear. But, Rose, I must warn you of one thing; don't let uncle spoil you."

"But I like to be spoilt, auntie."

"I don't doubt it; but if you turn out badly when the year is over he will be blamed, and his experiment prove a failure. That would be a pity, wouldn't it? when he wants to do so much for you, and can do it if his kind heart does not get in the way of his good judgment."

"I never thought of that, and I'll try not to be

spoilt. But how *can* I help it?" asked Rose anxiously.

"By not complaining of the wholesome things he wants you to do; by giving him cheerful obedience as well as love; and even making some small sacrifices for his sake."

"I will, I truly will! and when I get in a worry about things may I come to you? Uncle told me to, and I feel as if I shouldn't be afraid."

"You may, darling; this is the place where little troubles are best cured, and this is what mothers are for, I fancy;" and Aunt Jessie drew the curly head to her shoulder with a tender look that proved how well she knew what medicine the child most needed.

It was so sweet and comfortable that Rose sat still enjoying it till a little voice said,—

"Mamma, don't you think Pokey would like some of my shells? Rose gave Phebe some of her nice things, and it was very good of her. Can I?"

"Who is Pokey?" asked Rose, popping up her head, attracted by the odd name.

"My dolly; do you want to see her?" asked Jamie, who had been much impressed by the tale of adoption he had overheard.

"Yes; I'm fond of dollies, only don't tell the boys, or they will laugh at me."

"They don't laugh at me, and they play with my dolly a great deal; but she likes me best;" and Jamie ran away to produce his pet.

"I brought my old doll, but I keep her hidden

because I am too big to play with her, and yet I can't bear to throw her away, I'm so fond of her," said Rose, continuing her confidences in a whisper.

"You can come and play with Jamie's whenever you like, for we believe in dollies up here," began Aunt Jessie, smiling to herself as if something amused her.

Just then Jamie came back, and Rose understood the smile, for his dolly proved to be a pretty four-year-old little girl, who trotted in as fast as her fat legs would carry her, and, making straight for the shells, scrambled up an armful, saying, with a laugh that showed her little white teeth,—

"All for Dimmy and me, for Dimmy and me!"

"That's my dolly; isn't she a nice one?" asked Jamie, proudly surveying his pet with his hands behind him and his short legs rather far apart,—a manly attitude copied from his brothers.

"She is a dear dolly. But why call her Pokey?" asked Rose, charmed with the new plaything.

"She is such an inquisitive little body she is always poking that mite of a nose into every thing; and as Paul Pry did not suit, the boys fell to calling her Pokey. Not a pretty name, but very expressive."

It certainly was, for, having examined the shells, the busy tot laid hold of every thing she could find, and continued her researches till Archie caught her sucking his carved ivory chessmen to see if they were not barley-sugar. Rice-paper pictures were also discovered crumpled up in her tiny pocket, and she nearly smashed Will's ostrich egg by trying to sit upon it.

"Here, Jim, take her away; she's worse than the puppies, and we can't have her round," commanded the elder brother, picking her up and handing her over to the little fellow, who received her with open arms and the warning remark,—

"You'd better mind what you do, for I'm going to 'dopt Pokey like Rose did Phebe, and then you'll have to be very good to her, you big fellows."

" 'Dopt away, baby, and I'll give you a cage to keep her in, or you won't have her long, for she is getting worse than a monkey;" and Archie went back to his mates, while Aunt Jessie, foreseeing a crisis, proposed that Jamie should take his dolly home, as she was borrowed, and it was time her visit ended.

"*My* dolly is better than yours, isn't she? 'cause she can walk and talk and sing and dance, and yours can't do any thing, can she?" asked Jamie with pride, as he regarded his Pokey, who just then had been moved to execute a funny little jig and warble the well-known couplet,

" 'Puss-tat, puss-tat, where you been?'
'I been Lunnin, to saw a Tween.' "

After which superb display she retired, escorted by Jamie, both making a fearful din blowing on conch shells.

"We must tear ourselves away, Rose, because I want to get you home before sunset. Will you come for a drive, Jessie?" said Dr. Alec, as the music died away in the distance.

"No, thank you; but I see the boys want a scamper, so, if you don't mind, they may escort you home, but not go in. That is only allowed on holidays."

The words were hardly out of Aunt Jessie's mouth when Archie said, in a tone of command,—

"Pass the word, lads. Boot and saddle, and be quick about it."

"All right!" And in a moment not a vestige of boy remained but the litter on the floor.

The cavalcade went down the hill at a pace that made Rose cling to her uncle's arm, for the fat old horses got excited by the antics of the ponies careering all about them, and went as fast as they could pelt, with the gay dog-cart rattling in front, for Archie and Charlie scorned shelties since this magnificent equipage had been set up. Ben enjoyed the fun, and the lads cut up capers till Rose declared that "circus" was the proper name for them after all.

When they reached the house they dismounted, and stood, three on each side the steps, in martial attitudes, while her ladyship was handed out with great elegance by Uncle Alec. Then the clan saluted, mounted at word of command, and with a wild whoop tore down the avenue in what they considered the true Arab style.

"That was splendid, now it is safely ended," said Rose, skipping up the steps with her head over her shoulder to watch the dear tassels bob about.

"I shall get you a pony as soon as you are a little stronger," said Dr. Alec, watching her with a smile.

"Oh, I couldn't ride one of those horrid, frisky little beasts! They roll their eyes and bounce about so, I should die of fright," cried Rose, clasping her hands tragically.

"Are you a coward?"

"About horses I am."

"Never mind, then; come and see my new room;" and he led the way upstairs without another word.

As Rose followed she remembered her promise to Aunt Jessie, and was sorry she had objected so decidedly. She was a great deal more sorry five minutes later, and well she might be.

"Now take a good look, and tell me what you think of it," said Dr. Alec, opening the door and letting her enter before him, while Phebe was seen whisking down the backstairs with a dust-pan.

Rose walked to the middle of the room, stood still, and gazed about her with eyes that brightened as they looked, for all was changed.

This chamber had been built out over the library to suit some fancy, and had been unused for years, except at Christmas times, when the old house overflowed. It had three windows,—one to the east, that overlooked the bay; one to the south, where the horse-chestnuts waved their green fans; and one to the west, toward the hills and the evening sky. A ruddy sunset burned there now, filling the room with an enchanted glow; the soft murmur of the sea was heard, and a robin chirped "Good night!" among the budding trees.

Rose saw and heard these things first, and felt their beauty with a child's quick instinct; then her eye took in the altered aspect of the room, once so shrouded, still and solitary, now so full of light and warmth and simple luxury.

India matting covered the floor, with a gay rug here and there; the antique andirons shone on the wide hearth, where a cheery blaze dispelled the dampness of the long-closed room. Bamboo lounges and chairs stood about, and quaint little tables in cosey corners; one bearing a pretty basket, one a desk, and on a third lay several familiar-looking books. In a recess stood a narrow white bed, with a lovely Madonna hanging over it. The Japanese screen half folded back showed a delicate toilet-service of blue and white set forth on a marble slab, and near by was the great bath-pan, with Turkish towels and a sponge as big as Rose's head.

"Uncle must love cold water like a duck," she thought, with a shiver.

Then her eye went on to the tall cabinet, where a half-open door revealed a tempting array of the drawers, shelves, and "cubby holes," which so delight the hearts of children.

"What a grand place for my new things," she

thought, wondering what her uncle kept in that cedar retreat.

"Oh me, what a sweet toilet-table!" was her next mental exclamation, as she approached this inviting spot.

A round old-fashioned mirror hung over it, with a gilt eagle a-top, holding in his beak the knot of blue ribbon that tied up a curtain of muslin falling on either side of the table, where appeared little ivory-handled brushes, two slender silver candlesticks, a porcelain match-box, several pretty trays for small matters, and, most imposing of all, a plump blue silk cushion, coquettishly trimmed with lace, and pink rose-buds at the corners.

That cushion rather astonished Rose; in fact, the whole table did, and she was just thinking, with a sly smile,—

"Uncle is a dandy, but I never should have guessed it," when he opened the door of a large closet, saying, with a careless wave of the hand,—

"Men like plenty of room for their rattle-traps; don't you think that ought to satisfy me?"

Rose peeped in and gave a start, though all she saw was what one usually finds in closets,—clothes and boots, boxes and bags. Ah! but you see these clothes were small black and white frocks; the row of little boots that stood below had never been on Dr. Alec's feet; the green bandbox had a gray veil straying out of it, and,—yes! the bag hanging on the door was certainly her own piece-bag, with a hole in one corner. She gave a quick look round the room and understood now why it had seemed too dainty for a man, why *her* Testament and Prayer-book were on the table by the bed, and what those rose-buds meant on the blue cushion. It came upon her in one delicious burst that this little paradise was all for her, and, not knowing how else to express her gratitude, she caught Dr. Alec round the neck, saying impetuously,—

"O uncle, you are *too* good to me! I'll do any thing you ask me; ride wild horses and take freezing baths and eat bad-tasting messes, and let my clothes hang on me, to show how much I thank you for this dear, sweet, lovely room!"

"You like it, then? But why do you think it is yours, my lass?" asked Dr. Alec, as he sat down looking well pleased, and drew his excited little niece to his knee.

"I don't *think,* I *know* it is for me; I see it in your face, and I feel as if I didn't half deserve it. Aunt Jessie said you would spoil me, and I must not let you. I'm afraid this looks like it, and perhaps,—oh me!—perhaps I ought not to have this beautiful room after all!" and Rose tried to look as if she could be heroic enough to give it up if it was best.

"I owe Mrs. Jessie one for that," said Dr. Alec, trying to frown, though in his secret soul he felt that she was quite right. Then he smiled that cordial smile, which was like sunshine on his brown face, as he said,—

"This is part of the cure, Rose, and I put you here that you might take my three great remedies in the best and easiest way. Plenty of sun, fresh air, and cold water; also cheerful surroundings and some work; for Phebe is to show you how to take care of this room, and be your little maid as well as friend and teacher. Does that sound hard and disagreeable to you, dear?"

"No, sir; very, very pleasant, and I'll do my best to be a good patient. But I really don't think any one *could* be sick in this delightful room," she said, with a long sigh of happiness as her eye went from one pleasant object to another.

"Then you like my sort of medicine better than Aunt Myra's, and don't want to throw it out of the window, hey?"

A TRIP TO CHINA

"Come, little girl, I've got another dose for you. I fancy you won't take it as well as you did the last, but you will like it better after a while," said Dr. Alec, about a week after the grand surprise.

Rose was sitting in her pretty room, where she would gladly have spent all her time if it had been allowed; but she looked up with a smile, for she had ceased to fear her uncle's remedies, and was always ready to try a new one. The last had been a set of light gardening tools, with which she had helped him put the flower-beds in order, learning all sorts of new and pleasant things about the plants as she worked, for, though she had studied botany at school, it seemed very dry stuff compared with Uncle Alec's lively lesson.

"What is it now?" she asked, shutting her work-box without a murmur.

"Salt-water."

"How must I take it?"

"Put on the new suit Miss Hemming sent home yesterday, and come down to the beach; then I'll show you."

"Yes, sir," answered Rose obediently, adding to

herself, with a shiver, as he went off: "It is too early for bathing, so I *know* it is something to do with a dreadful boat."

Putting on the new suit of blue flannel, prettily trimmed with white, and the little sailor-hat with long streamers, diverted her mind from the approaching trial, till a shrill whistle reminded her that her uncle was waiting. Away she ran through the garden, down the sandy path, out upon the strip of beach that belonged to the house, and here she found Dr. Alec busy with a slender red and white boat that lay rocking on the rising tide.

"That is a dear little boat; and 'Bonnie Belle' is a pretty name," she said, trying not to show how nervous she felt.

"It is for you; so sit in the stern and learn to steer, till you are ready to learn to row."

"Do all boats wiggle about in that way?" she asked, lingering as if to tie her hat more firmly.

"Oh, yes, pitch about like nut-shells when the sea is a bit rough," answered her sailor uncle, never guessing her secret woe.

"Is it rough to-day?"

"Not very; it looks a trifle squally to the eastward, but we are all right till the wind changes. Come."

"Can you swim, uncle?" asked Rose, clutching at his arm as he took her hand.

"Like a fish. Now then."

"Oh, please hold me *very* tight till I get there! Why *do* you have the stern so far away?" and, stifling several squeaks of alarm in her passage, Rose crept to the distant seat, and sat there holding on with both hands and looking as if she expected every wave to bring a sudden shipwreck.

Uncle Alec took no notice of her fear, but patiently instructed her in the art of steering, till she was so absorbed in remembering which was starboard and which larboard, that she forgot to say "Ow!" every time a big wave slapped against the boat.

"Now where shall we go?" she asked, as the wind blew freshly in her face, and a few long, swift strokes sent them half across the little bay.

"Suppose we go to China?"

"Isn't that rather a long voyage?"

"Not as I go. Steer round the Point into the harbor, and I'll give you a glimpse of China in twenty minutes or so."

"I should like that!" and Rose sat wondering what he meant, while she enjoyed the new sights all about her.

Behind them the green Aunt-hill sloped gently upward to the grove at the top, and all along the seaward side stood familiar houses, stately, cosey, or picturesque. As they rounded the Point, the great bay opened before them full of shipping, and the city lay beyond, its spires rising above the tall masts with their gay streamers.

"Are we going there?" she asked, for she had never seen this aspect of the rich and busy old city before.

"Yes. Uncle Mac has a ship just in from Hong Kong, and I thought you would like to go and see it."

"Oh, I should! I love dearly to go poking about in the warehouses with Uncle Mac; every thing is so curious and new to me; and I'm specially interested in China because you have been there."

"I'll show you two genuine Chinamen who have just arrived. You will like to welcome Whang Lo and Fun See, I'm sure."

"Don't ask me to speak to them, uncle; I shall be sure to laugh at the odd names and the pig-tails and the slanting eyes. Please let me just trot round after you; I like that best."

"Very well; now steer toward the wharf where the big ship with the queer flag is. That's the 'Rajah,' and we will go aboard if we can."

In among the ships they went, by the wharves where the water was green and still, and queer barnacles grew on the slippery piles. Odd smells saluted her nose, and odd sights met her eyes, but Rose liked it all, and played she was really landing in Hong Kong when they glided up to the steps in the shadow of the tall "Rajah." Boxes and bales were rising out of the hold and being carried into the warehouse by stout porters, who tugged and bawled and clattered about with small trucks, or worked cranes with iron claws that came down and clutched heavy weights, whisking them aloft to where wide doors like mouths swallowed them up.

Dr. Alec took her aboard the ship, and she had

the satisfaction of poking her inquisitive little nose into every available corner, at the risk of being crushed, lost, or drowned.

"Well, child, how would you like to take a voyage round the world with me in a jolly old craft like this?" asked her uncle, as they rested a minute in the captain's cabin.

"I should like to see the world, but not in such a small, untidy, smelly place as this. We would go in a yacht all clean and comfortable; Charlie says that is the proper way," answered Rose, surveying the close quarters with little favor.

"You are not a true Campbell if you don't like the smell of tar and salt-water, nor Charlie either, with his luxurious yacht. Now come ashore and chin-chin with the Celestials."

After a delightful progress through the great warehouse, peeping and picking as they went, they found Uncle Mac and the yellow gentlemen in his private room, where samples, gifts, curiosities, and newly arrived treasures of all sorts were piled up in pleasing pro-fusion and con-fusion.

As soon as possible Rose retired to a corner, with a porcelain god on one side, a green dragon on the other, and, what was still more embarrassing, Fun See sat on a tea-chest in front, and stared at her with his beady black eyes till she did not know where to look.

Mr. Whang Lo was an elderly gentleman in American costume, with his pig-tail neatly wound round his head. He spoke English, and was talking busily with Uncle Mac in the most commonplace way,—so Rose considered *him* a failure. But Fun See was delightfully Chinese from his junk-like shoes to the button on his pagoda hat; for he had got himself up in style, and was a mass of silk jackets and slouchy trousers. He was short and fat, and waddled comically; his eyes were very "slanting," as Rose said; his queue was long, so were his nails; his yellow face was plump and shiny, and he was altogether a highly satisfactory Chinaman.

Uncle Alec told her that Fun See had come out to be educated, and could only speak a little pigeon English; so she must be kind to the poor fellow, for he was only a lad, though he looked nearly as old as Mr. Whang Lo. Rose said she would be kind; but had not the least idea how to entertain the queer guest, who looked as if he had walked out of one of the rice-paper landscapes on the wall, and sat nodding at her so like a toy Mandarin that she could hardly keep sober.

In the midst of her polite perplexity, Uncle Mac saw the two young people gazing wistfully at one another, and seemed to enjoy the joke of this making acquaintance under difficulties. Taking a box from his table, he gave it to Fun See with an order that seemed to please him very much.

Descending from his perch, he fell to unpacking it with great neatness and despatch, while Rose watched him, wondering what was going to happen. Presently, out from the wrappings came a teapot, which caused her to clasp her hands with delight, for it was made in the likeness of a plump little Chinaman. His hat was the cover, his queue the handle, and his pipe the nose. It stood upon feet in shoes turned up at the toes, and the smile on the fat, sleepy face was so like that on Fun's when he displayed the teapot, that Rose couldn't help laughing, which pleased him much.

Two pretty cups with covers, and a fine scarlet tray, completed the set, and made one long to have a "dish of tea," even in Chinese style, without cream or sugar.

When he had arranged them on a little table before her, Fun signified in pantomime that they were hers, from her uncle. She returned her thanks in the same way, whereupon he returned to his tea-chest, and, having no other means of communication, they sat smiling and nodding at one another in an absurd sort of way till a new idea seemed to strike Fun. Tumbling off his seat, he waddled away as fast as his petticoats permitted, leaving Rose hoping that he had not gone to get a roasted rat, a stewed puppy, or any other foreign mess which civility would oblige her to eat.

While she waited for her funny new friend, she improved her mind in a way that would have charmed Aunt Jane. The gentlemen were talking over all sorts of things, and she listened attentively, storing up much of what she heard, for she had an excellent memory, and longed to distinguish herself by being able to produce some useful information when reproached with her ignorance.

She was just trying to impress upon her mind that Amoy was two hundred and eighty miles from Hong Kong, when Fun came scuffling back, bearing what she thought was a small sword, till he unfurled an immense fan, and presented it with a string of Chinese compliments, the meaning of which would have amused her even more than the sound if she could have understood it.

She had never seen such an astonishing fan, and at once became absorbed in examining it. Of course, there was no perspective whatever, which only gave it a peculiar charm to Rose, for in one place a lovely lady, with blue knitting-needles in her hair, sat directly upon the spire of a stately pagoda. In another charming view a brook appeared to flow in at the front door of a stout gentleman's house, and out at his chimney. In a third a zigzag wall went up into the sky like a flash of lightning, and a bird with two tails was apparently brooding over a fisherman whose boat was just going aground upon the moon.

It was altogether a fascinating thing, and she would have sat wafting it to and fro all the afternoon, to Fun's great satisfaction, if Dr. Alec's attention had not suddenly been called to her by a breeze from the big fan that blew his hair into his eyes, and reminded him that they must go. So the pretty china was repacked, Rose furled her fan, and with several parcels of choice teas for the old ladies stowed away in Dr. Alec's pockets, they took their leave, after Fun had saluted them with the "three bendings and the nine knockings," as they salute the Emperor, or "Son of Heaven," at home.

"I feel as if I had really been to China, and I'm sure I look so," said Rose, as they glided out of the shadow of the "Rajah."

She certainly did, for Mr. Whang Lo had given her a Chinese umbrella; Uncle Alec had got some lanterns to light up her balcony; the great fan lay in her lap, and the tea-set reposed at her feet.

"This is not a bad way to study geography, is it?" asked her uncle, who had observed her attention to the talk.

"It is a very pleasant way, and I really think I have learned more about China to-day than in all the lessons I had at school, though I used to rattle off the answers as fast as I could go. No one explained any thing to us, so all I remember is that tea and silk come from there, and the women have little bits of feet. I saw Fun looking at mine, and he must have thought them perfectly immense," answered Rose, surveying her stout boots with sudden contempt.

"We will have out the maps and the globe, and I'll show you some of my journeys, telling stories as we go. That will be next best to doing it actually."

"You are so fond of travelling, I should think it would be very dull for you here, uncle. Do you know, Aunt Plenty says she is sure you will be off in a year or two."

"Very likely."

"Oh me! what *shall* I do then?" sighed Rose, in a

tone of despair that made Uncle Alec's face brighten with a look of genuine pleasure as he said significantly,—

"Next time I go I shall take my little anchor with me. How will that suit?"

"Really, uncle?"

"Really, niece."

Rose gave a little bounce of rapture which caused the boat to "wiggle" in a way that speedily quieted her down. But she sat beaming joyfully and trying to think which of some hundred questions she would ask first, when Dr. Alec said, pointing to a boat that was coming up behind them in great style,—

"How well those fellows row! Look at them, and take notes for your own use by and by."

The "Stormy Petrel" was manned by half a dozen jaunty-looking sailors, who made a fine display of blue shirts and shiny hats, with stars and anchors in every direction.

"How beautifully they go, and they are only boys. Why, I do believe they are *our* boys! Yes, I see Charlie laughing over his shoulder. Row, uncle, row! oh, please do, and not let them catch up with us!" cried Rose, in such a state of excitement that the new umbrella nearly went overboard.

"All right, here we go!" and away they did go with a long steady sweep of the oars that carried the "Bonnie Belle" through the water with a rush.

The lads pulled their prettiest, but Dr. Alec

would have reached the Point first, if Rose, in her flurry, had not retarded him by jerking the rudder ropes in a most unseamanlike way, and just as she got right again her hat blew off. That put an end to the race, and while they were still fishing for the hat the other boat came alongside, with all the oars in the air, and the jolly young tars ready for a frolic.

"Did you catch a crab, uncle?"

"No, a blue-fish," he answered, as the dripping hat was landed on a seat to dry.

"What have you been doing?"

"Seeing Fun."

"Good for you, Rose! I know what you mean. We are going to have him up to show us how to fly the big kite, for we can't get the hang of it. Isn't he great fun, though?"

"No, little Fun."

"Come, stop joking, and show us what you've got."

"You'd better hoist that fan for a sail."

"Lend Dandy your umbrella; he hates to burn his pretty nose."

"I say, uncle, are you going to have a Feast of Lanterns?"

"No, I'm going to have a feast of bread and butter, for it's tea-time. If that black cloud doesn't lie, we shall have a gust before long, so you had better get home as soon as you can, or your mother will be anxious, Archie."

"Ay, ay, skipper. Good-night, Rose; come out

often, and we'll teach you all there is to know about rowing," was Charlie's modest invitation.

Then the boats parted company, and across the water from the "Petrel's" crew came a verse from one of the Nonsense Songs in which the boys delighted.

"Oh, Timballoo! how happy we are,
We live in a sieve and a crockery jar!
And all night long, in the starlight pale, .
We sail away, with a pea-green sail,
And whistle and warble a moony song
To the echoing sound of a coppery gong.
Far and few, far and few
Are the lands where the Jumblies live;
Their heads are green, and their hands are blue,
And they went to sea in a sieve."

And What Came of It

"Uncle, could you lend me a ninepence? I'll return it as soon as I get my pocket-money," said Rose, coming into the library in a great hurry that evening.

"I think I could, and I won't charge any interest for it, so you need not be in any hurry to repay me. Come back here and help me settle these books if you have nothing pleasanter to do," answered Dr. Alec, handing out the money with that readiness which is so delightful when we ask small loans.

"I'll come in a minute; I've been longing to fix my books, but didn't dare to touch them, because you always shake your head when I read."

"I shall shake my head when you write, if you don't do it better than you did in making out this catalogue."

"I know it's bad, but I was in a hurry when I did it, and I am in one now." And away went Rose, glad to escape a lecture.

But she got it when she came back, for Uncle Alec was still knitting his brows over the list of books, and sternly demanded, pointing to a tipsy looking title staggering down the page,—

"Is that meant for 'Pulverized Bones,' ma'am?"

"No, sir; it's 'Paradise Lost.' "

"Well, I'm glad to know it, for I began to think you were planning to study surgery or farming. And what is this, if you please? 'Babies' Aprons' is all *I* can make of it."

Rose looked hard at the scrawl, and presently announced, with an air of superior wisdom,—

"Oh, that's 'Bacon's Essays.' "

"Miss Power did not teach any thing so old-fashioned as writing, I see. Now look at this little memorandum Aunt Plenty gave me, and see what a handsome plain hand that is. She went to a dame-school and learnt a few useful things well; that is better than a smattering of half a dozen so-called higher branches, I take the liberty of thinking."

"Well, I'm sure I was considered a bright girl at school, and learned every thing I was taught. Luly and me were the first in all our classes, and 'specially praised for our French and music and those sort of things," said Rose, rather offended at Uncle Alec's criticism.

"I dare say; but if your French grammar was no better than your English, I think the praise was not deserved, my dear."

"Why, uncle, we *did* study English grammar, and I could parse beautifully. Miss Power used to have us up to show off when people came. I don't see but I talk as right as most girls."

"I dare say you do, but we are all too careless

about our English. Now, think a minute and tell me if these expressions are correct,—'Luly and me,' 'those sort of things,' and 'as right as most girls.'"

Rose pulled her pet curl and put up her lip, but had to own that she was wrong, and said meekly, after a pause which threatened to be sulky,—

"I suppose I should have said 'Luly and I,' in that case, and 'that sort of things' and 'rightly,' though 'correctly' would have been a better word, I guess."

"Thank you; and if you will kindly drop 'I guess,' I shall like my little Yankee all the better. Now, see here, Rosy, I don't pretend to set myself up for a model in any thing, and you may come down on my grammar, manners, or morals as often as you think I'm wrong, and I'll thank you. I've been knocking about the world for years, and have got careless, but I want my girl to be what *I* call well educated, even if she studies nothing but the 'three Rs' for a year to come. Let us be thorough, no matter how slowly we go."

He spoke so earnestly and looked so sorry to have ruffled her that Rose went and sat on the arm of his chair, saying, with a pretty air of penitence,—

"I'm sorry I was cross, uncle, when I ought to thank you for taking so much interest in me. I guess,—no, I think you are right about being thorough, for I used to understand a great deal better when papa taught me a few lessons than when Miss Power hurried me through so many. I declare my head used to be such a jumble of French and German, history and arithmetic, grammar and music, I used to feel sometimes as if it would split. I'm sure I don't wonder it ached." And she held on to it as if the mere memory of the "jumble" made it swim.

"Yet that is considered an excellent school, I find, and I dare say it would be if the benighted lady did not think it necessary to cram her pupils like Thanksgiving turkeys, instead of feeding them in a natural and wholesome way. It is the fault with most American schools, and the poor little heads will go on aching till we learn better."

This was one of Dr. Alec's hobbies, and Rose was afraid he was off for a gallop, but he reined himself in and gave her thoughts a new turn by saying suddenly, as he pulled out a fat pocketbook,—

"Uncle Mac has put all your affairs into my hands now, and here is your month's pocket-money. You keep your own little accounts, I suppose?"

"Thank you. Yes, Uncle Mac gave me an account-book when I went to school, and I used to put down my expenses, but I couldn't make them go very well, for figures are the one thing I am not at all clever about," said Rose, rummaging in her desk for a dilapidated little book, which she was ashamed to show when she found it.

"Well, as figures are rather important things to most of us, and you may have a good many accounts to keep some day, wouldn't it be wise to begin at once and learn to manage your pennies before the pounds come to perplex you?"

"I thought you would do all that fussy part and take care of the pounds, as you call them. Need I worry about it? I do hate sums so!"

"I shall take care of things till you are of age, but I mean that you shall know how your property is managed and do as much of it as you can by and by; then you won't be dependent on the honesty of other people."

"Gracious me! as if I wouldn't trust you with millions of billions if I had them," cried Rose, scandalized at the mere suggestion.

"Ah, but I might be tempted; guardians are sometimes; so you'd better keep your eye on me, and in order to do that you must learn all about these affairs," answered Dr. Alec, as he made an entry in his own very neat account-book.

Rose peeped over his shoulder at it, and then turned to the arithmetical puzzle in her hand with a sigh of despair.

"Uncle, when you add up your expenses do you ever find you have got more money than you had in the beginning?"

"No; I usually find that I have a good deal less than I had in the beginning. Are you troubled in the peculiar way you mention?"

"Yes; it is very curious, but I never *can* make things come out square."

"Perhaps I can help you," began Uncle Alec, in the most respectful tone.

"I think you had better, for if I have got to keep accounts I may as well begin in the right way. But please don't laugh! I know I'm very stupid, and my book is a disgrace, but I never *could* get it straight." And with great trepidation Rose gave up her funny little accounts.

It really *was* good in Dr. Alec not to laugh, and Rose felt deeply grateful when he said, in a mildly suggestive tone,—

"The dollars and cents seem to be rather mixed; perhaps if I just straighten them out a bit we should find things all right."

"Please do, and then show me on a fresh leaf how to make mine look nice and ship-shape as yours do."

As Rose stood by him watching the ease with which he quickly brought order out of chaos, she privately resolved to hunt up her old arithmetic and perfect herself in the first four rules, with a good tug at fractions, before she read any more fairy tales.

"Am I a rich girl, uncle?" she asked suddenly, as he was copying a column of figures.

"Rather a poor one, I should say, since you had to borrow a ninepence."

"That was your fault, because you forgot my

pocket-money. But, really, shall I be rich by and by?"

"I am afraid you will."

"Why afraid, uncle?"

"Too much money is a bad thing."

"But I can give it away, you know; that is always the pleasantest part of having it, *I* think."

"I'm glad you feel so, for you *can* do much good with your fortune if you know how to use it well."

"You shall teach me, and when I am a woman we will set up a school where nothing but the three Rs shall be taught, and all the children live on oatmeal, and the girls have waists a yard round," said Rose, with a sudden saucy smile dimpling her cheeks.

"You are an impertinent little baggage, to turn on me in that way right in the midst of my first attempt at teaching. Never mind, I'll have an extra bitter dose for you next time, miss."

"I knew you wanted to laugh, so I gave you a chance. Now I will be good, master, and do my lesson nicely."

So Dr. Alec had his laugh, and then Rose sat down and took a lesson in accounts which she never forgot.

"Now come and read aloud to me; my eyes are tired, and it is pleasant to sit here by the fire while the rain pours outside and Aunt Jane lectures upstairs," said Uncle Alec, when last month's accounts had been put in good order and a fresh page neatly begun.

Rose liked to read aloud, and gladly gave him

the chapter in "Nicholas Nickleby" where the Miss Kenwigses take their French lesson. She did her very best, feeling that she was being criticised, and hoping that she might not be found wanting in this as in other things.

"Shall I go on, sir?" she asked very meekly when the chapter ended.

"If you are not tired, dear. It is a pleasure to hear you, for you read remarkably well," was the answer that filled her heart with pride and pleasure.

"Do you really think so, uncle? I'm so glad! papa taught me, and I read for hours to him, but I thought, perhaps, he liked it because he was fond of me."

"So am I; but you really do read unusually well, and I am very glad of it, for it is a rare accomplishment, and one I value highly. Come here in this cosey, low chair; the light is better, and I can pull these curls if you go too fast. I see you are going to be a great comfort as well as a great credit to your old uncle, Rosy." And Dr. Alec drew her close beside him with such a fatherly look and tone that she felt it would be very easy to love and obey him since he knew how to mix praise and blame so pleasantly together.

Another chapter was just finished, when the sound of a carriage warned them that Aunt Jane was about to depart. Before they could go to meet her, however, she appeared in the door-way looking like an unusually tall mummy in her waterproof, with her glasses shining like cat's eyes from the depths of the hood.

"Just as I thought! petting that child to death and letting her sit up late reading trash. I do hope you feel the weight of the responsibility you have taken upon yourself, Alec," she said, with a certain grim sort of satisfaction at seeing things go wrong.

"I think I have a very realizing sense of it, sister Jane," answered Dr. Alec, with a comical shrug of the shoulders and a glance at Rose's bright face.

"It is sad to see a great girl wasting these precious hours so. Now, my boys have studied all day, and Mac is still at his books, I've no doubt, while you have not had a lesson since you came, I suspect."

"I have had five to-day, ma'am," was Rose's very unexpected answer.

"I'm glad to hear it; and what were they, pray?"

Rose looked very demure as she replied,—

"Navigation, geography, grammar, arithmetic, and keeping my temper."

"Queer lessons, I fancy; and what have you learned from this remarkable mixture, I should like to know?"

A naughty sparkle came into Rose's eyes as she answered, with a droll look at her uncle,—

"I can't tell you all, ma'am, but I have collected some useful information about China, which you may like, especially the teas. The best are Lapsing Souchong, Assam Pekoe, rare Ankoe, Flowery Pekoe, Howqua's mixture, Scented Caper, Padral tea, black Congou, and green Twankey. Shanghai is on the Woosung River. Hong Kong means 'Island of sweet waters.' Singapore is 'Lion's Town.' 'Chops' are the boats they live in; and they drink tea out of little saucers. Principal productions are porcelain, tea, cinnamon, shawls, tin, tamarinds, and opium. They have beautiful temples and queer gods; and in Canton is the Dwelling of the Holy Pigs, fourteen of them, very big, and all blind."

The effect of this remarkable burst was immense, especially the fact last mentioned. It entirely took the wind out of Aunt Jane's sails; it was so sudden, so varied and unexpected, that she had not a word to say. The glasses remained fixed full upon Rose for a moment, and then, with a hasty "Oh, indeed!" the excellent lady bundled into her carriage and drove away, somewhat bewildered and very much disturbed.

She would have been more so if she had seen her reprehensible brother-in-law dancing a triumphal polka down the hall with Rose in honor of having silenced the enemy's battery for once.

PHEBE'S SECRET

"Why do you keep smiling to yourself, Phebe?" asked Rose, as they were working together one morning, for Dr. Alec considered house-work the best sort of gymnastics for girls; so Rose took lessons of Phebe in sweeping, dusting, and bed-making.

"I was thinking about a nice little secret I know, and couldn't help smiling."

"Shall I know it sometime?"

"Guess you will."

"Shall I like it?"

"Oh, won't you, though!"

"Will it happen soon?"

"Sometime this week."

"I know what it is! The boys are going to have fire-works on the Fourth, and have got some surprise for me. Haven't they?"

"That's telling."

"Well, I can wait; only tell me one thing,—is uncle in it?"

"Of course he is; there's never any fun without him."

"Then it is all right, and sure to be nice."

Rose went out on the balcony to shake the rugs, and, having given them a vigorous beating, hung them on the balustrade to air, while she took a look at her plants. Several tall vases and jars stood there, and a month of June sun and rain had worked wonders with the seeds and slips she had planted. Morning-glories and nasturtiums ran all over the bars, making haste to bloom. Scarlet beans and honeysuckles were climbing up from below to meet their pretty neighbors, and the woodbine was hanging its green festoons wherever it could cling.

The waters of the bay were dancing in the sunshine, a fresh wind stirred the chestnut-trees with a pleasant sound, and the garden below was full of roses, butterflies, and bees. A great chirping and twittering went on among the birds, busy with their summer housekeeping, and, far away, the white-winged gulls were dipping and diving in the sea, where ships, like larger birds, went sailing to and fro.

"Oh, Phebe, it's such a lovely day, I do wish your fine secret was going to happen right away! I feel just like having a good time; don't you?" said Rose, waving her arms as if she was going to fly.

"I often feel that way, but I have to wait for my good times, and don't stop working to wish for 'em. There, now you can finish as soon as the dust settles; I must go do my stairs," and Phebe trudged away with the broom, singing as she went.

Rose leaned where she was, and fell to thinking how many good times she had had lately, for the

gardening had prospered finely, and she was learning to swim and row, and there were drives and
walks, and quiet hours of reading and talk with
Uncle Alec, and, best of all, the old pain and *ennui*
seldom troubled her now. She could work and play
all day, sleep sweetly all night, and enjoy life with
the zest of a healthy, happy child. She was far from
being as strong and hearty as Phebe, but she was
getting on; the once pale cheeks had color in them
now, the hands were growing plump and brown,
and the belt was not much too loose. No one
talked to her about her health, and she forgot that
she had "no constitution." She took no medicine
but Dr. Alec's three great remedies, and they
seemed to suit her excellently. Aunt Plenty said it
was the pills; but, as no second batch ever followed
the first, I think the old lady was mistaken.

Rose looked worthy of her name as she stood
smiling to herself over a happier secret than any
Phebe had,—a secret which she did not know herself till she found out, some years later, the magic
of good health.

" 'Look only,' said the brownie,
   'At the pretty gown of blue,
At the kerchief pinned about her head,
   And at her little shoe,' "

said a voice from below, as a great cabbage-rose
came flying against her cheek.

"What is the princess dreaming about up there

in her hanging-garden?" added Dr. Alec as she flung back a morning-glory.

"I was wishing I could do something pleasant this fine day; something very new and interesting, for the wind makes me feel frisky and gay."

"Suppose we take a pull over to the Island? I intended to go this afternoon; but if you feel more like it now, we can be off at once."

"I do! I do! I'll come in fifteen minutes, uncle. I *must* just scrabble my room to rights, for Phebe has got a great deal to do."

Rose caught up the rugs and vanished as she spoke, while Dr. Alec went in, saying to himself, with an indulgent smile,—

"It may upset things a trifle, but half a child's pleasure consists in having their fun *when* they want it."

Never did duster flap more briskly than the one Rose used that day, and never was a room "scrabbled" to rights in such haste as hers. Tables and chairs flew into their places as if alive; curtains shook as if a gale was blowing; china rattled and small articles tumbled about as if a young earthquake was playing with them. The boating suit went on in a twinkling, and Rose was off with a hop and a skip, little dreaming how many hours it would be before she saw her pretty room again.

Uncle Alec was putting a large basket into the boat when she arrived, and before they were off Phebe came running down with a queer, knobby bundle done up in a water-proof.

"We can't eat half that luncheon, and I know we shall not need so many wraps. I wouldn't lumber the boat up so," said Rose, who still had secret scares when on the water.

"Couldn't you make a smaller parcel, Phebe?" asked Dr. Alec, eying the bundle suspiciously.

"No, sir, not in such a hurry," and Phebe laughed as she gave a particularly large knob a good poke.

"Well, it will do for ballast. Don't forget the note to Mrs. Jessie, I beg of you."

"No, sir. I'll send it right off," and Phebe ran up the bank as if she had wings to her feet.

"We'll take a look at the light-house first, for you have not been there yet, and it is worth seeing. By the time we have done that it will be pretty warm, and we will have lunch under the trees on the Island."

Rose was ready for any thing, and enjoyed her visit to the light-house on the Point very much, especially climbing up the narrow stairs and going inside the great lantern. They made a long stay, for Dr. Alec seemed in no hurry to go, and kept looking through his spy-glass as if he expected to discover something remarkable on sea or land. It was past twelve before they reached the Island, and Rose was ready for her lunch long before she got it.

"Now this *is* lovely! I do wish the boys were here. Won't it be nice to have them with us all their vacation? Why, it begins to-day, doesn't it? Oh, I wish I'd remembered it sooner, and perhaps they would have come with us," she said, as they lay luxuriously eating sandwiches under the old apple-tree.

"So we might. Next time we won't be in such a hurry. I expect the lads will take our heads off when they find us out," answered Dr. Alec, placidly drinking cold tea.

"Uncle, I smell a frying sort of a smell," Rose said, pausing suddenly as she was putting away the remains of the lunch half an hour later.

"So do I; it is fish, I think."

For a moment they both sat with their noses in the air, sniffing like hounds; then Dr. Alec sprang up, saying with great decision,—

"Now this won't do! No one is permitted on this island without asking leave. I must see who dares to fry fish on my private property."

Taking the basket on one arm and the bundle on the other, he strode away toward the traitorous smell, looking as fierce as a lion, while Rose marched behind under her umbrella.

"We are Robinson Crusoe and his man Friday going to see if the savages have come," she said presently, for her fancy was full of the dear old stories that all children love so well.

"And there they are! Two tents and two boats, as I live! These rascals mean to enjoy themselves, that's evident."

"There ought to be more boats and no tents. I wonder where the prisoners are?"

"There are traces of them," and Dr. Alec

pointed to the heads and tails of fishes strewn on the grass.

"And there are more," said Rose, laughing, as she pointed to a scarlet heap of what looked like lobsters.

"The savages are probably eating their victims now; don't you hear the knives rattle in that tent?"

"We ought to creep up and peep; Crusoe was cautious, you know, and Friday scared out of his wits," added Rose, still keeping up the joke.

"But this Crusoe is going to pounce upon them regardless of consequences. If I am killed and eaten, you seize the basket and run for the boat; there are provisions enough for your voyage home."

With that Uncle Alec slipped round to the front of the tent, and, casting in the big bundle like a bombshell, roared out, in a voice of thunder,—

"Pirates, surrender!"

A crash, a shout, a laugh, and out came the savages, brandishing knives and forks, chicken bones, and tin mugs, and all fell upon the intruder, pommelling him unmercifully as they cried,—

"You came too soon! We are not half ready! You've spoilt it all! Where is Rose?"

"Here I am," answered a half-stifled voice, and Rose was discovered sitting on the pile of red flannel bathing-clothes, which she had mistaken for lobsters, and where she had fallen in a fit of merriment when she discovered that the cannibals were her merry cousins.

"You good-for-nothing boys! You are always bursting out upon me in some ridiculous way, and I always get taken in because I'm not used to such pranks. Uncle is as bad as the rest, and it's great fun," she said, as the lads came round her, half scolding, half welcoming, and wholly enjoying the double surprise.

"You were not to come till afternoon, and mamma was to be here to receive you. Every thing is in a mess now, except your tent; we got that in order the first thing, and you can sit there and see us work," said Archie, doing the honors as usual.

"Rose felt it in her bones, as Debby says, that something was in the wind, and wanted to be off at once. So I let her come, and should have kept her away an hour longer if your fish had not betrayed you," explained Uncle Alec, subsiding from a ferocious Crusoe into his good-natured self again.

"As this seat is rather damp, I think I'll rise," said Rose, as the excitement lessened a little.

Several fishy hands helped her up, and Charlie said, as he scattered the scarlet garments over the grass with an oar,—

"We had a jolly good swim before dinner, and I told the Brats to spread these to dry. Hope you brought *your* things, Rose, for you belong to the Lobsters, you know, and we can have no end of fun teaching you to dive and float and tread water."

"I didn't bring any thing—" began Rose, but was interrupted by the Brats (otherwise Will and

Geordie), who appeared bearing the big bundle, so much demoralized by its fall that a red flannel tunic trailed out at one end and a little blue dressing-gown at the other, while the knobs proved to be a toilet-case, rubbers, and a silver mug.

"Oh, that sly Phebe! This was the secret, and she bundled up those things after I went down to the boat," cried Rose, with sparkling eyes.

"Guess something is smashed inside, for a bit of glass fell out," observed Will, as they deposited the bundle at her feet.

"Catch a girl going anywhere without a looking-glass. We haven't got one among the whole lot of us," added Mac, with masculine scorn.

"Dandy has; I caught him touching up his wig behind the trees after our swim," cut in Geordie, wagging a derisive finger at Steve, who promptly silenced him by a smart rap on the head with the drum-stick he had just polished off.

"Come, come, you lazy lubbers, fall to work, or we shall not be ready for mamma. Take Rose's things to her tent, and tell her all about it, Prince. Mac and Steve, you cut away and bring up the rest of the straw; and you small chaps clear off the table, if you have stuffed all you can. Please, uncle, I'd like your advice about the boundary lines and the best place for the kitchen."

Every one obeyed the Chief, and Rose was escorted to her tent by Charlie, who devoted himself to her service. She was charmed with her quarters, and still more so with the programme which he unfolded before her as they worked.

"We always camp out somewhere in vacation, and this year we thought we'd try the Island. It is handy, and our fire-works will show off well from here."

"Shall we stay over the Fourth? Three whole days! Oh, me! what a frolic it will be!"

"Bless your heart, we often camp for a week, we big fellows; but this year the small chaps wanted to come, so we let them. We have great larks, as you'll see; for we have a cave and play Captain Kidd, and have shipwrecks, and races, and all sorts of games. Arch and I are rather past that kind of thing now, but we do it to please the children," added Charlie, with a sudden recollection of his sixteen years.

"I had no idea boys had such good times. Their plays never seemed a bit interesting before. But I suppose that was because I never knew any boys very well, or perhaps you are unusually nice ones," observed Rose, with an artless air of appreciation that was very flattering.

"We are a pretty clever set, I fancy; but we have a good many advantages, you see. There are a tribe of us, to begin with; then our family has been here for ages, and we have plenty of 'spondulics,' so we can rather lord it over the other fellows and do as we like. There, ma'am, you can hang your smashed glass on that nail and do up your back hair as fine as you please. You can have a blue blanket or a red one, and a straw pillow or an air cushion for your head, whichever you like. You can trim up to any extent, and be as free and easy as squaws in a wigwam, for this corner is set apart for you ladies, and we never cross the line uncle is drawing until we ask leave. Any thing more I can do for you, cousin?"

"No, thank you. I think I'll leave the rest till auntie comes, and go and help you somewhere else, if I may."

"Yes, indeed, come on and see to the kitchen. Can you cook?" asked Charlie, as he led the way to the rocky nook where Archie was putting up a sail-cloth awning.

"I can make tea and toast bread."

"Well, we'll show you how to fry fish and make chowder. Now you just set these pots and pans round tastefully, and sort of tidy up a bit, for Aunt Jessie insists on doing some of the work, and I want it to be decent here."

By four o'clock the camp was in order, and the weary workers settled down on Lookout Rock to watch for Mrs. Jessie and Jamie, who was never far from mamma's apron-string. They looked like a flock of blue-birds, all being in sailor rig, with blue ribbon enough flying from the seven hats to have set up a milliner. Very tuneful blue-birds they were, too, for all the lads sang, and the echo of their happy voices reached Mrs. Jessie long before she saw them.

The moment the boat hove in sight up went the Island flag, and the blue-jackets cheered lustily, as they did on every possible occasion, like true young Americans. This welcome was answered by the flapping of a handkerchief and the shrill "Rah! Rah! Rah!" of the one small tar who stood in the stern waving his hat manfully, while a maternal hand clutched him firmly in the rear.

Cleopatra landing from her golden galley never received a heartier greeting than "Little Mum" as she was borne to her tent by the young folk, for love of whom she smilingly resigned herself to three days of discomfort; while Jamie immediately attached himself to Rose, assuring her of his protection from the manifold perils which might assail them.

Taught by long experience that boys are *always* hungry, Aunt Jessie soon proposed supper, and proceeded to get it, enveloped in an immense apron, with an old hat of Archie's stuck atop of her cap. Rose helped, and tried to be as handy as Phebe, though the peculiar style of table she had to set made it no easy task. It was accomplished at last, and a very happy party lay about under the trees, eating and drinking out of any one's plate and cup, and quite untroubled by the frequent appearance of ants and spiders in places which these interesting insects are not expected to adorn.

"I never thought I should like to wash dishes, but I do," said Rose, as she sat in a boat after supper lazily rinsing plates in the sea, and rocking luxuriously as she wiped them.

"Mum is mighty particular; *we* just give 'em a scrub with sand, and dust 'em off with a bit of paper. It's much the best way, *I* think," replied Geordie, who reposed in another boat alongside.

"How Phebe would like this! I wonder uncle did not have her come."

"I believe he tried to, but Debby was as cross as two sticks, and said she couldn't spare her. I'm sorry, for we all like the Phebe bird, and she'd chirp like a good one out here, wouldn't she?"

"She ought to have a holiday like the rest of us. It's too bad to leave her out."

This thought came back to Rose several times that evening, for Phebe would have added much to the little concert they had in the moonlight, would have enjoyed the stories told, been quick at guessing the conundrums, and laughed with all her heart at the fun. The merry going to bed would have been best of all, for Rose wanted some one to cuddle under the blue blanket with her, there to whisper and giggle and tell secrets, as girls delight to do.

Long after the rest were asleep, Rose lay wide awake, excited by the novelty of all about her, and a thought that had come into her mind. Far away she heard a city clock strike twelve; a large star like a mild eye peeped in at the opening of the tent, and the soft plash of the waves seemed calling her to come out. Aunt Jessie lay fast asleep, with Jamie rolled up like a kitten at her feet, and neither stirred as Rose in her wrapper crept out to see how the world looked at midnight.

She found it very lovely, and sat down on a cracker keg to enjoy it with a heart full of the innocent sentiment of her years. Fortunately, Dr. Alec saw her before she had time to catch cold, for coming out to tie back the door-flap of his tent for more air, he beheld the small figure perched in the moonlight. Having no fear of ghosts, he quietly approached, and, seeing that she was wide awake, said, with a hand on her shining hair,—

"What is my girl doing here?"

"Having a good time," answered Rose, not at all startled.

"I wonder what she was thinking about with such a sober look?"

"The story you told of the brave sailor who gave up his place on the raft to the woman, and the last drop of water to the poor baby. People who make sacrifices are very much loved and admired, aren't they?" she asked, earnestly.

"If the sacrifice is a true one. But many of the bravest never are known, and get no praise. That does not lessen their beauty, though perhaps it makes them harder, for we all like sympathy," and Dr. Alec sighed a patient sort of sigh.

"I suppose you have made a great many? Would you mind telling me one of them?" asked Rose, arrested by the sigh.

"My last was to give up smoking," was the very unromantic answer to her pensive question.

"Why did you?"

"Bad example for the boys."

"That was very good of you, uncle! Was it hard?"

"I'm ashamed to say it was. But as a wise old fellow once said, 'It is necessary to do right; it is not necessary to be happy.' "

Rose pondered over the saying as if it pleased her, and then said, with a clear, bright look,—

"A real sacrifice is giving up something you want or enjoy very much, isn't it?"

"Yes."

"Doing it one's own self because one loves another person very much and wants her to be happy?"

"Yes."

"And doing it pleasantly, and being glad about it, and not minding the praise if it doesn't come?"

"Yes, dear, that is the true spirit of self-sacrifice; you seem to understand it, and I dare say you will have many chances in your life to try the real thing. I hope they won't be very hard ones."

"I think they will," began Rose, and there stopped short.

"Well, make one now, and go to sleep, or my girl will be ill to-morrow, and then the aunts will say camping out was bad for her."

"I'll go,—good night!" and throwing him a kiss, the little ghost vanished, leaving Uncle Alec to pace the shore and think about some of the unsuspected sacrifices that had made him what he was.

10

ROSE'S SACRIFICE

There certainly were "larks" on Campbell's Island next day, as Charlie had foretold, and Rose took her part in them like one intent on enjoying every minute to the utmost. There was a merry breakfast, a successful fishing expedition, and then the lobsters came out in full force, for even Aunt Jessie appeared in red flannel. There was nothing Uncle Alec could not do in the water, and the boys tried their best to equal him in strength and skill, so there was a great diving and ducking, for every one was bent on distinguishing himself.

Rose swam far out beyond her depth, with uncle to float her back; Aunt Jessie splashed placidly in the shallow pools, with Jamie paddling near by like a little whale beside its mother; while the lads careered about, looking like a flock of distracted flamingoes, and acting like the famous dancing party in "Alice's Adventures in Wonderland."

Nothing but chowder would have lured them from their gambols in the briny deep; that time-honored dish demanded the concentrated action of several mighty minds; so the "Water Babies" came ashore and fell to cooking.

It is unnecessary to say that, when done, it was the most remarkable chowder ever cooked, and the quantity eaten would have amazed the world if the secret had been divulged. After this exertion a *siesta* was considered the thing, and people lay about in tents or out as they pleased, the boys looking like warriors slumbering where they fell.

The elders had just settled to a comfortable nap when the youngsters rose, refreshed and ready for further exploits. A hint sent them all off to the cave, and there were discovered bows and arrows, battle clubs, old swords, and various relics of an interesting nature. Perched upon a commanding rock, with Jamie to "splain" things to her, Rose beheld a series of stirring scenes enacted with great vigor and historical accuracy by her gifted relatives.

Captain Cook was murdered by the natives of Owhyhee in the most thrilling manner. Captain Kidd buried untold wealth in the chowder kettle at the dead of night, and shot both the trusting villains who shared the secret of the hiding-place. Sinbad came ashore there and had manifold adventures, and numberless wrecks bestrewed the sands.

Rose considered them by far the most exciting dramas she had ever witnessed; and when the performance closed with a grand ballet of Feejee Islanders, whose barbaric yells alarmed the gulls, she had no words in which to express her gratification.

Another swim at sunset, another merry evening on the rocks watching the lighted steamers pass seaward and the pleasure-boats come into port, ended the second day of the camping out, and sent every one to bed early that they might be ready for the festivities of the morrow.

"Archie, didn't I hear uncle ask you to row home in the morning for fresh milk and things?"

"Yes; why?"

"Please, may I go too? I have something of *great* importance to arrange; you know I was carried off in a hurry," Rose said in a confidential whisper as she was bidding her cousins good-night.

"I'm willing, and I guess Charlie won't mind."

"Thank you; be sure you stand by me when I ask leave in the morning, and don't say any thing till then, except to Charlie. Promise," urged Rose, so eagerly that Archie struck an attitude, and cried dramatically,—

"By yonder moon I swear!"

"Hush! it's all right, go along;" and Rose departed as if satisfied.

"She's a queer little thing, isn't she, Prince?"

"Rather a nice little thing, *I* think. I'm quite fond of her."

Rose's quick ears caught both remarks, and she retired to her tent, saying to herself with sleepy dignity,—

"Little thing, indeed! Those boys talk as if I was a baby. They will treat me with more respect after tomorrow, I guess."

Archie did stand by her in the morning, and her request was readily granted, as the lads were coming directly back. Off they went, and Rose waved her hand to the islanders with a somewhat pensive air, for an heroic purpose glowed within her, and the spirit of self-sacrifice was about to be illustrated in a new and touching manner.

While the boys got the milk Rose ran to Phebe, ordered her to leave her dishes, to put on her hat and take a note back to Uncle Alec, which would explain this somewhat mysterious performance. Phebe obeyed, and when she went to the boat Rose accompanied her, telling the boys she was not ready to go yet, but they could some of them come for her when she hung a white signal on her balcony.

"But why not come now? What are you about, miss? Uncle won't like it," protested Charlie, in great amazement.

"Just do as I tell you, little boy; uncle will understand and explain. Obey, as Phebe does, and ask no questions. *I* can have secrets as well as other people;" and Rose walked off with an air of lofty independence that impressed her friends immensely.

"It's some plot between uncle and herself, so we won't meddle. All right, Phebe? Pull away, Prince;" and off they went, to be received with much surprise by the islanders.

This was the note Phebe bore:—

"DEAR UNCLE,—I am going to take Phebe's place to-day, and let her have all the fun she can. Please don't mind what she says, but keep her, and tell the boys to be very good to her for my sake. Don't think it is easy to do this; it is very hard to give up the best day of all, but I feel so selfish to have all the pleasure, and Phebe none, that I wish to make this sacrifice. Do let me, and don't laugh at it; I truly do not wish to be praised, and I truly want to do it. Love to all from   "ROSE."

"Bless the little dear, what a generous heart she has! Shall we go after her, Jessie, or let her have her way?" said Dr. Alec, after the first mingled amusement and astonishment had subsided.

"Let her alone, and don't spoil her little sacrifice. She means it, I know, and the best way in which we can show our respect for her effort is to give Phebe a pleasant day. I'm sure she has earned it;" and Mrs. Jessie made a sign to the boys to suppress their disappointment and exert themselves to please Rose's guest.

Phebe was with difficulty kept from going straight home, and declared that she should not enjoy herself one bit without Miss Rose.

"She won't hold out all day, and we shall see her paddling back before noon, I'll wager any thing," said Charlie; and the rest so strongly inclined to his opinion that they resigned themselves to the loss of the little queen of the revels, sure that it would be only a temporary one.

But hour after hour passed, and no signal appeared on the balcony, though Phebe watched it hopefully. No passing boat brought the truant back, though more than one pair of eyes looked out for the bright hair under the round hat; and sunset came, bringing no Rose but the lovely color in the western sky.

"I really did not think the child had it in her. I fancied it was a bit of sentiment, but I see she *was* in earnest, and means that her sacrifice shall be a true one. Dear little soul! I'll make it up to her a thousand times over, and beg her pardon for thinking it might be done for effect," Dr. Alec said remorsefully, as he strained his eyes through the dusk, fancying he saw a small figure sitting in the garden as it had sat on the keg the night before, laying the generous little plot that had cost more than he could guess.

"Well, she can't help seeing the fire-works any way, unless she is goose enough to think she must hide in a dark closet and not look," said Archie, who was rather disgusted at Rose's seeming ingratitude.

"She will see ours capitally, but miss the big ones on the hill, unless papa has forgotten all about them," added Steve, cutting short the harangue Mac had begun upon the festivals of the ancients.

"I'm sure the sight of her will be better than the finest fire-works that ever went off," said Phebe, meditating an elopement with one of the boats if she could get a chance.

"Let things work; if she resists the brilliant invitation we give her she will be a heroine," added Uncle Alec, secretly hoping that she would not.

Meanwhile Rose had spent a quiet, busy day helping Debby, waiting on Aunt Peace, and steadily resisting Aunt Plenty's attempts to send her back to the happy island. It had been hard in the morning to come in from the bright world outside, with flags flying, cannon booming, crackers popping, and every one making ready for a holiday, and go to washing cups, while Debby grumbled and the aunts lamented. It was very hard to see the day go by, knowing how gay each hour must have been across the water, and how a word from her would take her where she longed to be with all her heart. But it was hardest of all when evening came and Aunt Peace was asleep, Aunt Plenty seeing a gossip in the parlor, Debby established in the porch to enjoy the show, and nothing left for the little maid to do but sit alone in her balcony and watch the gay rockets whizz up from island, hill, and city, while bands played and boats laden with happy people went to and fro in the fitful light.

Then it must be confessed that a tear or two dimmed the blue eyes, and once, when a very brilliant display illuminated the island for a moment, and she fancied she saw the tents, the curly head went down on the railing, and a wide-awake nasturtium heard a little whisper,—

"I hope some one wishes I was there!"

The tears were all gone, however, and she was watching the hill and island answer each other with what Jamie called "whizzers, whirligigs, and busters," and smiling as she thought how hard the boys must be working to keep up such a steady fire, when Uncle Mac came walking in upon her, saying hurriedly,—

"Come, child, put on your tippet, pelisse, or whatever you call it, and run off with me. I came to get Phebe, but aunt says she is gone, so I want you. I've got Fun down in the boat, and I want you to go with us and see my fire-works. Got them up for you, and you mustn't miss them, or I shall be disappointed."

"But, uncle," began Rose, feeling as if she ought to refuse even a glimpse of bliss, "perhaps—"

"I know, my dear, I know; aunt told me; but no one needs you now so much as I do, and I insist on your coming," said Uncle Mac, who seemed in a great hurry to be off, yet was unusually kind.

So Rose went and found the little Chinaman with a funny lantern waiting to help her in and convulse her with laughter trying to express his emotions in pigeon English. The city clocks were striking nine as they got out into the bay, and the island fire-works seemed to be over, for no rocket answered the last Roman candle that shone on the Aunt-hill.

"Ours are done, I see, but they are going up all

round the city, and how pretty they are," said Rose, folding her mantle about her and surveying the scene with a pensive interest.

"Hope my fellows have not got into trouble up there," muttered Uncle Mac, adding, with a satisfied chuckle, as a spark shone out, "No; there it goes! Look, Rosy, and see how you like this one; it was ordered especially in honor of your coming."

Rose looked with all her eyes, and saw the spark grow into the likeness of a golden vase, then green leaves came out, and then a crimson flower glowing on the darkness with a splendid lustre.

"Is it a rose, uncle?" she asked, clasping her hands with delight as she recognized the handsome flower.

"Of course it is! Look again, and guess what those are," answered Uncle Mac, chuckling and enjoying it all like a boy.

A wreath of what looked at first like purple brooms appeared below the vase, but Rose guessed what they were meant for and stood straight up, holding by his shoulder, and crying excitedly,—

"Thistles, uncle, Scotch thistles! There are seven of them,—one for each boy! Oh, what a joke!" and she laughed so that she plumped into the bottom of the boat and stayed there till the brilliant spectacle was quite gone.

"That was rather a neat thing, I flatter myself," said Uncle Mac in high glee at the success of his illumination. "Now, shall I leave you on the Island or take you home again, my good little girl?" he added, lifting her up with such a tone of approbation in his voice that Rose kissed him on the spot.

"Home, please, uncle; and I thank you very, very much for the beautiful fire-works you got up for me. I'm so glad I saw it; and I know I shall dream about it," answered Rose steadily, though a wistful glance went toward the Island, now so near that she could smell powder and see shadowy figures flitting about.

Home they went; and Rose fell asleep saying to herself, "It was harder than I thought, but I'm glad I did it, and I truly don't want any reward but Phebe's pleasure."

11
POOR MAC

Rose's sacrifice was a failure in one respect, for, though the elders loved her the better for it, and showed that they did, the boys were not inspired with the sudden respect which she had hoped for. In fact, her feelings were much hurt by overhearing Archie say that he couldn't see any sense in it; and the Prince added another blow by pronouncing her "the queerest chicken ever seen."

It is apt to be so, and it is hard to bear; for, though we do not want trumpets blown, we do like to have our little virtues appreciated, and cannot help feeling disappointed if they are not.

A time soon came, however, when Rose, quite unconsciously, won not only the respect of her cousins, but their gratitude and affection likewise.

Soon after the Island episode, Mac had a sunstroke, and was very ill for some time. It was so sudden that every one was startled, and for some days the boy's life was in danger. He pulled through, however; and then, just as the family were rejoicing, a new trouble appeared which cast a gloom over them all.

Poor Mac's eyes gave out; and well they might,

for he had abused them, and never being very strong, they suffered doubly now.

No one dared to tell him the dark predictions of the great oculist who came to look at them, and the boy tried to be patient, thinking that a few weeks of rest would repair the overwork of several years.

He was forbidden to look at a book, and as that was the one thing he most delighted in, it was a terrible affliction to the Worm. Every one was very ready to read to him, and at first the lads contended for this honor. But as week after week went by, and Mac was still condemned to idleness and a darkened room, their zeal abated, and one after the other fell off. It *was* hard for the active fellows, right in the midst of their vacation; and nobody blamed them when they contented themselves with brief calls, running of errands, and warm expressions of sympathy.

The elders did their best, but Uncle Mac was a busy man, Aunt Jane's reading was of a funereal sort, impossible to listen to long, and the other aunties were all absorbed in their own cares, though they supplied the boy with every delicacy they could invent.

Uncle Alec was a host in himself, but he could not give all his time to the invalid; and if it had not been for Rose, the afflicted Worm would have fared ill. Her pleasant voice suited him, her patience was unfailing, her time of no apparent value, and her eager good-will was very comforting.

The womanly power of self-devotion was strong in the child, and she remained faithfully at her post when all the rest dropped away. Hour after hour she sat in the dusky room, with one ray of light on her book, reading to the boy, who lay with shaded eyes silently enjoying the only pleasure that lightened the weary days. Sometimes he was peevish and hard to please, sometimes he growled because his reader could not manage the dry books he wished to hear, and sometimes he was so despondent that her heart ached to see him. Through all these trials Rose persevered, using all her little arts to please him. When he fretted, she was patient; when he growled, she ploughed bravely through the hard pages,—not dry to her in one sense, for quiet tears dropped on them now and then; and when Mac fell into a despairing mood, she comforted him with every hopeful word she dared to offer.

He said little, but she knew he was grateful, for she suited him better than any one else. If she was late, he was impatient; when she had to go, he seemed forlorn; and when the tired head ached worst, she could always soothe him to sleep, crooning the old songs her father used to love.

"I don't know what I *should* do without that child," Aunt Jane often said.

"She's worth all those racketing fellows put together," Mac would add, fumbling about to discover if the little chair was ready for her coming.

That was the sort of reward Rose liked, the

thanks that cheered her; and whenever she grew very tired, one look at the green shade, the curly head so restless on the pillow, and the poor groping hands, touched her tender heart and put new spirit into the weary voice.

She did not know how much she was learning, both from the books she read and the daily sacrifices she made. Stories and poetry were her delight, but Mac did not care for them; and since his favorite Greeks and Romans were forbidden, he satisfied himself with travels, biographies, and the history of great inventions or discoveries. Rose despised this taste at first, but soon got interested in Livingston's adventures, Hobson's stirring life in India, and the brave trials and triumphs of Watt and Arkwright, Fulton, and "Palissy, the Potter." The true, strong books helped the dreamy girl; her faithful service and sweet patience touched and won the boy; and long afterward both learned to see how useful those seemingly hard and weary hours had been to them.

One bright morning, as Rose sat down to begin a fat volume entitled "History of the French Revolution," expecting to come to great grief over the long names, Mac, who was lumbering about the room like a blind bear, stopped her by asking abruptly,—

"What day of the month is it?"

"The seventh of August, I believe."

"More than half my vacation gone, and I've only had a week of it! I call that hard," and he groaned dismally.

"So it is; but there is more to come, and you may be able to enjoy that."

"*May* be able! I *will* be able! Does that old noodle think I'm going to stay stived up here much longer?"

"I guess he does, unless your eyes get on faster than they have yet."

"Has he said any thing more lately?"

"I haven't seen him, you know. Shall I begin?— this looks rather nice."

"Read away; it's all one to me." And Mac cast himself down upon the old lounge, where his heavy head felt easiest.

Rose began with great spirit, and kept on gallantly for a couple of chapters, getting over the unpronounceable names with unexpected success, she thought, for her listener did not correct her once, and lay so still she fancied he was deeply interested. All of a sudden she was arrested in the middle of a fine paragraph by Mac, who sat bolt upright, brought both feet down with a thump, and said, in a rough, excited tone,—

"Stop! I don't hear a word, and you may as well save your breath to answer my question."

"What is it?" asked Rose, looking uneasy, for she had something on her mind, and feared that he suspected what it was. His next words proved that she was right.

"Now look here, I want to know something, and you've *got* to tell me."

"Please, don't,—" began Rose, beseechingly.

"You *must,* or I'll pull off this shade and stare at the sun as hard as ever I can stare. Come now!" and he half rose, as if ready to execute the threat.

"I will! oh, I will tell, if I know! But don't be reckless and do any thing so crazy as that," cried Rose, in great distress.

"Very well; then listen, and don't dodge, as every one else does. Didn't the doctor think my eyes worse the last time he came? Mother won't say, but you *shall.*"

"I believe he did," faltered Rose.

"I thought so! Did he say I should be able to go to school when it begins?"

"No, Mac," very low.

"Ah!"

That was all, but Rose saw her cousin set his lips together and take a long breath, as if she had hit him hard. He bore the disappointment bravely, however, and asked quite steadily in a minute,—

"How soon does he think I *can* study again?"

It was so hard to answer that! Yet Rose knew she must, for Aunt Jane had declared she *could* not do it, and Uncle Mac had begged her to break the truth to the poor lad.

"Not for a good many months."

"How many?" he asked with a pathetic sort of gruffness.

"A year, perhaps."

"A whole year! Why, I expected to be ready for college by that time." And, pushing up the shade,

Mac stared at her with startled eyes, that soon blinked and fell before the one ray of light.

"Plenty of time for that; you must be patient now, and get them thoroughly well, or they will trouble you again when it will be harder to spare them," she said, with tears in her own eyes.

"I won't do it! I *will* study and get through somehow. It's all humbug about taking care so long. These doctors like to keep hold of a fellow if they can. But I won't stand it,—I vow I won't!" and he banged his fist down on the unoffending pillow as if he were pommelling the hard-hearted doctor.

"Now, Mac, listen to me," Rose said very earnestly, though her voice shook a little and her heart ached. "You know you have hurt your eyes reading by firelight and in the dusk, and sitting up late, and now you'll have to pay for it; the doctor said so. You *must* be careful, and do as he tells you, or you will be—blind."

"No!"

"Yes, it is true, and he wanted us to tell you that nothing but entire rest would cure you. I know it's dreadfully hard, but we'll all help you; I'll read all day long, and lead you, and wait upon you, and try to make it easier—"

She stopped there, for it was evident that he did not hear a sound; the word "blind" seemed to have knocked him down, for he had buried his face in the pillow, and lay so still that Rose was frightened. She sat motionless for many minutes, longing to comfort him, but not knowing how, and wishing Uncle Alec would come, for he had promised to tell Mac.

Presently, a sort of choking sound came out of the pillow, and went straight to her heart,—the most pathetic sob she ever heard, for, though it was the most natural means of relief, the poor fellow must not indulge in it because of the afflicted eyes. The "French Revolution" tumbled out of her lap, and, running to the sofa, she knelt down by it, saying, with the motherly sort of tenderness girls feel for any sorrowing creature,—

"Oh, my dear, you mustn't cry! It is so bad for your poor eyes. Take your head out of that hot pillow, and let me cool it. I don't wonder you feel so, but please don't cry. I'll cry for you; it won't hurt *me*."

As she spoke, she pulled away the cushion with gentle force, and saw the green shade all crushed and stained with the few hot tears that told how bitter the disappointment had been. Mac felt her sympathy, but, being a boy, did not thank her for it; only sat up with a jerk, saying, as he tried to rub away the tell-tale drops with the sleeve of his jacket: "Don't bother; weak eyes always water. I'm all right."

But Rose cried out, and caught his arm: "Don't touch them with that rough woollen stuff! Lie down and let me bathe them, there's a dear boy; then there will be no harm done."

"They do smart confoundedly. I say, don't you

tell the other fellows that I made a baby of myself, will you?" he added, yielding with a sigh to the orders of his nurse, who had flown for the eye-wash and linen cambric handkerchief.

"Of course I won't; but any one would be upset at the idea of being—well—troubled in this way. I'm sure you bear it splendidly, and you know it isn't half so bad when you get used to it. Besides, it is only for a time, and you can do lots of pleasant things if you can't study. You'll have to wear blue goggles, perhaps; won't that be funny?"

And while she was pouring out all the comfortable words she could think of, Rose was softly bathing the eyes and dabbing the hot forehead with lavender-water, as her patient lay quiet with a look on his face that grieved her sadly.

"Homer was blind, and so was Milton, and they did something to be remembered by, in spite of it," he said, as if to himself, in a solemn tone, for even the blue goggles did not bring a smile.

"Papa had a picture of Milton and his daughters writing for him. It was a very sweet picture, I thought," observed Rose in a serious voice, trying to meet the sufferer on his own ground.

"Perhaps I could study if some one read and did the eye part. Do you suppose I could, by and by?" he asked, with a sudden ray of hope.

"I dare say, if your head is strong enough. This sun-stroke, you know, is what upset you, and your brains need rest, the doctor says."

"I'll have a talk with the old fellow next time he

comes, and find out just what I *may* do; then I shall know where I am. What a fool I was that day to be stewing my brains and letting the sun glare on my book till the letters danced before me! I see 'em now when I shut my eyes; black balls bobbing round, and stars and all sorts of queer things. Wonder if all blind people do?"

"Don't think about them; I'll go on reading, shall I? We shall come to the exciting part soon, and then you'll forget all this," suggested Rose.

"No, I never shall forget. Hang the old 'Revolution!' I don't want to hear another word of it. My head aches, and I'm hot. Oh, wouldn't I like to go for a pull in the 'Stormy Petrel!'" and poor Mac tossed about as if he did not know what to do with himself.

"Let me sing, and perhaps you'll drop off; then the day will seem shorter," said Rose, taking up a fan and sitting down beside him.

"Perhaps I shall; I didn't sleep much last night, and when I did I dreamed like fun. See here, you tell the people that I know, and it's all right, and I don't want them to talk about it or howl over me. That's all; now drone away, and I'll try to sleep. Wish I could for a year, and wake up cured."

"Oh, I wish, I wish you could!"

Rose said it so fervently, that Mac was moved to grope for her apron and hold on to a corner of it, as if it was comfortable to feel her near him. But all he said was,—

"You are a good little soul, Rosy. Give us 'The

Birks;' that is a drowsy one that always sends me off."

Quite contented with this small return for all her sympathy, Rose waved her fan and sang, in a dreamy tone, the pretty Scotch air, the burden of which is,—

"Bonny lassie, will ye gang, will ye gang
To the Birks of Aberfeldie?"

Whether the lassie went or not I cannot say, but the laddie was off to the land of Nod in about ten minutes, quite worn out with hearing the bad tidings and the effort to bear them manfully.

12

"The Other Fellows"

Rose did tell "the people" what had passed, and no one "howled" over Mac, or said a word to trouble him. He had his talk with the doctor, and got very little comfort out of it, for he found that "just what he might do" was nothing at all; though the prospect of some study by and by, if all went well, gave him courage to bear the woes of the present. Having made up his mind to this, he behaved so well that every one was astonished, never having suspected so much manliness in the quiet Worm.

The boys were much impressed, both by the greatness of the affliction which hung over him and by his way of bearing it. They were very good to him, but not always particularly wise in their attempts to cheer and amuse; and Rose often found him much downcast after a visit of condolence from the clan. She still kept her place as head-nurse and chief-reader, though the boys did their best in an irregular sort of way. They were rather taken aback sometimes at finding Rose's services preferred to theirs, and privately confided to one another that "Old Mac was getting fond of being molly-coddled." But they could not help seeing how useful she was, and owning that she alone had remained faithful,—a fact which caused some of them much secret compunction now and then.

Rose felt that she ruled in that room, if nowhere else, for Aunt Jane left a great deal to her, finding that her experience with her invalid father fitted her for a nurse, and in a case like this her youth was an advantage rather than a drawback. Mac soon came to think that no one could take care of him so well as Rose, and Rose soon grew fond of her patient, though at first she had considered this cousin the least attractive of the seven. He was not polite and sensible like Archie, nor gay and handsome like Prince Charlie, nor neat and obliging like Steve, nor amusing like the "Brats," nor confiding and affectionate like little Jamie. He was rough, absent-minded, careless, and awkward, rather priggish, and not at all agreeable to a dainty, beauty-loving girl like Rose.

But when his trouble came upon him, she discovered many good things in this cousin of hers, and learned not only to pity but to respect and love the poor Worm, who tried to be patient, brave, and cheerful, and found it a harder task than any one guessed, except the little nurse, who saw him in his gloomiest moods. She soon came to think that his friends did not appreciate him, and upon one occasion was moved to free her mind in a way that made a deep impression on the boys.

Vacation was almost over, and the time drawing near when Mac would be left outside the happy school-world which he so much enjoyed. This made him rather low in his mind, and his cousins exerted themselves to cheer him up, especially one afternoon when a spasm of devotion seemed to seize them all. Jamie trudged down the hill with a basket of blackberries which he had "picked all his ownself," as his scratched fingers and stained lips plainly testified. Will and Geordie brought their puppies to beguile the weary hours, and the three elder lads called to discuss base-ball, cricket, and kindred subjects, eminently fitted to remind the invalid of his privations.

Rose had gone to drive with Uncle Alec, who declared she was getting as pale as a potato sprout, living so much in a dark room. But her thoughts were with her boy all the while, and she ran up to him the moment she returned, to find things in a fine state of confusion.

With the best intentions in life, the lads had done more harm than good, and the spectacle that met Nurse Rose's eye was a trying one. The puppies were yelping, the small boys romping, and the big boys all talking at once; the curtains were up, the room close, berries scattered freely about, Mac's shade half off, his cheeks flushed, his temper ruffled, and his voice loudest of all as he disputed hotly with Steve about lending certain treasured books which he could no longer use.

Now Rose considered this her special kingdom, and came down upon the invaders with an energy which amazed them and quelled the riot at once.

They had never seen her roused before, and the effect was tremendous; also comical, for she drove the whole flock of boys out of the room like an indignant little hen defending her brood. They all went as meekly as sheep; the small lads fled from the house precipitately, but the three elder ones only retired to the next room, and remained there hoping for a chance to explain and apologize, and so appease the irate young lady, who had suddenly turned the tables and clattered them about their ears.

As they waited, they observed her proceedings through the half-open door, and commented upon them briefly but expressively, feeling quite bowed down with remorse at the harm they had innocently done.

"She's put the room to rights in a jiffy. What jacks we were to let those dogs in and kick up such a row," observed Steve, after a prolonged peep.

"The poor old Worm turns as if she was treading on him instead of cuddling him like a pussy cat. Isn't he cross, though?" added Charlie, as Mac was heard growling about his "confounded head."

"She will manage him; but it's mean in us to rumple him up and then leave her to smooth him down. I'd go and help, but I don't know how," said Archie, looking much depressed, for he was a conscientious fellow, and blamed himself for his want of thought.

"No more do I. Odd, isn't it, what a knack

women have for taking care of sick folks?" and Charlie fell a-musing over this undeniable fact.

"She has been ever so good to Mac," began Steve, in a self-reproachful tone.

"Better than his own brother, hey?" cut in Archie, finding relief for his own regret in the delinquencies of another.

"Well, you needn't preach; you didn't any of you do any more, and you might have, for Mac likes you better than he does me. I always fret him, he says, and it isn't my fault if I am a quiddle," protested Steve, in self-defence.

"We have all been selfish and neglected him, so we won't fight about it, but try and do better," said Archie, generously taking more than his share of blame, for he had been less inattentive than either of the others.

"Rose has stood by him like a good one, and it's no wonder he likes to have her round best. I should myself if I was down on my luck as he is," put in Charlie, feeling that he really had not done "the little thing" justice.

"I'll tell you what it is, boys,—we haven't been half good enough to Rose, and we've got to make it up to her somehow," said Archie, who had a very manly sense of honor about paying his debts, even to a girl.

"I'm awfully sorry I made fun of her doll when Jamie lugged it out; and I called her 'baby bunting' when she cried over the dead kitten. Girls *are* such geese sometimes, I can't help it," said Steve, confessing his transgressions handsomely, and feeling quite ready to atone for them if he only knew how.

"I'll go down on my knees and beg her pardon for treating her as if she was a child. Don't it make her mad, though? Come to think of it, she's only two years or so younger than I am. But she is so small and pretty, she always seems like a dolly to me," and the Prince looked down from his lofty height of five feet five as if Rose was indeed a pygmy beside him.

"That dolly has got a real good little heart, and a bright mind of her own, you'd better believe. Mac says she understands some things quicker than he can, and mother thinks she is an uncommonly nice girl, though she don't know all creation. You needn't put on airs, Charlie, though you *are* a tall one, for Rose likes Archie better than you; she said she did because he treated her respectfully."

"Steve looks as fierce as a game-cock; but don't you get excited, my son, for it won't do a bit of good. Of course, everybody likes the Chief best; they ought to, and I'll punch their heads if they don't. So calm yourself, Dandy, and mend your own manners before you come down on other people's."

Thus the Prince with great dignity and perfect good nature, while Archie looked modestly gratified with the flattering opinions of his kinsfolk, and Steve subsided, feeling he had done his duty as a cousin and a brother. A pause ensued, during which Aunt Jane appeared in the other room, accompanied by a tea-tray sumptuously spread, and prepared to feed her big nestling, as that was a task she allowed no one to share with her.

"If you have a minute to spare before you go, child, I wish you'd just make Mac a fresh shade; this has got a berry stain on it, and he must be tidy, for he is to go out to-morrow if it is a cloudy day," said Mrs. Jane, spreading toast in a stately manner, while Mac slopped his tea about without receiving a word of reproof.

"Yes, aunt," answered Rose, so meekly that the boys could hardly believe it could be the same voice which had issued the stern command, "Out of this room, every one of you!" not very long ago.

They had not time to retire, without unseemly haste, before she walked into the parlor and sat down at the work-table without a word. It was funny to see the look the three tall lads cast at the little person sedately threading a needle with green silk. They all wanted to say something expressive of repentance, but no one knew how to begin, and it was evident, from the prim expression of Rose's face, that she intended to stand upon her dignity till they had properly abased themselves. The pause was becoming very awkward, when Charlie, who possessed all the persuasive arts of a born scapegrace, went slowly down upon his knees before her, beat his breast, and said, in a heartbroken tone,—

"Please forgive me this time, and I'll never do so any more."

It was very hard to keep sober, but Rose managed it, and answered gravely,—

"It is Mac's pardon you should ask, not mine, for you haven't hurt me, and I shouldn't wonder if you had him a great deal, with all that light and racket, and talk about things that only worry him."

"Do you really think we've hurt him, cousin?" asked Archie, with a troubled look, while Charlie settled down in a remorseful heap among the table legs.

"Yes, I do, for he has got a raging headache, and his eyes are as red as—as this emery bag," answered Rose, solemnly plunging her needle into a fat flannel strawberry.

Steve tore his hair, metaphorically speaking, for he clutched his cherished top-knot and wildly dishevelled it, as if that was the heaviest penance he could inflict upon himself at such short notice. Charlie laid himself out flat, melodramatically begging some one to take him away and hang him; but Archie, who felt worst of all, said nothing except to vow within himself that he would read to Mac till his own eyes were as red as a dozen emery bags combined.

Seeing the wholesome effects of her treatment upon these culprits, Rose felt that she might relent and allow them a gleam of hope. She found it impossible to help trampling upon the prostrate Prince a little, in words at least, for he had hurt her feelings oftener than he knew; so she gave him a thimble-pie on the top of his head, and said, with the air of an infinitely superior being,—

"Don't be silly, but get up, and I'll tell you something much better to do than sprawling on the floor and getting all over lint."

Charlie obediently sat himself upon a hassock at her feet; the other sinners drew near to catch the words of wisdom about to fall from her lips, and Rose, softened by this gratifying humility, addressed them in her most maternal tone.

"Now, boys, if you really want to be good to Mac, you can do it in this way. Don't keep talking about things he can't do, or go and tell what fun you have had batting your ridiculous balls about. Get some nice book and read quietly; cheer him up about school, and offer to help him study by and by; *you* can do that better than I, because I'm only a girl, and don't learn Greek and Latin and all sorts of headachy stuff."

"Yes, but you can do heaps of things better than we can; you've proved that," said Archie, with an approving look that delighted Rose, though she could not resist giving Charlie one more rebuke, by saying, with a little bridling up of the head, and a curl of the lip that wanted to smile instead,—

"I'm glad you think so, though I *am* a 'queer chicken.' "

This scathing remark caused the Prince to hide his face for shame, and Steve to erect his head in the proud consciousness that this shot was not meant for him. Archie laughed, and Rose, seeing a merry blue eye winking at her from behind two brown hands, gave Charlie's ear a friendly tweak, and extended the olive-branch of peace.

"Now we'll all be good, and plan nice things for poor Mac," she said, smiling so graciously that the boys felt as if the sun had suddenly burst out from behind a heavy cloud and was shining with great brilliancy.

The storm had cleared the air, and quite a heavenly calm succeeded, during which plans of a most varied and surprising sort were laid, for every one burned to make noble sacrifices upon the shrine of "poor Mac," and Rose was the guiding star to whom the others looked with most gratifying submission. Of course, this elevated state of things could not endure long, but it was *very* nice while it lasted, and left an excellent effect upon the minds of all when the first ardor had subsided.

"There, that's ready for to-morrow, and I do hope it will be cloudy," said Rose, as she finished off the new shade, the progress of which the boys had watched with interest.

"I'd bespoken an extra sunny day, but I'll tell the clerk of the weather to change it. He's an obliging fellow, and he'll attend to it; so make yourself easy," said Charlie, who had become quite perky again.

"It is very easy for you to joke, but how would you like to wear a blinder like that for weeks and weeks, sir?" and Rose quenched his rising spirits by slipping the shade over his eyes, as he still sat on the cushion at her feet.

"It's horrid! Take it off, take it off! I don't wonder the poor old boy has the blues with a thing like that on;" and Charlie sat looking at what seemed to him an instrument of torture, with such a sober face that Rose took it gently away, and went in to bid Mac good-night.

"I shall go home with her, for it is getting darkish, and she is rather timid," said Archie, forgetting that he had often laughed at this very timidity.

"I think *I* might, for she's taking care of my brother," put in Steve, asserting his rights.

"Let's all go; that will please her," proposed Charlie, with a burst of gallantry which electrified his mates.

"We will!" they said with one voice, and they did, to Rose's great surprise and secret contentment; though Archie had all the care of her, for the other two were leaping fences, running races, and having wrestling matches all the way down.

They composed themselves on reaching the door, however; shook hands cordially all round, made their best bows, and retired with great elegance and dignity, leaving Rose to say to herself, with girlish satisfaction, as she went in,—

"Now, *that* is the way I like to be treated."

13

COSEY CORNER

Vacation was over, the boys went back to school, and poor Mac was left lamenting. He was out of the darkened room now, and promoted to blue goggles, through which he took a gloomy view of life, as might have been expected; for there was nothing he could do but wander about, and try to amuse himself without using his eyes. Any one who has ever been condemned to that sort of idleness knows how irksome it is, and can understand the state of mind which caused Mac to say to Rose in a desperate tone one day,—

"Look here, if you don't invent some new employment or amusement for me, I shall knock myself on the head as sure as you live."

Rose flew to Uncle Alec for advice, and he ordered both patient and nurse to the mountains for a month, with Aunt Jessie and Jamie as escort. Pokey and her mother joined the party, and one bright September morning six very happy-looking people were aboard the express train for Portland,—two smiling mammas, laden with luncheon baskets and wraps; a pretty young girl with a bag of books on her arm; a tall, thin lad with his hat over his eyes; and two small children, who sat with their short legs straight out before them, and their chubby faces beaming with the first speechless delight of "truly travelling."

An especially splendid sunset seemed to have been prepared to welcome them when, after a long day's journey, they drove into a wide, green dooryard, where a white colt, a red cow, two cats, four kittens, many hens, and a dozen people, old and young, were gayly disporting themselves. Every one nodded and smiled in the friendliest manner, and a lively old lady kissed the new-comers all round, as she said heartily,—

"Well, now, I'm proper glad to see you! Come right in and rest, and we'll have tea in less than no time, for you must be tired. Lizzie, you show the folks upstairs; Kitty, you fly round and help father in with the trunks; and Jenny and I will have the table all ready by the time you come down. Bless the dears, they want to go see the pussies, and so they shall!"

The three pretty daughters did "fly round," and every one felt at home at once, all were so hospitable and kind. Aunt Jessie had raptures over the home-made carpets, quilts, and quaint furniture; Rose could not keep away from the windows, for each framed a lovely picture; and the little folks made friends at once with the other children, who filled their arms with chickens and kittens, and did the honors handsomely.

The toot of a horn called all to supper, and a

goodly party including six children besides the Campbells, assembled in the long dining-room, armed with mountain appetites and the gayest spirits. It was impossible for any one to be shy or sober, for such gales of merriment arose they blew the starch out of the stiffest, and made the saddest jolly. Mother Atkinson, as all called their hostess, was the merriest there, and the busiest; for she kept flying up to wait on the children, to bring out some new dish, or to banish the live stock, who were of such a social turn that the colt came into the entry and demanded sugar; the cats sat about in people's laps, winking suggestively at the food; and speckled hens cleared the kitchen floor of crumbs, as they joined in the chat with a cheerful clucking.

Everybody turned out after tea to watch the sunset till all the lovely red was gone, and mosquitoes wound their shrill horns to sound the retreat. The music of an organ surprised the new-comers, and in the parlor they found Father Atkinson playing sweetly on the little instrument made by himself. All the children gathered about him, and, led by the tuneful sisters, sang prettily till Pokey fell asleep behind the door, and Jamie gaped audibly right in the middle of his favorite,—

"Coo," said the little doves: "Coo," said she,
    "All in the top of the old pine-tree."

The older travellers, being tired, went to "bye low" at the same time, and slept like tops in homespun sheets, on husk mattresses made by Mother Atkinson, who seemed to have put some soothing powder among them, so deep and sweet was the slumber that came.

Next day began the wholesome out-of-door life, which works such wonders with tired minds and feeble bodies. The weather was perfect, and the mountain air made the children as frisky as young lambs; while the elders went about smiling at one another, and saying, "Isn't it splendid?" Even Mac, the "slow coach," was seen to leap over a fence as if he really could not help it; and when Rose ran after him with his broad-brimmed hat, he made the spirited proposal to go into the woods and hunt for a catamount.

Jamie and Pokey were at once enrolled in the Cosey Corner Light Infantry,—a truly superb company, composed entirely of officers, all wearing cocked hats, carrying flags, waving swords, or beating drums. It was a spectacle to stir the dullest soul when this gallant band marched out of the yard in full regimentals, with Captain Dove—a solemn, big-headed boy of eleven—issuing his orders with the gravity of a general, and his Falstaffian regiment obeying them with more docility than skill. The little Snow children did very well, and Lieutenant Jack Dove was fine to see; so was Drummer Frank, the errand-boy of the house, as he rub-a-dub-dubbed with all his heart and drumsticks. Jamie had "trained" before, and was made a colonel at once; but Pokey was the best of all, and called forth a spontaneous burst of applause from the spectators as she brought up the rear, her cocked hat all over one eye, her flag trailing over her shoulder, and her wooden sword straight up in the air; her face beaming and every curl bobbing with delight as her fat legs tottered in the vain attempt to keep step manfully.

Mac and Rose were picking blackberries in the bushes beside the road when the soldiers passed without seeing them, and they witnessed a sight that was both pretty and comical. A little farther on was one of the family burial spots so common in those parts, and just this side of it Captain Fred Dove ordered his company to halt, explaining his reason for so doing in the following words:—

"That's a graveyard, and it's proper to muffle the drums and lower the flags as we go by, and we'd better take off our hats, too; it's more respectable, I think."

"Isn't that cunning of the dears?" whispered Rose, as the little troop marched slowly by to the muffled roll of the drums, every flag and sword held low, all the little heads uncovered, and the childish faces very sober as the leafy shadows flickered over them.

"Let's follow and see what they are after," proposed Mac, who found sitting on a wall and being fed with blackberries luxurious but tiresome.

So they followed and heard the music grow lively, saw the banners wave in the breeze again when the graveyard was passed, and watched the company file into the dilapidated old church that stood at the corner of three woodland roads. Presently the sound of singing made the outsiders quicken their steps, and, stealing up, they peeped in at one of the broken windows.

Captain Dove was up in the old wooden pulpit, gazing solemnly down upon his company, who, having stacked their arms in the porch, now sat in the bare pews singing a Sunday-school hymn with great vigor and relish.

"Let us pray," said Captain Dove, with as much reverence as an army chaplain; and, folding his hands, he repeated a prayer which he thought all would know,—an excellent little prayer, but not exactly appropriate to the morning, for it was,—

"Now I lay me down to sleep."

Every one joined in saying it, and it was a pretty sight to see the little creatures bowing their curly heads and lisping out the words they knew so well. Tears came into Rose's eyes as she looked; Mac took his hat off involuntarily, and then clapped it on again as if ashamed of showing any feeling.

"Now I shall preach you a short sermon, and my text is, 'Little children, love one another.' I asked mamma to give me one, and she thought that would be good; so you all sit still and I'll preach it. You mustn't whisper, Marion, but hear *me*. It means that we should be good to each other, and play fair, and not quarrel as we did this very day about the wagon. Jack can't always drive, and needn't be mad because I like to go with Frank. Annette ought to be horse sometimes and not always driver; and Willie may as well make up his mind to let Marion build her house by his, for she *will* do it, and he needn't fuss about it. Jamie seems to be a good boy, but I shall preach to him if he isn't. No, Pokey, people don't kiss in church or put their hats on. Now you must all remember what I tell you, because I'm the captain, and you should mind me."

Here Lieutenant Jack spoke right out in meeting with the rebellious remark,—

"Don't care if you are; you'd better mind yourself, and tell how you took away my strap, and kept the biggest doughnut, and didn't draw fair when we had the truck."

"Yes, and you slapped Frank; I saw you," bawled Willie Snow, bobbing up in his pew.

"And you took my book away and hid it 'cause I wouldn't go and swing when you wanted me to," added Annette, the oldest of the Snow trio.

"I *shan't* build my house by Willie's if he don't want me to, so now!" put in little Marion, joining the mutiny.

"I *will* tiss Dimmy! and I tored up my hat 'tause a pin picked me," shouted Pokey, regardless of Jamie's efforts to restrain her.

Captain Dove looked rather taken aback at this outbreak in the ranks; but, being a dignified and calm personage, he quelled the rising rebellion with great tact and skill by saying, briefly,—

"We will sing the last hymn; 'Sweet, sweet good-by,'—you all know that, so do it nicely, and then we will go and have luncheon."

Peace was instantly restored, and a burst of melody drowned the suppressed giggles of Rose and Mac, who found it impossible to keep sober during the latter part of this somewhat remarkable service. Fifteen minutes of repose rendered it a physical impossibility for the company to march out as quietly as they had marched in. I grieve to state that the entire troop raced home as hard as they could pelt, and were soon skirmishing briskly over their lunch, utterly oblivious of what Jamie (who had been much impressed by the sermon) called "the captain's beautiful teck."

It was astonishing how much they all found to do at Cosey Corner; and Mac, instead of lying in a hammock and being read to, as he had expected, was busiest of all. He was invited to survey and lay out Skeeterville, a town which the children were getting up in a huckleberry pasture; and he found much amusement in planning little roads, staking off house-lots, attending to the water-works, and consulting with the "selectmen" about the best sites for public buildings; for Mac was a boy still, in spite of his fifteen years and his love of books.

Then he went fishing with a certain jovial gentleman from the West; and though they seldom caught any thing but colds, they had great fun and exercise chasing the phantom trout they were bound to have. Mac also developed a geological mania, and went tapping about at rocks and stones, discoursing wisely of "strata, periods, and fossil remains;" while Rose picked up leaves and lichens, and gave him lessons in botany, in return for his lectures on geology.

They led a very merry life; for the Atkinson girls kept up a sort of perpetual picnic; and did it so capitally, that one was never tired of it. So their visitors throve finely, and long before the month was out it was evident that Dr. Alec had prescribed the right medicine for his patients.

14

A HAPPY BIRTHDAY

The twelfth of October was Rose's birthday, but no one seemed to remember that interesting fact, and she felt delicate about mentioning it, so fell asleep the night before wondering if she would have any presents. That question was settled early the next morning, for she was awakened by a soft tap on her face, and opening her eyes she beheld a little black and white figure sitting on her pillow, staring at her with a pair of round eyes very like blueberries, while one downy paw patted her nose to attract her notice. It was Kitty Comet, the prettiest of all the pussies, and Comet evidently had a mission to perform, for a pink bow adorned her neck, and a bit of paper was pinned to it bearing the words, "For Miss Rose, from Frank."

That pleased her extremely, and that was only the beginning of the fun, for surprises and presents kept popping out in the most delightful manner all through the day, the Atkinson girls being famous jokers and Rose a favorite. But the best gift of all came on the way to Mount Windy-top, where it was decided to picnic in honor of the great occasion. Three jolly loads set off soon after breakfast, for everybody went, and everybody seemed bound to have an extra good time, especially Mother Atkinson, who wore a hat as broad-brimmed as an umbrella, and took the dinner-horn to keep her flock from straying away.

"I'm going to drive aunty and a lot of the babies, so you must ride the pony. And please stay behind us a good bit when we go to the station, for a parcel is coming, and you are not to see it till dinnertime. You won't mind, will you?" said Mac in a confidential aside during the wild flurry of the start.

"Not a bit," answered Rose. "It hurts my feelings *very* much to be told to keep out of the way at any other time, but birthdays and Christmas it is part of the fun to be blind and stupid, and poked into corners. I'll be ready as soon as you are, Giglamps."

"Stop under the big maple till I call,—then you can't possibly see any thing," added Mac, as he mounted her on the pony his father had sent up for his use. "Barkis" was so gentle and so "willin," however, that Rose was ashamed to be afraid to ride him; so she had learned, that she might surprise Dr. Alec when she got home; meantime she had many a fine canter "over the hills and far away" with Mac, who preferred Mr. Atkinson's old Sorrel.

Away they went, and, coming to the red maple, Rose obediently paused; but could not help stealing a glance in the forbidden direction before the call came. Yes, there was a hamper going under the seat, and then she caught sight of a tall man whom Mac seemed to be hustling into the carriage in a great hurry. One look was enough, and, with a cry of delight, Rose was off down the road as fast as Barkis could go.

"Now I'll astonish uncle," she thought. "I'll dash up in grand style, and show him that I am not a coward, after all."

Fired by this ambition, she startled Barkis by a sharp cut, and still more bewildered him by leaving him to his own guidance down the steep, stony road. The approach would have been a fine success if, just as Rose was about to pull up and salute, two or three distracted hens had not scuttled across the road with a great squawking, which caused Barkis to shy and stop so suddenly that his careless rider landed in an ignominious heap just under old Sorrel's astonished nose.

Rose was up again before Dr. Alec was out of the carryall, and threw two dusty arms about his neck, crying with a breathless voice,—

"O uncle, I'm *so* glad to see you! It is better than a cart-load of goodies, and so dear of you to come!"

"But aren't you hurt, child? That was a rough tumble, and I'm afraid you must be damaged somewhere," answered the Doctor, full of fond anxiety, as he surveyed his girl with pride.

"My feelings are hurt, but my bones are all safe. It's too bad! I was going to do it so nicely, and those stupid hens spoilt it all," said Rose, quite crest-fallen, as well as much shaken.

"I couldn't believe my eyes when I asked 'Where is Rose?' and Mac pointed to the little Amazon pelting down the hill at such a rate. You couldn't have done any thing that would please me more, and I'm delighted to see how well you ride. Now, will you mount again, or shall we turn Mac out and take you in?" asked Dr. Alec, as Aunt Jessie proposed a start, for the others were beckoning them to follow.

"Pride goeth before a fall,—better not try to show off again, ma'am," said Mac, who would have been more than mortal if he had refrained from teasing when so good a chance offered.

"Pride does go before a fall, but I wonder if a sprained ankle always comes after it?" thought Rose, bravely concealing her pain, as she answered, with great dignity,—

"I *prefer* to ride. Come on, and see who will catch up first."

She was up and away as she spoke, doing her best to efface the memory of her downfall by sitting very erect, elbows down, head well up, and taking the motion of the pony as Barkis cantered along as easily as a rocking-chair.

"You ought to see her go over a fence and race when we ride together. She can scud, too, like a deer when we play 'Follow the leader,' and skip stones and bat balls almost as well as I can," said Mac, in reply to his uncle's praise of his pupil.

"I'm afraid you will think her a sad tomboy, Alec; but really she seems so well and happy, I have not the heart to check her. She has broken out in the most unexpected way, and frisks like a colt; for she says she feels so full of spirits she *must* run and shout whether it is proper or not," added Mrs. Jessie, who had been a pretty hoyden years ago herself.

"Good,—good! that's the best news you could tell me;" and Dr. Alec rubbed his hands heartily. "Let the girl run and shout as much as she will,— it is a sure sign of health, and as natural to a happy child as frisking is to any young animal full of life. Tomboys make strong women usually, and I had far rather find Rose playing foot-ball with Mac than puttering over bead-work like that affected midget, Ariadne Blish."

"But she cannot go on playing foot-ball very long; and we must not forget that she has a woman's work to do by and by," began Mrs. Jessie.

"Neither will Mac play foot-ball much longer, but he will be all the better fitted for business, because of the health it gives him. Polish is easily added, if the foundations are strong; but no amount of gilding will be of use if your timber is not sound. I'm sure I'm right, Jessie; and if I can do as well by my girl during the next six months as I have the last, my experiment *will* succeed."

"It certainly will; for when I contrast that bright, blooming face with the pale, listless one that made my heart ache a while ago, I can believe in almost any miracle," said Mrs. Jessie, as Rose looked round to point out a lovely view, with cheeks like the ruddy apples in the orchard near by, eyes clear as the autumn sky overhead, and vigor in every line of her girlish figure.

A general scramble among the rocks was followed by a regular gypsy lunch, which the young folks had the rapture of helping to prepare. Mother Atkinson put on her apron, turned up her sleeves, and fell to work as gayly as if in her own kitchen, boiling the kettle slung on three sticks over a fire of cones and fir-boughs; while the girls spread the mossy table with a feast of country goodies, and the children tumbled about in every one's way till the toot of the horn made them settle down like a flock of hungry birds.

As soon as the merry meal and a brief interval of repose were over, it was unanimously voted to have some charades. A smooth, green spot between two stately pines was chosen for the stage; shawls hung up, properties collected, audience and actors separated, and a word quickly chosen.

The first scene discovered Mac in a despondent attitude and shabby dress, evidently much troubled in mind. To him entered a remarkable creature with a brown-paper bag over its head. A little pink nose peeped through one hole in the middle, white teeth through another, and above two eyes glared fiercely. Spires of grass stuck in each side of the mouth seemed meant to represent whiskers;

the upper corners of the bag were twisted like ears, and no one could doubt for a moment that the black scarf pinned on behind was a tail.

This singular animal seemed in pantomime to be comforting his master and offering advice, which was finally acted upon, for Mac pulled off his boots, helped the little beast into them, and gave him a bag; then, kissing his paw with a hopeful gesture, the creature retired, purring so successfully that there was a general cry of "Cat, puss, boots!"

"Cat is the word," replied a voice, and the curtain fell.

The next scene was a puzzler, for in came another animal, on all-fours this time, with a new sort of tail and long ears. A gray shawl concealed its face, but an inquisitive sunbeam betrayed the glitter as of goggles under the fringe. On its back rode a small gentleman in Eastern costume, who appeared to find some difficulty in keeping his seat as his steed jogged along. Suddenly a spirit appeared, all in white, with long newspaper wings upon its back and golden locks about its face. Singularly enough, the beast beheld this apparition and backed instantly, but the rider evidently saw nothing and whipped up unmercifully, also unsuccessfully, for the spirit stood directly in the path, and the amiable beast would not budge a foot. A lively skirmish followed, which ended in the Eastern gentleman's being upset into a sweet-fern bush, while the better-bred animal abased itself before the shining one.

The children were all in the dark till Mother Atkinson said, in an inquiring tone,—

"If that isn't Balaam and the ass, I'd like to know what it is. Rose makes a sweet angel, don't she?"

"Ass" was evidently the word, and the angel retired, smiling with mundane satisfaction over the compliment that reached her ears.

The next was a pretty little scene from the immortal story of "Babes in the Wood." Jamie and Pokey came trotting in, hand-in-hand, and, having been through the parts many times before, acted with great ease and much fluency, audibly directing each other from time to time as they went along. The berries were picked, the way lost, tears shed, baby consolation administered, and then the little pair lay down among the brakes and died with their eyes wide open and the toes of their four little boots turned up to the daisies in the most pathetic manner.

"Now the wobins tum. You be twite dead, Dimmy, and I'll peep and see 'em," one defunct innocent was heard to say.

"I hope they'll be quick, for I'm lying on a stone, and ants are walking up my leg like fury," murmured the other.

Here the robins came flapping in with red scarfs over their breasts and leaves in their mouths, which they carefully laid upon the babes wherever they would show best. A prickly blackberry-leaf placed directly over Pokey's nose caused her to sneeze so violently that her little legs flew into the air; Jamie gave a startled "Ow!" and the pitying fowls fled giggling.

After some discussion it was decided that the syllable must be "strew or strow," and then they waited to see if it was a good guess.

This scene discovered Annette Snow in bed, evidently very ill; Miss Jenny was her anxious mamma, and her merry conversation amused the audience till Mac came in as a physician, and made great fun with his big watch, pompous manner, and absurd questions. He prescribed one pellet with an unpronounceable name, and left after demanding twenty dollars for his brief visit.

The pellet was administered, and such awful agonies immediately set in that the distracted mamma bade a sympathetic neighbor run for Mother Know-all. The neighbor ran, and in came a brisk little old lady in cap and specs, with a bundle of herbs under her arm, which she at once applied in all sorts of funny ways, explaining their virtues as she clapped a plantain poultice here, put a pounded catnip plaster there, or tied a couple of mullein leaves round the sufferer's throat. Instant relief ensued, the dying child sat up and demanded baked beans, the grateful parent offered fifty dollars; but Mother Know-all indignantly refused it and went smiling away, declaring that a neighborly turn needed no reward, and a doctor's *fee* was all a humbug.

The audience were in fits of laughter over this

scene, for Rose imitated Mrs. Atkinson capitally, and the herb-cure was a good hit at the excellent lady's belief that "yarbs" would save mankind if properly applied. No one enjoyed it more than herself, and the saucy children prepared for the grand *finale* in high feather.

This closing scene was brief but striking, for two trains of cars whizzed in from opposite sides, met with a terrible collision in the middle of the stage, and a general smash-up completed the word *catastrophe.*

"Now let us act a proverb. I've got one all ready," said Rose, who was dying to distinguish herself in some way before Uncle Alec.

So every one but Mac, the gay Westerner, and Rose, took their places on the rocky seats and discussed the late beautiful and varied charade, in which Pokey frankly pronounced her own scene the "bestest of all."

In five minutes the curtain was lifted; nothing appeared but a very large sheet of brown paper pinned to a tree, and on it was drawn a clock-face, the hands pointing to four. A small note below informed the public that 4 A.M. was the time. Hardly had the audience grasped this important fact when a long water-proof serpent was seen uncoiling itself from behind a stump. An inch-worm, perhaps, would be a better description, for it travelled in the same humpy way as that pleasing reptile. Suddenly a very wide-awake and active fowl advanced, pecking, chirping, and scratching vigorously. A tuft of green leaves waved upon his crest, a larger tuft of brakes made an umbrageous tail, and a shawl of many colors formed his flapping wings. A truly noble bird, whose legs had the genuine strut, whose eyes shone watchfully, and whose voice had a ring that evidently struck terror into the caterpillar's soul, if it was a caterpillar. He squirmed, he wriggled, he humped as fast as he could, trying to escape; but all in vain. The tufted bird espied him, gave one warbling sort of crow, pounced upon him, and flapped triumphantly away.

"That early bird got such a big worm he could hardly carry him off," laughed Aunt Jessie, as the children shouted over the joke suggested by Mac's nickname.

"That is one of uncle's favorite proverbs, so I got it up for his especial benefit," said Rose, coming up with the two-legged worm beside her.

"Very clever; what next?" asked Dr. Alec as she sat down beside him.

"The Dove boys are going to give us an 'Incident in the Life of Napoleon,' as they call it; the children think it very splendid, and the little fellows do it rather nicely," answered Mac with condescension.

A tent appeared, and pacing to and fro before it was a little sentinel, who, in a brief soliloquy, informed the observers that the elements were in a great state of confusion, that he had marched some hundred miles or so that day, and that he was dying for want of sleep. Then he paused, leaned upon his gun, and seemed to doze; dropped slowly down, overpowered with slumber, and finally lay flat, with his gun beside him, a faithless little sentinel. Enter Napoleon, cocked hat, gray coat, high boots, folded arms, grim mouth, and a melodramatic stride. Freddy Dove always covered himself with glory in this part, and "took the stage" with a Napoleonic attitude that brought down the house; for the big-headed boy, with solemn, dark eyes and square brow, was "the very moral of that rascal, Boneyparty," Mother Atkinson said.

Some great scheme was evidently brewing in his mighty mind,—a trip across the Alps, a bonfire at Moscow, or a little skirmish at Waterloo, perhaps, for he marched in silent majesty till suddenly a gentle snore disturbed the imperial reverie. He saw the sleeping soldier and glared upon him, saying in an awful tone,—

"Ha! asleep at his post! Death is the penalty,— he must die!"

Picking up the musket, he is about to execute summary justice, as emperors are in the habit of doing, when something in the face of the weary sentinel appears to touch him. And well it might, for a most engaging little warrior was Jack as he lay with his shako half off, his childish face trying to keep sober, and a great black moustache over his rosy mouth. It would have softened the heart of any Napoleon, and the Little Corporal proved himself a man by relenting, and saying, with a lofty gesture of forgiveness,—

"Brave fellow, he is worn out; I will let him sleep, and mount guard in his place."

Then, shouldering the gun, this noble being strode to and fro with a dignity which thrilled the younger spectators. The sentinel awakes, sees what has happened, and gives himself up for lost. But the Emperor restores his weapon, and, with that smile which won all hearts, says, pointing to a high rock whereon a crow happens to be sitting: "Be brave, be vigilant, and remember that from yonder Pyramid generations are beholding you," and with these memorable words he vanishes, leaving the grateful soldier bolt upright, with his hand at his temple and deathless devotion stamped upon his youthful countenance.

The applause which followed this superb piece had hardly subsided, when a sudden splash and a shrill cry caused a general rush toward the waterfall that went gambolling down the rocks, singing sweetly as it ran. Pokey had tried to gambol also, and had tumbled into a shallow pool, whither Jamie had gallantly followed, in a vain attempt to fish her out, and both were paddling about half frightened, half pleased with the unexpected bath.

This mishap made it necessary to get the dripping infants home as soon as possible; so the wagons were loaded up, and away they went, as merry as if the mountain air had really been "Oxygenated Sweets not Bitters," as Dr. Alec suggested when Mac said he felt as jolly as if he had been drinking champagne instead of the currant wine that came with a great frosted cake wreathed with sugar roses in Aunt Plenty's hamper of goodies.

Rose took part in all the fun, and never betrayed by look or word the twinges of pain she suffered in her ankle. She excused herself from the games in the evening, however, and sat talking to Uncle Alec in a lively way, that both amazed and delighted him; for she confided to him that she played horse with the children, drilled with the light infantry, climbed trees, and did other dreadful things that would have caused the aunts to cry aloud if they knew of them.

"I don't care a pin what they say if you don't mind, uncle," she answered, when he pictured the dismay of the good ladies.

"Ah, it's all very well to defy *them*, but you are getting so rampant, I'm afraid you will defy me next, and then where are we?"

"No, I won't! I shouldn't dare; because you are my guardian, and can put me in a strait-jacket if you like"; and Rose laughed in his face, even while she nestled closer with a confiding gesture pleasant to see.

"Upon my word, Rosy, I begin to feel like the man who bought an elephant, and then didn't know what to do with him. I thought I had got a pet and plaything for years to come; but here you are growing up like a bean-stalk, and I shall find I've got a strong-minded little woman on my hands before I can turn round. There's a predicament for a man and an uncle!"

Dr. Alec's comic distress was mercifully relieved for the time being by a dance of goblins on the lawn, where the children, with pumpkin lanterns on their heads, frisked about like will-o'-the-wisps, as a parting surprise.

When Rose went to bed, she found that Uncle Alec had not forgotten her; for on the table stood a delicate little easel, holding two miniatures set in velvet. She knew them both, and stood looking at them till her eyes brimmed over with tears that were both sweet and sad; for they were the faces of her father and mother, beautifully copied from portraits fast fading away.

Presently she knelt down, and, putting her arms round the little shrine, kissed one after the other, saying with an earnest voice, "I'll truly try to make them glad to see me by and by."

And that was Rose's little prayer on the night of her fourteenth birthday.

Two days later, the Campbells went home, a larger party than when they came; for Dr. Alec was escort, and Kitty Comet was borne in state in a basket, with a bottle of milk, some tiny sandwiches, and a doll's dish to drink out of, as well as a bit of carpet to lie on in her palace car, out of which she kept popping her head in the most fascinating manner.

There was a great kissing and cuddling, waving of handkerchiefs, and last good-bys, as they went; and when they had started, Mother Atkinson came running after them, to tuck in some little pies, hot from the oven, "for the dears, who might get tired of bread and butter during that long day's travel."

Another start, and another halt; for the Snow children came shrieking up to demand the three kittens that Pokey was coolly carrying off in a travelling-bag. The unhappy kits were rescued, half smothered, and restored to their lawful owners, amid dire lamentation from the little kidnapper, who declared that she only "tooked um 'cause they'd want to go wid their sister Tomie."

Start number three and stoppage number three, as Frank hailed them with the luncheon-basket, which had been forgotten, after every one had protested that it was safely in.

All went well after that, and the long journey was pleasantly beguiled by Pokey and Pussy, who played together so prettily that they were considered public benefactors.

"Rose doesn't want to go home, for she knows the aunts won't let her rampage as she did up at Cosey Corner," said Mac, as they approached the old house.

"I *can't* rampage if I want to,—for a time, at least; and I'll tell you why. I sprained my ankle when I tumbled off of Barkis, and it gets worse and worse; though I've done all I know to cure it and hide it, so it shouldn't trouble any one," whispered Rose, knitting her brows with pain, as she prepared to descend, wishing her uncle would take her instead of her bundles.

How he did it, she never knew; but Mac had her

up the steps and on the parlor sofa before she could put her foot to the ground.

"There you are,—right side up with care; and mind, now, if your ankle bothers you, and you are laid up with it, *I* am to be your footman. It's only fair, you know; for I don't forget how good you have been to me." And Mac went to call Phebe, so full of gratitude and good-will that his very goggles shone.

15

EAR-RINGS

Rose's sprain proved to be a serious one, owing to neglect, and Dr. Alec ordered her to lie on the sofa for a fortnight at least; whereat she groaned dismally, but dared not openly complain, lest the boys turn upon her with some of the wise little sermons on patience which she had delivered for their benefit.

It was Mac's turn now, and honorably did he repay his debt; for, as school was still forbidden, he had plenty of leisure, and devoted most of it to Rose. He took many steps for her, and even allowed her to teach him to knit, after assuring himself that many a brave Scotchman knew how to "click the pricks." She was obliged to take a solemn vow of secrecy, however, before he would consent; for, though he did not mind being called "Giglamps," "Granny" was more than his boyish soul could bear, and at the approach of any of the clan his knitting vanished as if by magic, which frequent "chucking" out of sight did not improve the stripe he was doing for Rose's new afghan.

She was busy with this pretty work one bright October afternoon, all nicely established on her sofa in the upper hall, while Jamie and Pokey (lent for her amusement) were keeping house in a corner, with Comet and Rose's old doll for their "childerns."

Presently, Phebe appeared with a card. Rose read it, made a grimace, then laughed and said,—

"I'll see Miss Bliss," and immediately put on her company face, pulled out her locket, and settled her curls.

"You dear thing, how *do* you do? I've been trying to call every day since you got back, but I have so many engagements, I really couldn't manage it till to-day. So glad you are alone, for mamma said I could sit awhile, and I brought my lace-work to show you, for it's perfectly lovely," cried Miss Bliss, greeting Rose with a kiss, which was not very warmly returned, though Rose politely thanked her for coming, and bid Phebe roll up the easy chair.

"How nice to have a maid!" said Annabel, as she settled herself with much commotion. "Still, dear, you must be very lonely, and feel the need of a bosom friend."

"I have my cousins," began Rose, with dignity, for her visitor's patronizing manner ruffled her temper.

"Gracious, child! you don't make friends of those great boys, do you? Mamma says she really doesn't think it's proper for you to be with them so much."

"They are like brothers, and my aunts *do* think

it's proper," replied Rose, rather sharply, for it struck her that this was none of Miss Bliss's business.

"I was merely going to say I should be glad to have you for *my* bosom friend, for Hatty Mason and I have had an awful quarrel, and don't speak. She is too mean to live, so I gave her up. Just think, she never paid back one of the caramels I've given her, and never invited me to her party. I could have forgiven the caramels, but to be left out in that rude way was more than I could bear, and I told her never to look at me again as long as she lived."

"You are very kind, but I don't think I want a bosom friend, thank you," said Rose, as Annabel stopped to bridle and shake her flaxen head over the delinquent Hatty Mason.

Now, in her heart Miss Bliss thought Rose "a stuck-up puss," but the other girls wanted to know her and couldn't, the old house was a charming place to visit, the lads were considered fine fellows, and the Campbells "are one of our first families," mamma said. So Annabel concealed her vexation at Rose's coolness, and changed the subject as fast as possible.

"Studying French, I see; who is your teacher?" she asked, flirting over the leaves of "Paul and Virginia," that lay on the table.

"I don't *study* it, for I read French as well as English, and uncle and I often speak it for hours. He talks like a native, and says I have a remarkably good accent."

Rose really could not help this small display of superiority, for French was one of her strong points, and she was vain of it, though she usually managed to hide this weakness. She felt that Annabel would be the better for a little crushing, and could not resist the temptation to patronize in her turn.

"Oh, indeed!" said Miss Bliss, rather blankly, for French was not *her* strong point by any means.

"I am to go abroad with uncle in a year or two, and he knows how important it is to understand the languages. Half the girls who leave school can't speak decent French, and when they go abroad they are *so* mortified. I shall be very glad to help you, if you like, for of course *you* have no one to talk with at home."

Now Annabel, though she *looked* like a wax doll, had feelings within her instead of sawdust, and these feelings were hurt by Rose's lofty tone. She thought her more "stuck up" than ever, but did not know how to bring her down, yet longed to do it, for she felt as if she had received a box on the ear, and involuntarily put her hand up to it. The touch of an ear-ring consoled her, and suggested a way of returning tit for tat in a telling manner.

"Thank you, dear; I don't need any help, for our teacher is from Paris, and of course *he* speaks better French than your uncle." Then she added, with a gesture of her head that set the little bells on her ears to tingling: "How do you like my new ear-rings? Papa gave them to me last week, and every one says they are lovely."

Rose came down from her high horse with a rapidity that was comical, for Annabel had the upper hand now. Rose adored pretty things, longed to wear them, and the desire of her girlish soul was to have her ears bored, only Dr. Alec thought it foolish, so she never had done it. She would gladly have given all the French she could jabber for a pair of golden bells with pearl-tipped tongues, like those Annabel wore; and, clasping her hands, she answered, in a tone that went to the hearer's heart,—

"They are *too* sweet for any thing! If uncle would only let me wear some, I should be *perfectly* happy."

"I wouldn't mind what he says. Papa laughed at me at first, but he likes them now, and says I shall have diamond solitaires when I am eighteen," said Annabel, quite satisfied with her shot.

"I've got a pair now that were mamma's, and a beautiful little pair of pearl and turquoise ones, that I am dying to wear," sighed Rose.

"Then do it. I'll pierce your ears, and you must wear a bit of silk in them till they are well; your curls will hide them nicely; then, some day, slip in your smallest ear-rings, and see if your uncle don't like them."

"I asked him if it wouldn't do my eyes good once when they were red, and he only laughed.

People do cure weak eyes that way, don't they?"

"Yes, indeed, and yours *are* sort of red. Let me see. Yes, I really think you ought to do it before they get worse," said Annabel, peering into the large clear eye offered for inspection.

"Does it hurt much?" asked Rose, wavering.

"Oh dear, no! just a prick and a pull, and it's all over. I've done lots of ears, and know just how. Come, push up your hair and get a big needle."

"I don't quite like to do it without asking uncle's leave," faltered Rose, when all was ready for the operation.

"Did he ever forbid it?" demanded Annabel hovering over her prey like a vampire.

"No, never!"

"Then do it, unless you are *afraid*," cried Miss Bliss, bent on accomplishing the deed.

That last word settled the matter, and, closing her eyes, Rose said "Punch!" in the tone of one giving the fatal order "Fire!"

Annabel punched, and the victim bore it in heroic silence, though she turned pale and her eyes were full of tears of anguish.

"There! Now pull the bits of silk often, and cold-cream your ears every night, and you'll soon be ready for the rings," said Annabel, well pleased with her job, for the girl who spoke French with "a fine accent" lay flat upon the sofa, looking as exhausted as if she had had both ears cut off.

"It does hurt dreadfully, and I know uncle won't like it," sighed Rose, as remorse began to gnaw.

"Promise not to tell, or I shall be teased to death," she added, anxiously, entirely forgetting the two little pitchers gifted with eyes as well as ears, who had been watching the whole performance from afar.

"Never. Mercy me, what's that?" and Annabel started as a sudden sound of steps and voices came up from below.

"It's the boys! Hide the needle. Do my ears show? Don't breathe a word!" whispered Rose, scrambling about to conceal all traces of their iniquity from the sharp eyes of the clan.

Up they came, all in good order, laden with the proceeds of a nutting expedition, for they always reported to Rose and paid tribute to their queen in the handsomest manner.

"How many, and how big! We'll have a grand roasting frolic after tea, won't we?" said Rose, plunging both hands into a bag of glossy brown nuts, while the clan "stood at ease" and nodded to Annabel.

"That lot was picked especially for you, Rosy. I got every one myself, and they are extra whackers," said Mac, presenting a bushel or so.

"You should have seen Giglamps when he was after them. He pitched out of the tree, and would have broken his blessed old neck if Arch had not caught him," observed Steve, as he lounged gracefully in the window seat.

"You needn't talk, Dandy, when you didn't know a chestnut from a beech, and kept on thrashing till I told you of it," retorted Mac, festooning himself over the back of the sofa, being a privileged boy.

"I don't make mistakes when I thrash you, old Worm, so you'd better mind what you are about," answered Steve, without a ray of proper respect for his elder brother.

"It is getting dark, and I must go, or mamma will be alarmed," said Annabel rising in sudden haste, though she hoped to be asked to remain to the nut-party.

No one invited her; and all the while she was putting on her things and chatting to Rose the boys were telegraphing to one another the sad fact that some one ought to escort the young lady home. Not a boy felt heroic enough to cast himself into the breach, however; even polite Archie shirked the duty, saying to Charlie, as they quietly slipped into an adjoining room,—

"I'm not going to do all the gallivanting. Let Steve take that chit home and show his manners."

"I'll be hanged if I do!" answered Prince, who disliked Miss Bliss because she tried to be coquettish with him.

"Then I will," and, to the dismay of both recreant lads, Dr. Alec walked out of the room to offer his services to the "chit."

He was too late, however, for Mac, obeying a look from Rose, had already made a victim of himself, and trudged meekly away, wishing the gentle Annabel at the bottom of the Red Sea.

"Then I will take this lady down to tea, as the other one has found a *gentleman* to go home with her. I see the lamps are lighted below, and I smell a smell which tells me that aunty has something extra nice for us to-night."

As he spoke, Dr. Alec was preparing to carry Rose downstairs as usual; but Archie and Prince rushed forward, begging with penitent eagerness for the honor of carrying her in an arm-chair. Rose consented, fearing that her uncle's keen eye would discover the fatal bits of silk; so the boys crossed hands, and, taking a good grip of each curly pate, she was borne down in state, while the others followed by way of the banisters.

Tea was ordered earlier than usual, so that Jamie and his dolly could have a taste, at least, of the holiday fun, for they were to stay till seven, and be allowed twelve roasted chestnuts apiece, which they were under bonds not to eat till next day.

Tea was despatched rapidly, therefore, and the party gathered round the wide hearth in the dining-room, where the nuts were soon dancing gayly on hot shovels or bouncing out among the company, thereby causing delightful panics among the little ones.

"Come, Rosy, tell us a story while we work, for you can't help much, and must amuse us as your share," proposed Mac, who sat in the shade pricking nuts, and who knew by experience what a capital little Scheherazade his cousin was.

"Yes, we poor monkeys can't burn our paws for

nothing, so tell away, Pussy," added Charlie, as he threw several hot nuts into her lap and shook his fingers afterward.

"Well, I happen to have a little story with a moral to it in my mind, and I will tell it, though it is intended for younger children than you," answered Rose, who was rather fond of telling instructive tales.

"Fire away," said Geordie, and she obeyed, little thinking what a disastrous story it would prove to herself.

"Well, once upon a time, a little girl went to see a young lady who was very fond of her. Now, the young lady happened to be lame, and had to have her foot bandaged up every day; so she kept a basketful of bandages, all nicely rolled and ready. The little girl liked to play with this basket, and one day, when she thought no one saw her, she took one of the rolls without asking leave, and put it in her pocket."

Here Pokey, who had been peering lovingly down at the five warm nuts that lay at the bottom of her tiny pocket, suddenly looked up and said, "Oh!" in a startled tone, as if the moral tale had become intensely interesting all at once.

Rose heard and saw the innocent betrayal of the small sinner, and went on in a most impressive manner, while the boys nudged one another and winked as they caught the joke.

"But an eye did see this naughty little girl, and whose eye do you think it was?"

"Eye of Dod," murmured conscience-stricken Pokey, spreading two chubby little hands before the round face, which they were not half big enough to hide.

Rose was rather taken aback by this reply, but, feeling that she was producing a good effect, she added, seriously,—

"Yes, God saw her, and so did the young lady, but she did not say any thing; she waited to see what the little girl would do about it. She had been very happy before she took the bandage, but when it was in her pocket she seemed troubled, and pretty soon stopped playing and sat down in a corner, looking very sober. She thought a few minutes, and then went and put back the roll very softly, and her face cleared up, and she was a happy child again. The young lady was glad to see that, and wondered what made the little girl put it back."

"Tonscience p'icked her," murmured a contrite voice from behind the small hands pressed tightly over Pokey's red face.

"And why did she take it, do you suppose?" asked Rose, in a school-marmish tone, feeling that all the listeners were interested in her tale and its unexpected application.

"It was *so* nice and wound, and she wanted it deffly," answered the little voice.

"Well, I'm glad she had such a good conscience. The moral is that people who steal don't enjoy what they take, and are not happy till they put it back. What makes that little girl hide her face?" asked Rose, as she concluded.

"Me's so 'shamed of Pokey," sobbed the small culprit, quite overcome by remorse and confusion at this awful disclosure.

"Come, Rose, it's too bad to tell her little tricks before every one, and preach at her in that way; you wouldn't like it yourself," began Dr. Alec, taking the weeper on his knee and administering consolation in the shape of kisses and nuts.

Before Rose could express her regret, Jamie, who had been reddening and ruffling like a little turkey-cock for several minutes, burst out indignantly, bent on avenging the wound given to his beloved dolly,—

"*I* know something bad that *you* did, and I'm going to tell right out. You thought we didn't see you, but we did, and you said uncle wouldn't like it, and the boys would tease, and you made Annabel promise not to tell, and she punched holes in your ears to put ear-rings in. So now! and that's much badder than to take an old piece of rag; and I hate you for making my Pokey cry."

Jamie's somewhat incoherent explosion produced such an effect that Pokey's small sin was instantly forgotten, and Rose felt that her hour had come.

"What! what! what!" cried the boys in a chorus, dropping their shovels and knives to gather round Rose, for a guilty clutching at her ears betrayed her, and with a feeble cry of "Annabel made me!"

she hid her head among the pillows like an absurd little ostrich.

"Now she'll go prancing round with bird-cages and baskets and carts and pigs, for all I know, in her ears, as the other girls do, and won't she look like a goose?" asked one tormentor, tweaking a curl that strayed out from the cushions.

"I didn't think she'd be so silly," said Mac, in a tone of disappointment that told Rose she had sunk in the esteem of her wise cousin.

"That Bliss girl is a nuisance, and ought not to be allowed to come here with her nonsensical notions," said the Prince, feeling a strong desire to shake that young person as an angry dog might shake a mischievous kitten.

"How do *you* like it, uncle?" asked Archie, who, being the head of a family himself, believed in preserving discipline at all costs.

"I am very much surprised; but I see she is a girl, after all, and must have her vanities like all the rest of them," answered Dr. Alec, with a sigh, as if he had expected to find Rose a sort of angel, above all earthly temptation.

"What shall you do about it, sir?" inquired Geordie, wondering what punishment would be inflicted on a feminine culprit.

"As she is fond of ornaments, perhaps we had better give her a nose-ring also. I have one somewhere that a Fiji belle once wore; I'll look it up," and, leaving Pokey to Jamie's care, Dr. Alec rose as if to carry out his suggestion in earnest.

"Good! good! We'll do it right away! Here's a gimlet, so you hold her, boys, while I get her dear little nose all ready," cried Charlie, whisking away the pillows as the other boys danced about the sofa in true Fiji style.

It was a dreadful moment, for Rose could not run away,—she could only grasp her precious nose with one hand and extend the other, crying distractedly,—

"O uncle, save me, save me!"

Of course he saved her; and when she was securely barricaded by his strong arm, she confessed her folly in such humiliation of spirit that the lads, after a good laugh at her, decided to forgive her and lay all the blame on the tempter, Annabel. Even Dr. Alec relented so far as to propose two gold rings for the ears instead of one copper one for the nose; a proceeding which proved that if Rose had all the weakness of her sex for jewellery, he had all the inconsistency of his in giving a pretty penitent exactly what she wanted, spite of his better judgment.

16

BREAD AND BUTTON-HOLES

"What in the world is my girl thinking about all alone here, with such a solemn face?" asked Dr. Alec, coming into the study, one November day, to find Rose sitting there with folded hands and a very thoughtful aspect.

"Uncle, I want to have some serious conversation with you, if you have time," she said, coming out of a brown study, as if she had not heard his question.

"I'm entirely at your service, and most happy to listen," he answered, in his politest manner, for when Rose put on her womanly little airs he always treated her with a playful sort of respect that pleased her very much.

Now, as he sat down beside her, she said, very soberly,—

"I've been trying to decide what trade I would learn, and I want you to advise me."

"Trade, my dear?" and Dr. Alec looked so astonished that she hastened to explain.

"I forgot that you didn't hear the talk about it up at Cosey Corner. You see we used to sit under the pines and sew, and talk a great deal,—all the

ladies, I mean,—and I liked it very much. Mother
Atkinson thought that every one should have a
trade, or something to make a living out of, for rich
people may grow poor, you know, and poor people
have to work. Her girls were very clever, and could
do ever so many things, and Aunt Jessie thought
the old lady was right; so when I saw how happy
and independent those young ladies were, I
wanted to have a trade, and then it wouldn't matter about money, though I like to have it well
enough."

Dr. Alec listened to this explanation with a curious mixture of surprise, pleasure, and amusement
in his face, and looked at his little niece as if she
had suddenly changed into a young woman. She
had grown a good deal in the last six months, and
an amount of thinking had gone on in that young
head which would have astonished him greatly
could he have known it all, for Rose was one of the
children who observe and meditate much, and
now and then nonplus their friends by a wise or
curious remark.

"I quite agree with the ladies, and shall be glad
to help you decide on something if I can," said the
Doctor seriously. "What do you incline to? A natural taste or talent is a great help in choosing, you
know."

"I haven't any talent, or any especial taste that I
can see, and that is why I can't decide, uncle. So,
I think it would be a good plan to pick out some
very *useful* business and learn it, because I don't do

it for pleasure, you see, but as a part of my education, and to be ready in case I'm ever poor," answered Rose, looking as if she rather longed for a little poverty so that her useful gift might be exercised.

"Well, now, there is one very excellent, necessary, and womanly accomplishment that no girl should be without, for it is a help to rich and poor, and the comfort of families depends upon it. This fine talent is neglected nowadays, and considered old-fashioned, which is a sad mistake, and one that I don't mean to make in bringing up my girl. It should be a part of every girl's education, and I know of a most accomplished lady who will teach you in the best and pleasantest manner."

"Oh, what is it?" cried Rose eagerly, charmed to be met in this helpful and cordial way.

"Housekeeping!" answered Dr. Alec.

"Is that an accomplishment?" asked Rose, while her face fell, for she had indulged in all sorts of vague, delightful dreams.

"Yes; it is one of the most beautiful as well as useful of all the arts a woman can learn. Not so romantic, perhaps, as singing, painting, writing, or teaching, even; but one that makes many happy and comfortable, and home the sweetest place in the world. Yes, you may open your big eyes; but it is a fact that I had rather see you a good housekeeper than the greatest belle in the city. It need not interfere with any talent you may possess, but it *is* a necessary part of your training, and I hope that you will set about it at once, now that you are well and strong."

"Who is the lady?" asked Rose, rather impressed by her uncle's earnest speech.

"Aunt Plenty."

"Is *she* accomplished?" began Rose in a wondering tone, for this great-aunt of hers had seemed the least cultivated of them all.

"In the good old-fashioned way she is very accomplished, and has made this house a happy home to us all, ever since we can remember. She is not elegant, but genuinely good, and so beloved and respected that there will be universal mourning for her when her place is empty. No one can fill it, for the solid, homely virtues of the dear soul have gone out of fashion, as I say, and nothing new can be half so satisfactory, to me at least."

"I should like to have people feel so about me. Can she teach me to do what she does, and to grow as good?" asked Rose, with a little prick of remorse for even thinking that Aunt Plenty was a commonplace old lady.

"Yes, if you don't despise such simple lessons as she can give. I know it would fill her dear old heart with pride and pleasure to feel that any one cared to learn of her, for she fancies her day gone by. Let her teach you how to be what she has been,—a skilful, frugal, cheerful housewife; the maker and the keeper of a happy home, and by and by you will see what a valuable lesson it is."

"I will, uncle. But how shall I begin?"

"I'll speak to her about it, and she will make it all right with Debby, for cooking is one of the main things, you know."

"So it is! I don't mind that a bit, for I like to mess, and used to try at home; but I had no one to tell me, so I never did much but spoil my aprons. Pies are great fun, only Debby is *so* cross, I don't believe she will ever let me do a thing in the kitchen."

"Then we'll cook in the parlor. I fancy Aunt Plenty will manage her, so don't be troubled. Only mind this, I'd rather you learned how to make good bread than the best pies ever baked. When you bring me a handsome, wholesome loaf, entirely made by yourself, I shall be more pleased than if you offered me a pair of slippers embroidered in the very latest style. I don't wish to bribe you, but I'll give you my heartiest kiss, and promise to eat every crumb of the loaf myself."

"It's a bargain! it's a bargain! Come and tell aunty all about it, for I'm in a hurry to begin," cried Rose, dancing before him toward the parlor, where Miss Plenty sat alone knitting contentedly, yet ready to run at the first call for help of any sort, from any quarter.

No need to tell how surprised and gratified she was at the invitation she received to teach the child the domestic arts which were her only accomplishments, nor to relate how energetically she set about her pleasant task. Debby dared not grumble, for Miss Plenty was the one person whom she obeyed, and Phebe openly rejoiced, for these new lessons brought Rose nearer to her, and glorified the kitchen in the good girl's eyes.

To tell the truth, the elder aunts had sometimes felt that they did not have quite their share of the little niece who had won their hearts long ago, and was the sunshine of the house. They talked it over together sometimes, but always ended by saying that as Alec had all the responsibility, he should have the larger share of the dear girl's love and time, and they would be contented with such crumbs of comfort as they could get.

Dr. Alec had found out this little secret, and, after reproaching himself for being blind and selfish, was trying to devise some way of mending matters without troubling any one, when Rose's new whim suggested an excellent method of weaning her a little from himself. He did not know how fond he was of her till he gave her up to the new teacher, and often could not resist peeping in at the door, to see how she got on, or stealing sly looks through the slide when she was deep in dough, or listening intently to some impressive lecture from Aunt Plenty. They caught him at it now and then, and ordered him off the premises at the point of the rolling-pin; or, if unusually successful, and, therefore, in a milder mood, they lured him away with bribes of gingerbread, a stray pickle, or a tart that was not quite symmetrical enough to suit their critical eyes.

Of course he made a point of partaking copiously

of all the delectable messes that now appeared at table, for both the cooks were on their mettle, and he fared sumptuously every day. But an especial relish was given to any dish when, in reply to his honest praise of it, Rose colored up with innocent pride, and said modestly,—

"I made that, uncle, and I'm glad you like it."

It was some time before the perfect loaf appeared, for bread-making is an art not easily learned, and Aunt Plenty was very thorough in her teaching; so Rose studied yeast first, and through various stages of cake and biscuit came at last to the crowning glory of the "handsome, wholesome loaf." It appeared at tea-time, on a silver salver, proudly borne in by Phebe, who could not refrain from whispering, with a beaming face, as she set it down before Dr. Alec,—

"Ain't it just lovely, sir?"

"It is a regularly splendid loaf! Did my girl make it all herself?" he asked, surveying the shapely, sweet-smelling object, with real interest and pleasure.

"Every particle herself, and never asked a bit of help or advice from any one," answered Aunt Plenty, folding her hands with an air of unmitigated satisfaction, for her pupil certainly did her great credit.

"I've had so many failures and troubles that I really thought I never should be able to do it alone. Debby let one splendid batch burn up because I forgot it. She was there and smelt it, but never did a thing, for she said, when I undertook to bake bread I must give my whole mind to it. Wasn't it hard? She might have called me at least," said Rose, recollecting, with a sigh, the anguish of that moment.

"She meant you should learn by experience, as Rosamond did in that little affair of the purple jar, you remember."

"I always thought it very unfair in her mother not to warn the poor thing a little bit; and she was regularly mean when Rosamond asked for a bowl to put the purple stuff in, and she said, in such a provoking way, 'I did not agree to lend you a bowl, but I will, my dear.' Ugh! I always want to shake that hateful woman, though she *was* a moral mamma."

"Never mind her now, but tell me all about my loaf," said Dr. Alec, much amused at Rose's burst of indignation.

"There's nothing to tell, uncle, except that I did my best, gave my mind to it, and sat watching over it all the while it was in the oven till I was quite baked myself. Every thing went right this time, and it came out a nice, round, crusty loaf, as you see. Now taste it, and tell me if it is good as well as handsome."

"Must I cut it? Can't I put it under a glass cover and keep it in the parlor as they do wax flowers and fine works of that sort?"

"What an idea, uncle! It would mould and be spoilt. Besides, people would laugh at us, and make fun of my old-fashioned accomplishment. You promised to eat it, and you must; not all at once, but as soon as you can, so I can make you some more."

Dr. Alec solemnly cut off his favorite crusty slice, and solemnly ate it; then wiped his lips, and brushing back Rose's hair, solemnly kissed her on the forehead, saying heartily,—

"My dear, it is perfect bread, and you are an honor to your teacher. When we have our model school I shall offer a prize for the best bread, and *you* will get it."

"I've got it already, and I'm quite satisfied," said Rose, slipping into her seat, and trying to hide her right hand which had a burn on it.

But Dr. Alec saw it, guessed how it came there, and after tea insisted on easing the pain which she would hardly confess.

"Aunt Clara says I am spoiling my hands, but I don't care, for I've had *such* good times with Aunt Plenty, and I think she has enjoyed it as much as I have. Only one thing troubles me, uncle, and I want to ask you about it," said Rose, as they paced up and down the hall in the twilight, the bandaged hand very carefully laid on Dr. Alec's arm.

"More little confidences? I like them immensely, so tell away, my dear."

"Well, you see I feel as if Aunt Peace would like to do something for me, and I've found out what it can be. You know she can't go about like Aunty Plen, and we are so busy nowadays that she is rather lonely, I'm afraid. So I want to take lessons in sewing of her. She works so beautifully, and it is a useful thing, you know, and I ought to be a good needlewoman as well as housekeeper, oughtn't I?"

"Bless your kind little heart, that is what I was thinking of the other day when Aunt Peace said she saw you very seldom now, you were so busy. I wanted to speak of it, but fancied you had as much on your hands as you could manage. It would delight the dear woman to teach you all her delicate handicraft, especially button-holes, for I believe that is where young ladies fail; at least I've heard them say so. So, do you devote your mind to button-holes; make 'em all over my clothes if you want something to practice on. I'll wear any quantity."

Rose laughed at this reckless offer, but promised to attend to that important branch, though she confessed that darning was her weak point. Whereupon Uncle Alec engaged to supply her with socks in all stages of dilapidation, and to have a new set at once, so that she could run the heels for him as a pleasant beginning.

Then they went up to make their request in due form, to the great delight of gentle Aunt Peace, who got quite excited with the fun that went on while they wound yarn, looked up darning-needles, and fitted out a nice little mending basket for her pupil.

Very busy and very happy were Rose's days now, for in the morning she went about the house with Aunt Plenty attending to linen-closets and store-rooms, pickling and preserving, exploring garret and cellar to see that all was right, and learning, in the good old-fashioned manner, to look well after the ways of the household.

In the afternoon, after her walk or drive, she sat with Aunt Peace plying her needle, while Aunt Plenty, whose eyes were failing, knit and chatted briskly, telling many a pleasant story of old times, till the three were moved to laugh and cry together, for the busy needles were embroidering all sorts of bright patterns on the lives of the workers, though they seemed to be only stitching cotton and darning hose.

It was a pretty sight to see the rosy-faced little maid sitting between the two old ladies, listening dutifully to their instructions, and cheering the lessons with her lively chatter and blithe laugh. If the kitchen had proved attractive to Dr. Alec when Rose was there at work, the sewing-room was quite irresistible, and he made himself so agreeable that no one had the heart to drive him away, especially when he read aloud or spun yarns.

"There! I've made you a new set of warm night-gowns with four button-holes in each. See if they are not neatly done," said Rose, one day, some weeks after the new lessons began.

"Even to a thread, and nice little bars across the end so I can't tear them when I twitch the buttons out. Most superior work, ma'am, and I'm deeply grateful; so much so, that I'll sew on these buttons myself, and save those tired fingers from another prick."

"You sew them on?" cried Rose, with her eyes wide open in amazement.

"Wait a bit till I get my sewing tackle, and then you shall see what *I* can do."

"Can he, really?" asked Rose of Aunt Peace, as Uncle Alec marched off with a comical air of importance.

"Oh, yes, I taught him years ago, before he went to sea; and I suppose he has had to do things for himself, more or less, ever since; so he has kept his hand in."

He evidently had, for he was soon back with a funny little work-bag, out of which he produced a thimble without a top; and, having threaded his needle, he proceeded to sew on the buttons so handily that Rose was much impressed and amused.

"I wonder if there is any thing in the world that *you* cannot do," she said, in a tone of respectful admiration.

"There are one or two things that I am not up to yet," he answered, with a laugh in the corner of his eye, as he waxed his thread with a flourish.

"I should like to know what?"

"Bread and button-holes, ma'am."

17

GOOD BARGAINS

It was a rainy Sunday afternoon, and four boys were trying to spend it quietly in the "liberry," as Jamie called the room devoted to books and boys, at Aunt Jessie's. Will and Geordie were sprawling on the sofa, deep in the adventures of the scapegraces and ragamuffins whose histories are now the fashion. Archie lounged in the easy chair surrounded by newspapers; Charlie stood upon the rug, in an Englishman's favorite attitude, and, I regret to say, both were smoking cigars.

"It is my opinion that this day will *never* come to an end," said Prince, with a yawn that nearly rent him asunder.

"Read and improve your mind, my son," answered Archie, peering solemnly over the paper behind which he had been dozing.

"Don't you preach, parson; but put on your boots and come out for a tramp, instead of mulling over the fire like a granny."

"No, thank you, tramps in an easterly storm don't strike me as amusing." There Archie stopped and held up his hand, for a pleasant voice was heard saying outside,—

"Are the boys in the library, auntie?"

"Yes, dear, and longing for sunshine; so run in and make it for them," answered Mrs. Jessie.

"It's Rose," and Archie threw his cigar into the fire.

"What's that for?" asked Charlie.

"Gentlemen don't smoke before ladies."

"True; but I'm not going to waste *my* weed," and Prince poked his into the empty inkstand that served them for an ash tray.

A gentle tap at the door was answered by a chorus of "Come in," and Rose appeared, looking blooming and breezy with the chilly air.

"If I disturb you, say so, and I'll go away," she began, pausing on the threshold with modest hesitation, for something in the elder boys' faces excited her curiosity.

"You never disturb us, cousin," said the smokers, while the readers tore themselves from the heroes of the bar-room and gutter long enough to nod affably to their guest.

As Rose bent to warm her hands, one end of Archie's cigar stuck out of the ashes, smoking furiously and smelling strongly.

"Oh, you bad boys, how could you do it, to-day of all days?" she said reproachfully.

"Where's the harm?" asked Archie.

"You know as well as I do; your mother doesn't like it, and it's a bad habit, for it wastes money and does you no good."

"Fiddle-sticks! every man smokes, even Uncle

Alec, whom you think so perfect," began Charlie, in his teasing way.

"No, he doesn't! He has given it up, and I know why," cried Rose eagerly.

"Now I think of it, I haven't seen the old meer-schaum since he came home. Did he stop it on our account?" asked Archie.

"Yes," and Rose told the little scene on the seashore in the camping-out time.

Archie seemed much impressed, and said man-fully,—"He won't have done that in vain so far as I'm concerned. I don't care a pin about smoking, so can give it up as easy as not, and I promise you I will. I only do it now and then for fun."

"You too?" and Rose looked up at the bonny Prince, who never looked less bonny than at that moment, for he had resumed his cigar, just to tor-ment her.

Now Charlie cared as little as Archie about smok-ing, but it would not do to yield too soon; so he shook his head, gave a great puff, and said loftily,—

"You women are always asking us to give up harmless little things, just because *you* don't ap-prove of them. How would you like it if we did the same by you, Miss?"

"If I did harmful or silly things, I'd thank you for telling me of them, and I'd try to mend my ways," answered Rose heartily.

"Well, now, we'll see if you mean what you say. I'll give up smoking to please you, if you will give up something to please me," said Prince, seeing a good chance to lord it over the weaker vessel at small cost to himself.

"I'll agree if it is as foolish as cigars."

"Oh, it's ever so much sillier."

"Then I promise; what is it?" and Rose quite trembled with anxiety to know which of her pet habits or possessions she must lose.

"Give up your ear-rings," and Charlie laughed wickedly, sure that she would never hold to that bargain.

Rose uttered a cry and clapped both hands to her ears where the gold rings hung.

"O Charlie, wouldn't any thing else do as well? I've been through so much teasing and trouble, I do want to enjoy my pretty ear-rings, for I can wear them now."

"Wear as many as you like, and I'll smoke in peace," returned this bad boy.

"Will *nothing* else satisfy you?" imploringly.

"Nothing," sternly.

Rose stood silent for a minute, thinking of something Aunt Jessie once said,—"You have more influence over the boys than you know; use it for their good, and I shall thank you all my life." Here was a chance to do some good by sacrificing a little vanity of her own. She felt it was right to do it, yet found it very hard, and asked wistfully,—

"Do you mean *never* wear them, Charlie?"

"*Never,* unless you want me to smoke."

"I never do."

"Then clinch the bargain."

He had no idea she would do it, and was much surprised when she took the dear rings from her ears, with a quick gesture, and held them out to him, saying, in a tone that made the color come up to his brown cheek, it was so full of sweet good will,—

"I care more for my cousins than for my ear-rings, so I promise, and I'll keep my word."

"For shame, Prince! let her wear her little danglers if she likes, and don't bargain about doing what you know is right," cried Archie, coming out of his grove of newspapers with an indignant bounce.

But Rose was bent on showing her aunt that she *could* use her influence for the boys' good, and said steadily,—

"It is fair, and I want it to be so, then you will believe I'm in earnest. Here, each of you wear one of these on your watch-guard to remind you. *I* shall not forget, because very soon I cannot wear ear-rings if I want to."

As she spoke, Rose offered a little ring to each cousin, and the boys, seeing how sincere she was, obeyed her. When the pledges were safe, Rose stretched a hand to each, and the lads gave hers a hearty grip, half pleased and half ashamed of their part in the compact.

Just at that moment Dr. Alec and Mrs. Jessie came in.

"What's this? Dancing Ladies Triumph on Sunday?" exclaimed Uncle Alec, surveying the trio with surprise.

"No, sir, it is the Anti-Tobacco League. Will you join?" said Charlie, while Rose slipped away to her aunt, and Archie buried both cigars behind the back log.

When the mystery was explained, the elders were well pleased, and Rose received a vote of thanks, which made her feel as if she had done a service to her country, as she had, for every boy who grows up free from bad habits bids fair to make a good citizen.

"I wish Rose would drive a bargain with Will and Geordie also, for I think these books are as bad for the small boys as cigars for the large ones," said Mrs. Jessie, sitting down on the sofa between the readers, who politely curled up their legs to make room for her.

"I thought they were all the fashion," answered Dr. Alec, settling in the big chair with Rose.

"So is smoking, but it is harmful. The writers of these popular stories intend to do good, I have no doubt, but it seems to me they fail because their motto is, 'Be smart, and you will be rich,' instead of 'Be honest, and you will be happy.' I do not judge hastily, Alec, for I have read a dozen, at least, of these stories, and, with much that is attractive to boys, I find a great deal to condemn in them, and other parents say the same when I ask them."

"Now, Mum, that's too bad! I like 'em tiptop. This one is a regular screamer," cried Will.

"They're bully books, and I'd like to know where's the harm," added Geordie.

"You have just shown us one of the chief evils, and that is slang," answered their mother quickly.

"Must have it, ma'am. If these chaps talked all right, there'd be no fun in 'em," protested Will.

"A boot-black *mustn't* use good grammar, and a newsboy *must* swear a little, or he wouldn't be natural," explained Geordie, both boys ready to fight gallantly for their favorites.

"But my sons are neither boot-blacks nor newsboys, and I object to hearing them use such words as 'screamer,' 'bully,' and 'buster.' In fact, I fail to see the advantage of writing books about such people unless it is done in a very different way. I cannot think they will help to refine the raga-muffins, if they read them, and I'm sure they can do no good to the better class of boys, who through these books are introduced to police courts, counterfeiters' dens, gambling houses, drinking saloons, and all sorts of low life."

"Some of them are about first-rate boys, mother; and they go to sea and study, and sail round the world, having great larks all the way."

"I have read about them, Geordie, and though they *are* better than the others, I am not satisfied with these *optical* delusions, as I call them. Now, I put it to you, boys, is it natural for lads from fifteen to eighteen to command ships, defeat pirates, out-wit smugglers, and so cover themselves with glory, that Admiral Farragut invites them to dinner, saying: 'Noble boy, you are an honor to your country!' Or, if the hero is in the army, he has hair-breadth escapes and adventures enough in one small volume to turn his hair white, and in the end he goes to Washington at the express desire of the President or Commander-in-Chief to be promoted to no end of stars and bars. Even if the hero is merely an honest boy trying to get his living, he is not permitted to do so in a natural way, by hard work and years of patient effort, but is suddenly adopted by a millionaire whose pocketbook he has returned; or a rich uncle appears from sea, just in the nick of time; or the remarkable boy earns a few dollars, speculates in pea-nuts or neck-ties, and grows rich so rapidly that Sinbad in the diamond valley is a pauper compared to him. Isn't it so, boys?"

"Well, the fellows in these books *are* mighty lucky, and very smart, I must say," answered Will, surveying an illustration on the open page before him, where a small but virtuous youth is upsetting a tipsy giant in a bar-room, and under it the elegant inscription: "Dick Dauntless punches the head of Sam Soaker."

"It gives boys such wrong ideas of life and business; shows them so much evil and vulgarity that they need not know about, and makes the one success worth having a fortune, a lord's daughter, or some worldly honor, often not worth the time it takes to win. It does seem to me that some one might write stories that should be lively, natural, and helpful,—tales in which the English should be good, the morals pure, and the characters such as we can love in spite of the faults that all may have. I can't bear to see such crowds of eager little fellows at the libraries reading such trash; weak, when it is not wicked, and totally unfit to feed the hungry minds that feast on it for want of something better. There! my lecture is done; now I should like to hear what you gentlemen have to say," and Aunt Jessie subsided with a pretty flush on the face that was full of motherly anxiety for her boys.

"Tom Brown just suits mother, and me too, so I wish Mr. Hughes would write another story as good," said Archie.

"You don't find things of this sort in Tom Brown; yet these books are all in the Sunday-school libraries"—and Mrs. Jessie read the following paragraph from the book she had taken from Will's hand:—

" 'In this place we saw a tooth of John the Baptist. Ben said he could see locust and wild honey sticking to it. I couldn't. Perhaps John used a piece of the true cross for a toothpick.' "

"A larky sort of a boy says that, Mum, and we skip the parts where they describe what they saw in the different countries," cried Will.

"And those descriptions, taken mostly from guide-books, I fancy, are the only parts of any real worth. The scrapes of the bad boys make up the rest of the story, and it is for those you read these books, I think," answered his mother, stroking back the hair off the honest little face that looked rather abashed at this true statement of the case.

"Any way, mother, the ship part is useful, for we learn how to sail her, and by and by that will all come handy when we go to sea," put in Geordie.

"Indeed; then you can explain this manoeuvre to me, of course—"and Mrs. Jessie read from another page the following nautical paragraph:—

"The wind is south-south-west, and we can have her up four points closer to the wind, and still be six points off the wind. As she luffs up we shall man the fore and main sheets, slack on the weather, and haul on the lee braces."

"I guess I could, if I wasn't afraid of uncle. He knows so much more than I do, he'd laugh," began Geordie, evidently puzzled by the question.

"Ho, you know you can't, so why make believe? We don't understand half of the sea lingo, Mum, and I dare say it's all wrong," cried Will, suddenly going over to the enemy, to Geordie's great disgust.

"I do wish the boys wouldn't talk to me as if *I* was a ship," said Rose, bringing forward a private grievance. "Coming home from church, this morning, the wind blew me about, and Will called out, right in the street, 'Brail up the foresail, and take in the flying-jib, that will ease her.' "

The boys shouted at the plaintive tone in which Rose repeated the words that offended her, and

Will vainly endeavored to explain that he only meant to tell her to wrap her cloak closer, and tie a veil over the tempest-tossed feathers in her hat.

"To tell the truth, if the boys *must* have slang, I can bear the 'sea lingo,' as Will calls it, better than the other. It afflicts me less to hear my sons talk about 'brailing up the foresail' than doing as they 'darn please,' and 'cut your cable' is decidedly preferable to 'let her rip.' I once made a rule that I would have no slang in the house. I give it up now, for I cannot keep it; but I will *not* have rubbishy books; so, Archie, please send these two after your cigars."

Mrs. Jessie held both the small boys fast with an arm round each neck, and when she took this base advantage of them they could only squirm with dismay. "Yes, right behind the back log," she continued, energetically. "There, my hearties—(you like sea slang, so I'll give you a bit)—now, I want you to promise not to read any more stuff for a month, and I'll agree to supply you with wholesome fare."

"O mother! not a single one?" cried Will.

"Couldn't we just finish those?" pleaded Geordie.

"The boys threw away half-smoked cigars; and your books must go after them. Surely you would not be outdone by the 'old fellows,' as you call them, or be less obedient to little Mum than they were to Rose."

"Course not! Come on, Geordie," and Will took the vow like a hero. His brother sighed, and obeyed, but privately resolved to finish his story the minute the month was over.

"You have laid out a hard task for yourself, Jessie, in trying to provide good reading for boys who have been living on sensation stories. It will be like going from raspberry tarts to plain bread and butter; but you will probably save them from a bilious fever," said Dr. Alec, much amused at the proceedings.

"I remember hearing grandpa say that a love for good books was one of the best safeguards a man could have," began Archie, staring thoughtfully at the fine library before him.

"Yes, but there's no time to read nowadays; a fellow has to keep scratching round to make money or he's nobody," cut in Charlie, trying to look worldly-wise.

"This love of money is the curse of America, and for the sake of it men will sell honor and honesty, till we don't know whom to trust, and it is only a genius like Agassiz who dares to say, 'I cannot waste my time in getting rich,' " said Mrs. Jessie sadly.

"Do you want us to be poor, mother?" asked Archie, wondering.

"No, dear, and you never need be, while you can use your hands; but I *am* afraid of this thirst for wealth, and the temptations it brings. O my boys! I tremble for the time when I must let you go, because I think it would break my heart to have you fail as so many fail. It would be far easier to see you dead if it could be said of you as of Sumner,—'No man dared offer him a bribe.' "

Mrs. Jessie was so earnest in her motherly anxiety that her voice faltered over the last words, and she hugged the yellow heads closer in her arms, as if she feared to let them leave that safe harbor for the great sea where so many little boats go down. The younger lads nestled closer to her, and Archie said, in his quiet, resolute way,—

"I cannot promise to be an Agassiz or a Sumner, mother; but I do promise to be an honest man, please God."

"Then I'm satisfied!" and holding fast the hand he gave her, she sealed his promise with a kiss that had all a mother's hope and faith in it.

"I don't see how they ever *can* be bad, she is so fond and proud of them," whispered Rose, quite touched by the little scene.

"You must help her make them what they should be. You have begun already, and when I see those rings where they are, my girl is prettier in my sight than if the biggest diamonds that ever twinkled shone in her ears," answered Dr. Alec, looking at her with approving eyes.

"I'm so glad you think I can do any thing, for I perfectly *ache* to be useful, every one is *so* good to me, especially Aunt Jessie."

"I think you are in a fair way to pay your debts, Rosy, for when girls give up their little vanities, and boys their small vices, and try to strengthen each other in well-doing, matters are going as they ought. Work away, my dear, and help their mother keep these sons fit friends for an innocent creature like yourself; they will be the manlier men for it, I can assure you."

18

FASHION AND PHYSIOLOGY

"Please, sir, I guess you'd better step up right away, or it will be too late, for I heard Miss Rose say she knew you wouldn't like it, and she'd never dare to let you see her."

Phebe said this as she popped her head into the study, where Dr. Alec sat reading a new book.

"They are at it, are they?" he said, looking up quickly, and giving himself a shake, as if ready for a battle of some sort.

"Yes, sir, as hard as they can talk, and Miss Rose don't seem to know what to do, for the things are ever so stylish, and she looks elegant in 'em; though I like her best in the old ones," answered Phebe.

"You are a girl of sense. I'll settle matters for Rosy, and you'll lend a hand. Is every thing ready in her room, and are you sure you understand how they go?"

"Oh, yes, sir; but they are so funny! I know Miss Rose will think it's a joke," and Phebe laughed as if something tickled her immensely.

"Never mind what she thinks so long as she obeys. Tell her to do it for my sake, and she will find it the best joke she ever saw. I expect to have a tough time of it, but we'll win yet," said the Doctor, as he marched upstairs with the book in his hand, and an odd smile on his face.

There was such a clatter of tongues in the sewing-room that no one heard his tap at the door, so he pushed it open and took an observation. Aunt Plenty, Aunt Clara, and Aunt Jessie were all absorbed in gazing at Rose, who slowly revolved between them and the great mirror, in a full winter costume of the latest fashion.

"Bless my heart! worse even than I expected," thought the Doctor, with an inward groan, for, to his benighted eyes, the girl looked like a trussed fowl, and the fine new dress had neither grace, beauty, nor fitness to recommend it.

The suit was of two peculiar shades of blue, so arranged that patches of light and dark distracted the eye. The upper skirt was tied so tightly back that it was impossible to take a long step, and the under one was so loaded with plaited frills that it "wobbled"—no other word will express it—ungracefully, both fore and aft. A bunch of folds was gathered up just below the waist behind, and a great bow rode a-top. A small jacket of the same material was adorned with a high ruff at the back, and laid well open over the breast, to display some lace and a locket. Heavy fringes, bows, puffs, ruffles, and *revers* finished off the dress, making one's head ache to think of the amount of work wasted, for not a single graceful line struck the eye, and the beauty of the material was quite lost in the profusion of ornament.

A high velvet hat, audaciously turned up in front, with a bunch of pink roses and a sweeping plume, was cocked over one ear, and, with her curls braided into a club at the back of her neck, Rose's head looked more like that of a dashing young cavalier than a modest little girl's. High-heeled boots tilted her well forward, a tiny muff pinioned her arms, and a spotted veil tied so closely over her face that her eyelashes were rumpled by it, gave the last touch of absurdity to her appearance.

"Now she looks like other girls, and as *I* like to see her," Mrs. Clara was saying, with an air of great satisfaction.

"She does look like a fashionable young lady, but somehow I miss my little Rose, for children dressed like children in my day," answered Aunt Plenty, peering through her glasses with a troubled look, for she could not imagine the creature before her ever sitting in her lap, running to wait upon her, or making the house gay with a child's blithe presence.

"Things have changed since your day, Aunt, and it takes time to get used to new ways. But you, Jessie, surely like this costume better than the dowdy things Rose has been wearing all summer. Now, be honest, and own you do," said Mrs. Clara, bent on being praised for her work.

"Well, dear, to be *quite* honest, then, I think it is

frightful," answered Mrs. Jessie with a candor that caused revolving Rose to stop in dismay.

"Hear, hear," cried a deep voice, and with a general start the ladies became aware that the enemy was among them.

Rose blushed up to her hat brim, and stood, looking, as she felt, like a fool, while Mrs. Clara hastened to explain.

"Of course I don't expect *you* to like it, Alec, but I don't consider you a judge of what is proper and becoming for a young lady. Therefore I have taken the liberty of providing a pretty street suit for Rose. She need not wear it if you object, for I know we promised to let you do what you liked with the poor dear for a year."

"It is a street costume, is it?" asked the Doctor, mildly. "Do you know, I never should have guessed that it was meant for winter weather and brisk locomotion. Take a turn, Rosy, and let me see all its beauties and advantages."

Rose tried to walk off with her usual free tread, but the under-skirt got in her way, the over-skirt was so tight she could not take a long step, and her boots made it impossible to carry herself perfectly erect.

"I haven't got used to it yet," she said, petulantly, kicking at her train, as she turned to toddle back again.

"Suppose a mad dog or a runaway horse was after you, could you get out of the way without upsetting, Colonel?" asked the Doctor, with a twinkle in the eyes that were fixed on the rakish hat.

"Don't think I could, but I'll try," and Rose made a rush across the room. Her boot-heels caught on a rug, several strings broke, her hat tipped over her eyes, and she plunged promiscuously into a chair, where she sat laughing so infectiously that all but Mrs. Clara joined in her mirth.

"I should say that a walking suit in which one could not walk, and a winter suit which exposes the throat, head, and feet to cold and damp, was rather a failure, Clara; especially as it has no beauty to reconcile one to its utter unfitness," said Dr. Alec, as he helped Rose undo her veil, adding, in a low tone, "Nice thing for the eyes; you'll soon see spots when it is off as well as when it is on, and, by and by, be a case for an oculist."

"No beauty!" cried Mrs. Clara, warmly. "Now that is just a man's blindness. This is the best of silk and camel's hair, real ostrich feathers, and an expensive ermine muff. What *could* be in better taste, or more proper for a young girl?"

"I'll show you, if Rose will go to her room and oblige me by putting on what she finds there," answered the Doctor, with unexpected readiness.

"Alec, if it is a Bloomer, I shall protest. I've been expecting it, but I know I *cannot* bear to see that pretty child sacrificed to your wild ideas of health. Tell me it *isn't* a Bloomer!" and Mrs. Clara clasped her hands imploringly.

"It is not."

"Thank Heaven!" and she resigned herself with

a sigh of relief, adding plaintively, "I did hope you'd accept my suit, for poor Rose has been afflicted with frightful clothes long enough to spoil the taste of any girl."

"You talk of *my* afflicting the child, and then make a helpless guy like that of her!" answered the Doctor, pointing to the little fashion plate that was scuttling out of sight as fast as it could go.

He closed the door with a shrug, but before any one could speak, his quick eye fell upon an object which caused him to frown, and demand in an indignant tone,—

"After all I have said, were you really going to tempt my girl with those abominable things?"

"I thought we put them away when she wouldn't wear them," murmured Mrs. Clara, whisking a little pair of corsets out of sight, with guilty haste. "I only brought them to try, for Rose is growing stout, and will have no figure if it is not attended to soon," she added, with an air of calm conviction that roused the Doctor still more, for this was one of his especial abominations.

"Growing stout! Yes, thank Heaven, she is, and shall continue to do it, for Nature knows how to mould a woman better than any corset-maker, and I won't have her interfered with. My dear Clara, *have* you lost your senses that you can for a moment dream of putting a growing girl into an instrument of torture like this?" and with a sudden gesture he plucked forth the offending corsets from under the sofa cushion, and held them out with the expression one would wear on beholding the thumb-screws or the rack of ancient times.

"Don't be absurd, Alec. There is no torture about it, for tight lacing is out of fashion, and we have nice, sensible things nowadays. Every one wears them; even babies have stiffened waists to support their weak little backs," began Mrs. Clara, rushing to the defence of the pet delusion of most women.

"I know it, and so the poor little souls have weak backs all their days, as their mothers had before them. It is vain to argue the matter, and I won't try, but I wish to state, once for all, that if I ever see a pair of corsets near Rose, I'll put them in the fire, and you may send the bill to me."

As he spoke, the corsets were on their way to destruction, but Mrs. Jessie caught his arm, exclaiming merrily, "Don't burn them, for mercy sake, Alec; they are full of whalebones, and will make a dreadful odor. Give them to me. I'll see that they do no harm."

"Whalebones indeed! A regular fence of them, and metal gate-posts in front. As if our own bones were not enough, if we'd give them a chance to do their duty," growled the Doctor, yielding up the bone of contention with a last shake of contempt. Then his face cleared suddenly, and he held up his finger, saying, with a smile, "Hear those girls laugh; cramped lungs could not make hearty music like that."

Peals of laughter issued from Rose's room, and

smiles involuntarily touched the lips of those who listened to the happy sound.

"Some new prank of yours, Alec?" asked Aunt Plenty, indulgently, for she had come to believe in most of her nephew's odd notions, because they seemed to work so well.

"Yes, ma'am, my last, and I hope you will like it. I discovered what Clara was at, and got my rival suit ready for to-day. I'm not going to 'afflict' Rose, but let her choose, and if I'm not entirely mistaken, she will like my rig best. While we wait I'll explain, and then you will appreciate the general effect better. I got hold of this little book, and was struck with its good sense and good taste, for it suggests a way to clothe women both healthfully and handsomely, and that is a great point. It begins at the foundations, as you will see if you will look at these pictures, and I should think women would rejoice at this lightening of their burdens."

As he spoke, the Doctor laid the book before Aunt Plenty, who obediently brought her spectacles to bear upon the illustrations, and after a long look exclaimed with a scandalized face,—

"Mercy on us, these things are like the night-drawers Jamie wears! You don't mean to say you want Rose to come out in this costume? It's not proper, and I won't consent to it!"

"I do mean it, and I'm sure my sensible aunt *will* consent when she understands that these,— well,—I'll call them by an Indian name, and say,— pajamas,—are for underwear, and Rose can have as pretty frocks as she likes outside. These two suits of flannel, each in one piece from head to foot, with a skirt or so hung on this easily fitting waist, will keep the child warm without burdening her with belts, and gathers, and buckles, and bunches round the waist, and leave free the muscles that need plenty of room to work in. She shall never have the backache if *I* can help it, nor the long list of ills you dear women think you cannot escape."

"*I* don't consider it modest, and I'm sure Rose will be shocked at it," began Mrs. Clara, but stopped suddenly as Rose appeared in the doorway, not looking shocked a bit.

"Come on, my hygienic model, and let us see you," said her uncle, with an approving glance, as she walked in looking so mischievously merry, that it was evident she enjoyed the joke.

"Well, I don't see any thing remarkable. That is a neat, plain suit; the materials are good, and it's not unbecoming, if you want her to look like a little school-girl; but it has not a particle of style, and no one would ever give it a second glance," said Mrs. Clara, feeling that her last remark condemned the whole thing.

"Exactly what I want," answered the provoking Doctor, rubbing his hands with a satisfied air. "Rosy looks now like what she is, a modest little girl, who does not want to be stared at. I think she would get a glance of approval, though, from people who liked sense and simplicity, rather than fuss and feathers. Revolve, my Hebe, and let me refresh my eyes by the sight of you."

There was very little to see, however, only a pretty Gabrielle dress, of a soft, warm shade of brown, coming to the tops of a trim pair of boots with low heels. A seal-skin sack, cap, and mittens, with a glimpse of scarlet at the throat, and the pretty curls tied up with a bright velvet of the same color, completed the external adornment, making her look like a robin redbreast,—wintry, yet warm.

"How do you like it, Rosy?" asked the Doctor, feeling that *her* opinion was more important to the success of his new idea than that of all the aunts on the hill.

"I feel very odd and light, but I'm warm as a toast, and nothing seems to be in my way," answered Rose, with a skip which displayed shapely gaiters on legs that now might be as free and active as a boy's under the modest skirts of the girl.

"You can run away from the mad dogs, and walk off at a smart pace without tumbling on your nose, now, I fancy?"

"Yes, uncle! suppose the dog coming, I just hop over a wall so—and when I walk of a cold day, I go like this—"

Entering fully into the spirit of the thing, Rose swung herself over the high back of the sofa as easily as one of her cousins, and then went down the long hall as if her stout boots were related to the famous seven-leaguers.

"There! you see how it will be; dress her in that

boyish way and she will act like a boy. I do hate all these inventions of strong-minded women!" exclaimed Mrs. Clara, as Rose came back at a run.

"Ah, but you see some of these sensible inventions come from the brain of a fashionable *modiste*, who will make you lovely, or what you value more,—'stylish' outside and comfortable within. Mrs. Van Tassel has been to Madame Stone, and is wearing a full suit of this sort. Van himself told me, when I asked how she was, that she had given up lying on the sofa, and was going about in a most astonishing way, considering her feeble health."

"You don't say so! Let me see that book a moment," and Aunt Clara examined the new patterns with a more respectful air, for if the elegant Mrs. Van Tassel wore these "dreadful things" it would never do to be left behind, in spite of her prejudices.

Dr. Alec looked at Mrs. Jessie, and both smiled, for "little Mum" had been in the secret, and enjoyed it mightily.

"I thought that would settle it," he said with a nod.

"I didn't wait for Mrs. Van to lead the way, and for once in my life I have adopted a new fashion before Clara. My freedom suit is ordered, and you *may* see me playing tag with Rose and the boys before long," answered Mrs. Jessie, nodding back at him.

Meantime Aunt Plenty was examining Rose's costume, for the hat and sack were off, and the girl was eagerly explaining the new under-garments.

"See, auntie, all nice scarlet flannel, and a gay little petticoat, and long stockings, oh, so warm! Phebe and I nearly died laughing when I put this rig on, but I like it ever so much. The dress is so comfortable, and doesn't need any belt or sash, and I can sit without rumpling any trimming, that's *such* a comfort! I like to be tidy, and so, when I wear fussed-up things, I'm thinking of my clothes all the time, and that's tiresome. Do say you like it. I resolved *I* would, just to please uncle, for he does know more about health than any one else, I'm sure, and I'd wear a bag if he asked me to do it."

"I don't ask that, Rose, but I wish you'd weigh and compare the two suits, and then choose which seems best. I leave it to your own common-sense," answered Dr. Alec, feeling pretty sure he had won.

"Why, I take this one, of course, uncle. The other is fashionable, and—yes—I must say I think it's pretty—but it's very heavy, and I should have to go round like a walking doll if I wore it. I'm much obliged to auntie, but I'll keep this, please."

Rose spoke gently but decidedly, though there was a look of regret when her eye fell on the other suit which Phebe had brought in; and it was very natural to like to look as other girls did. Aunt Clara sighed; Uncle Alec smiled, and said heartily,—

"Thank you, dear; now read this book and you will understand why I ask it of you. Then, if you like, I'll give you a new lesson; you asked for one yesterday, and this is more necessary than French or housekeeping."

"Oh, what?" and Rose caught up the book which Mrs. Clara had thrown down with a disgusted look.

Though Dr. Alec was forty, the boyish love of teasing was not yet dead in him, and, being much elated at his victory, he could not resist the temptation of shocking Mrs. Clara by suggesting dreadful possibilities, so he answered, half in earnest half in jest: "Physiology, Rose. Wouldn't you like to be a little medical student with Uncle Doctor for teacher, and be ready to take up his practice when he has to stop? If you agree, I'll hunt up my old skeleton to-morrow."

That was *too* much for Aunt Clara, and she hastily departed with her mind in a sad state of perturbation about Mrs. Van Tassel's new costume, and Rose's new study.

19

BROTHER BONES

Rose accepted her uncle's offer, as Aunt Myra discovered two or three days later. Coming in for an early call, and hearing voices in the study, she opened the door, gave a cry and shut it quickly, looking a good deal startled. The Doctor appeared in a moment, and begged to know what the matter was.

"How *can* you ask when that long box looks so like a coffin I thought it was one, and that dreadful thing stared me in the face as I opened the door," answered Mrs. Myra, pointing to the skeleton that hung from the chandelier cheerfully grinning at all beholders.

"This is a medical college where women are freely admitted, so walk in, madam, and join the class if you'll do me the honor," said the Doctor, waving her forward with his politest bow.

"Do, auntie; it's perfectly splendid," cried Rose's voice, and Rose's blooming face was seen behind the ribs of the skeleton, smiling and nodding in the gayest possible manner.

"What *are* you doing, child?" demanded Aunt Myra, dropping into a chair and staring about her.

"Oh, I'm learning bones to-day, and I like it so much. There are twelve ribs, you know, and the two lower ones are called floating ribs, because they are not fastened to the breast bone. That's why they go in so easily if you lace tight and squeeze the lungs and heart in the—let me see, what was that big word—oh, I know—thoracic cavity," and Rose beamed with pride as she aired her little bit of knowledge.

"Do you think that is a good sort of thing for her to be poking over? She is a nervous child, and I'm afraid it will be bad for her," said Aunt Myra, watching Rose as she counted vertebrae, and waggled a hip-joint in its socket with an inquiring expression.

"An excellent study, for she enjoys it, and I mean to teach her how to manage her nerves so that they won't be a curse to her, as many a woman's become through ignorance or want of thought. To make a mystery or a terror of these things is a mistake, and I mean Rose shall understand and respect her body so well that she won't dare to trifle with it as most women do."

"And she really likes it?"

"Very much, auntie! It's all so wonderful, and so nicely planned, you can hardly believe what you see. Just think, there are 600,000,000 air cells in one pair of lungs, and 2,000 pores to a square inch of surface; so you see what quantities of air we *must* have, and what care we should take of our skin so all the little doors will open and shut right.

And brains, auntie, you've no idea how curious they are; I haven't got to them yet, but I long to, and uncle is going to show me a manikin that you can take to pieces. Just think how nice it will be to see all the organs in their places; I only wish they could be made to work as ours do."

It was funny to see Aunt Myra's face as Rose stood before her talking rapidly with one hand laid in the friendliest manner on the skeleton's shoulder. Every word both the Doctor and Rose uttered hit the good lady in her weakest spot, and as she looked and listened a long array of bottles and pill-boxes rose up before her, reproaching her with the "ignorance and want of thought" that made her what she was, a nervous, dyspeptic, unhappy old woman.

"Well, I don't know but you may be right, Alec, only I wouldn't carry it too far. Women don't need much of this sort of knowledge, and are not fit for it. I couldn't bear to touch that ugly thing, and it gives me the creeps to hear about 'organs,'" said Aunt Myra, with a sigh and her hand on her side.

"Wouldn't it be a comfort to know that your liver was on the right side, auntie, and not on the left?" asked Rose with a naughty laugh in her eyes, for she had lately learned that Aunt Myra's liver complaint was not in the proper place.

"It's a dying world, child, and it don't much matter where the pain is, for sooner or later we all drop off and are seen no more," was Aunt Myra's cheerful reply.

"Well, I intend to know what kills me if I can,

and meantime I'm going to enjoy myself in spite of a dying world. I wish you'd do so too, and come and study with uncle, it would do you good I'm sure," and Rose went back to counting vertebrae with such a happy face that Aunt Myra had not the heart to say a word to dampen her ardor.

"Perhaps it's as well to let her do what she likes the little while she is with us. But pray be careful of her, Alec, and not allow her to overwork," she whispered as she went out.

"That's exactly what I'm trying to do, ma'am, and rather a hard job I find it," he added, as he shut the door, for the dear aunts were dreadfully in his way sometimes.

Half an hour later came another interruption in the shape of Mac, who announced his arrival by the brief but elegant remark,—

"Hullo! what new game is this?"

Rose explained, Mac gave a long whistle of surprise, and then took a promenade round the skeleton, observing gravely,—

"Brother Bones looks very jolly, but I can't say much for his beauty."

"You mustn't make fun of him, for he's a good old fellow, and you'd be just as ugly if your flesh was off," said Rose, defending her new friend with warmth.

"I dare say, so I'll keep my flesh on, thank you. You are so busy you can't read to a fellow, I suppose?" asked Mac, whose eyes were better, but still too weak for books.

"Don't you want to come and join my class? Uncle explains it all to us, and you can take a look at the plates as they come along. We'll give up bones to-day and have eyes instead; that will be more interesting to *you*," added Rose, seeing no ardent thirst for physiological information in his face.

"Rose, we must not fly about from one thing to another in this way," began Dr. Alec; but she whispered quickly, with a nod towards Mac, whose goggles were turned wistfully in the direction of the forbidden books,—

"He's blue to-day, and we must amuse him; give a little lecture on eyes, and it will do him good. No matter about me, uncle."

"Very well; the class will please be seated," and the Doctor gave a sounding rap on the table.

"Come, sit by me, dear, then we can both see the pictures; and if your head gets tired you can lie down," said Rose, generously opening her little college to a brother, and kindly providing for the weaknesses that all humanity is subject to.

Side by side they sat and listened to a very simple explanation of the mechanism of the eye, finding it as wonderful as a fairy tale, for fine plates illustrated it, and a very willing teacher did his best to make the lesson pleasant.

"Jove! if I'd known what mischief I was doing to that mighty delicate machine of mine, you wouldn't have caught me reading by firelight, or studying with a glare of sunshine on my book," said Mac, peering solemnly at a magnified eyeball; then, pushing it away, he added indignantly: "Why isn't a fellow taught all about his works, and how to manage 'em, and not left to go blundering into all sorts of worries? Telling him after he's down isn't much use, for then he's found it out himself and won't thank you."

"Ah, Mac, that's just what I keep lecturing about, and people *won't* listen. You lads need that sort of knowledge so much, and fathers and mothers ought to be able to give it to you. Few of them *are* able and so we all go blundering, as you say. Less Greek and Latin and more knowledge of the laws of health for *my* boys, if I had them. Mathematics are all very well, but morals are better, and I wish, *how* I wish that I could help teachers and parents to feel it as they ought."

"Some do; Aunt Jessie and her boys have capital talks, and I wish we could; but mother's so busy with her housekeeping, and father with his business, there never seems to be any time for that sort of thing; even if there was, it don't seem as if it would be easy to talk to them, because we've never got into the way of it, you know."

Poor Mac was right there, and expressed a want that many a boy and girl feels. Fathers and mothers *are* too absorbed in business and housekeeping to study their children, and cherish that sweet and natural confidence which is a child's surest safeguard, and a parent's subtlest power. So the young hearts hide trouble or temptation till the harm is done, and mutual regret comes too late. Happy the boys and girls who tell all things freely to father or mother, sure of pity, help, and pardon; and thrice happy the parents who, out of their own experience, and by their own virtues, can teach and uplift the souls for which they are responsible.

This longing stirred in the hearts of Rose and Mac, and by a natural impulse both turned to Dr. Alec, for in this queer world of ours, fatherly and motherly hearts often beat warm and wise in the breasts of bachelor uncles and maiden aunts; and it is my private opinion that these worthy creatures are a beautiful provision of nature for the cherishing of other people's children. They certainly get great comfort out of it, and receive much innocent affection that otherwise would be lost.

Dr. Alec was one of these, and his big heart had room for every one of the eight cousins, especially orphaned Rose and afflicted Mac; so, when the boy uttered that unconscious reproach to his parents, and Rose added with a sigh, "It must be beautiful to have a mother!"—the good Doctor yearned over them, and, shutting his book with a decided slam, said in that cordial voice of his,—

"Now, look here, children, you just come and tell *me* all your worries, and with God's help I'll settle them for you. That is what I'm here for, I believe, and it will be a great happiness to me if you can trust me."

"We can, uncle, and we will!" both answered with a heartiness that gratified him much.

"Good! now school is dismissed, and I advise you to go and refresh your 600,000,000 air cells by a brisk run in the garden. Come again whenever you like, Mac, and we'll teach you all we can about your 'works,' as you call them, so you can keep them running smoothly."

"We'll come, sir, much obliged," and the class in physiology went out to walk.

Mac did come again, glad to find something he could study in spite of his weak eyes, and learned much that was of more value than any thing his school had ever taught him.

Of course, the other lads made great fun of the whole thing, and plagued Dr. Alec's students half out of their lives. But they kept on persistently, and one day something happened which made the other fellows behave themselves for ever after.

It was a holiday, and Rose up in her room thought she heard the voices of her cousins, so she ran down to welcome them, but found no one there.

"Never mind, they will be here soon, and then we'll have a frolic," she said to herself, and thinking she had been mistaken she went into the study to wait. She was lounging over the table looking at a map when an odd noise caught her ear. A gentle tapping somewhere, and following the sound it seemed to come from the inside of the long case in which the skeleton lived when not professionally engaged. This case stood upright in a niche between two book-cases at the back of the room, a darkish corner, where Brother Bones, as the boys *would* call him, was out of the way.

As Rose stood looking in that direction, and wondering if a rat had got shut in, the door of the case swung slowly open, and with a great start she saw a bony arm lifted, and a bony finger beckon to her. For a minute she was frightened, and ran to the study door with a fluttering heart, but just as she touched the handle a queer, stifled sort of giggle made her stop short and turn red with anger. She paused an instant to collect herself, and then went softly toward the bony beckoner. A nearer look revealed black threads tied to the arm and fingers, the ends of threads disappearing through holes bored in the back of the case. Peeping into the deep recess, she also caught sight of the tip of an elbow covered with a rough gray cloth which she knew very well.

Quick as a flash she understood the joke, her fear vanished, and with a wicked smile, she whipped out her scissors, cut the threads, and the bony arm dropped with a rattle. Before she could say, "Come out, Charlie, and let my skeleton alone," a sudden irruption of boys all in a high state of tickle proclaimed to the hidden rogue that his joke was a failure.

"I told him not to do it, because it might give you a start," explained Archie, emerging from the closet.

"I had a smelling-bottle all ready if she fainted away," added Steve, popping up from behind the great chair.

"It's too bad of you not to squawk and run; we depended on it, it's such fun to howl after you," said Will and Geordie, rolling out from under the sofa in a promiscuous heap.

"You are getting altogether too strong-minded, Rose; most girls would have been in a jolly twitter to see this old fellow waggling his finger at them," complained Charlie, squeezing out from his tight quarters, dusty and disgusted.

"I'm used to your pranks now, so I'm always on the watch and prepared. But I won't have Brother Bones made fun of. I know uncle wouldn't like it, so please don't," began Rose just as Dr. Alec came in, and, seeing the state of the case at a glance, he said quietly,—

"Hear how I got that skeleton, and then I'm sure you will treat it with respect."

The boys settled down at once on any article of furniture that was nearest and listened dutifully.

"Years ago, when I was in the hospital, a poor fellow was brought there with a rare and very painful disease. There was no hope for him, but we did our best, and he was so grateful that when he died he left us his body that we might discover the mysteries of his complaint, and so be able to help others afflicted in the same way. It did do good, and his brave patience made us remember him long after he was gone. He thought I had been kind to him, and said to a fellow-student of mine: 'Tell the Doctor I lave him me bones, for I've nothing else in the wide world, and I'll not be wanting 'em at all, at all, when the great pain has kilt me entirely.' So that is how they came to be mine, and why I've kept them carefully; for, though only a poor, ignorant fellow, Mike Nolan did what he could to help others, and prove his gratitude to those who tried to help him."

As Dr. Alec paused, Archie closed the door of the case as respectfully as if the mummy of an Egyptian king was inside; Will and Geordie looked solemnly at one another, evidently much impressed, and Charlie pensively remarked from the coal-hod where he sat,—

"I've often heard of a skeleton in the house, but I think few people have one as useful and as interesting as ours."

20

UNDER THE MISTLETOE

Rose made Phebe promise that she would bring her stocking into the "Bower," as she called her pretty room, on Christmas morning, because that first delicious rummage loses half its charm if two little night-caps at least do not meet over the treasures, and two happy voices Oh and Ah together.

So when Rose opened her eyes that day they fell upon faithful Phebe, rolled up in a shawl, sitting on the rug before a blazing fire, with her untouched stocking laid beside her.

"Merry Christmas!" cried the little mistress, smiling gayly.

"Merry Christmas!" answered the little maid, so heartily that it did one good to hear her.

"Bring the stockings right away, Phebe, and let's see what we've got," said Rose, sitting up among the pillows, and looking as eager as a child.

A pair of long knobby hose were laid out upon the coverlet and their contents examined with delight, though each knew every blessed thing that had been put into the other's stocking.

Never mind what they were; it is evident that they were quite satisfactory, for as Rose leaned back, she said, with a luxurious sigh of satisfaction: "Now, I believe I've got every thing in the world that I want," and Phebe answered, smiling over a lapful of treasures: "This is the most splendid Christmas I ever had since I was born." Then, she added with an important air,—

"Do wish for something else, because I happen to know of two more presents outside the door this minute."

"Oh, me, what richness!" cried Rose, much excited. "I used to wish for a pair of glass slippers like Cinderella's, but as I can't have them, I really don't know what to ask for."

Phebe clapped her hands as she skipped off the bed and ran to the door, saying merrily: "One of them *is* for your feet any way. I don't know what you'll say to the other, but *I* think it's elegant."

So did Rose, when a shining pair of skates and a fine sled appeared.

"Uncle sent those; I know he did; and, now I see them, I remember that I did want to skate and coast. Isn't it a beauty? See! they fit nicely," and, sitting on the new sled, Rose tried a skate on her little bare foot, while Phebe stood by admiring the pretty *tableau.*

"Now we must hurry and get dressed, for there is a deal to do to-day, and I want to get through in time to try my sled before dinner."

"Gracious me, and I ought to be dusting my parlors this blessed minute!" and mistress and maid separated with such happy faces that any one would have known what day it was without being told.

"Birnam Wood has come to Dunsinane, Rosy," said Dr. Alec, as he left the breakfast table to open the door for a procession of holly, hemlock, and cedar boughs that came marching up the steps.

Snowballs and "Merry Christmases!" flew about pretty briskly for several minutes; then all fell to work trimming up the old house, for the family always dined together there on that day.

"I rode miles and mileses, as Ben says, to get this fine bit, and I'm going to hang it there as the last touch to the rig-a-madooning," said Charlie, as he fastened a dull green branch to the chandelier in the front parlor.

"It isn't very pretty," said Rose, who was trimming the chimney-piece with glossy holly sprays.

"Never mind that, it's mistletoe, and any one who stands under it will get kissed whether they like it or not. Now's your time, ladies," answered the saucy Prince, keeping his place and looking sentimentally at the girls, who retired precipitately from the dangerous spot.

"You won't catch me," said Rose, with great dignity.

"See if I don't!"

"I've got my eye on Phebe," observed Will, in a patronizing tone that made them all laugh.

"Bless the dear; I sha'n't mind it a bit," answered Phebe, with such a maternal air that Will's budding gallantry was chilled to death.

"Oh, the mistletoe bough!" sang Rose.

"Oh, the mistletoe bough!" echoed all the boys, and the teasing ended in the plaintive ballad they all liked so well.

There was plenty of time to try the new skates before dinner, and then Rose took her first lesson on the little bay, which seemed to have frozen over for that express purpose. She found tumbling down and getting up again warm work for a time, but, with six boys to teach her, she managed at last to stand alone; and, satisfied with that success, she refreshed herself with a dozen grand coasts on the Amazon, as her sled was called.

"Ah, that fatal color! it breaks my heart to see it," croaked Aunt Myra, as Rose came down a little late, with cheeks almost as ruddy as the holly berries on the wall, and every curl as smooth as Phebe's careful hands could make it.

"I'm glad to see that Alec allows the poor child to make herself pretty in spite of his absurd notions," added Aunt Clara, taking infinite satisfaction in the fact that Rose's blue silk dress had three frills on it.

"She is a very intelligent child, and has a nice little manner of her own," observed Aunt Jane, with unusual affability; for Rose had just handed Mac a screen to guard his eyes from the brilliant fire.

"If I had a daughter like that to show my Jem when he gets home, I should be a very proud and happy woman," thought Aunt Jessie, and then reproached herself for not being perfectly satisfied with her four brave lads.

Aunt Plenty was too absorbed in the dinner to have an eye for anything else; if she had not been, she would have seen what an effect her new cap produced upon the boys. The good lady owned that she did "love a dressy cap," and on this occasion her head-gear was magnificent; for the towering structure of lace was adorned with buff ribbons to such an extent that it looked as if a flock of yellow butterflies had settled on her dear old head. When she trotted about the rooms the ruches quivered, the little bows all stood erect, and the streamers waved in the breeze so comically that it was absolutely necessary for Archie to smother the Brats in the curtains till they had had their first laugh out.

Uncle Mac had brought Fun See to dinner, and it was a mercy he did, for the elder lads found a vent for their merriment in joking the young Chinaman on his improved appearance. He was in American costume now, with a cropped head, and spoke remarkably good English after six months at school; but, for all that, his yellow face and beady eyes made a curious contrast to the blond Campbells all about him. Will called him the "Typhoon," meaning Tycoon, and the name stuck to him to his great disgust.

Aunt Peace was brought down and set in the chair of state at table, for she never failed to join the family on this day, and sat smiling at them all "like an embodiment of Peace on earth," Uncle Alec said, as he took his place beside her, while

Uncle Mac supported Aunt Plenty at the other end.

"I ate hardly any breakfast, and I've done everything I know to make myself extra hungry, but I really don't think I *can* eat straight through, unless I burst my buttons off," whispered Geordie to Will, as he surveyed the bounteous stores before him with a hopeless sigh.

"A fellow never knows what he can do till he tries," answered Will, attacking his heaped-up plate with the evident intention of doing his duty like a man.

Everybody knows what a Christmas dinner is, so we need waste no words in describing this one, but hasten at once to tell what happened at the end of it. The end, by the way, was so long in coming that the gas was lighted before dessert was over, for a snow flurry had come on and the wintry daylight faded fast. But that only made it all the jollier in the warm, bright rooms, full of happy souls. Every one was very merry, but Archie seemed particularly uplifted,—so much so, that Charlie confided to Rose that he was afraid the Chief had been at the decanters.

Rose indignantly denied the insinuation, for when healths were drunk in the good old-fashioned way to suit the elders, she had observed that Aunt Jessie's boys filled their glasses with water, and had done the same herself in spite of the Prince's jokes about "the rosy."

But Archie certainly *was* unusually excited, and when some one remembered that it was the anniversary of Uncle Jem's wedding, and wished he was there to make a speech, his son electrified the family by trying to do it for him. It was rather incoherent and flowery, as maiden speeches are apt to be, but the end was considered superb; for, turning to his mother with a queer little choke in his voice, he said that she "deserved to be blessed with peace and plenty, to be crowned with roses and lads-love, and to receive the cargo of happiness sailing home to her in spite of wind or tide to add another Jem to the family jewels."

That allusion to the Captain, now on his return trip, made Mrs. Jessie sob in her napkin, and set the boys cheering. Then, as if that was not sensation enough, Archie suddenly dashed out of the room as if he had lost his wits.

"Too bashful to stay and be praised," began Charlie, excusing the peculiarities of his Chief as in duty bound.

"Phebe beckoned to him; I saw her," cried Rose, staring hard at the door.

"Is it more presents coming?" asked Jamie, just as his brother re-appeared looking more excited than ever.

"Yes; a present for mother, and here it is!" roared Archie, flinging wide the door to let in a tall man who cried out,—

"Where's my little woman? The first kiss for her, then the rest may come on as fast as they like."

Before the words were out of his mouth, Mrs. Jessie was half hidden under his rough great-coat, and four boys were prancing about him clamoring for their turn.

Of course, there was a joyful tumult for a time, during which Rose slipped into the window recess and watched what went on, as if it were a chapter in a Christmas story. It was good to see bluff Uncle Jem look proudly at his tall son, and fondly hug the little ones. It was better still to see him shake his brothers' hands as if he would never leave off, and kiss all the sisters in a way that made even solemn Aunt Myra brighten up for a minute. But it was best of all to see him finally established in grandfather's chair, with his "little woman" beside him, his three youngest boys in his lap, and Archie hovering over him like a large-sized cherub. That really was, as Charlie said, "A landscape to do one's heart good."

"All hearty and all here, thank God!" said Captain Jem in the first pause that came, as he looked about him with a grateful face.

"All but Rose," answered loyal little Jamie, remembering the absent.

"Faith, I forgot the child! Where is George's little girl?" asked the Captain, who had not seen her since she was a baby.

"You'd better say Alec's great girl," said Uncle Mac, who professed to be madly jealous of his brother.

"Here I am, sir," and Rose appeared from behind the curtains, looking as if she had rather have staid there.

"Saint George Germain, how the mite has

grown!" cried Captain Jem, as he tumbled the boys out of his lap, and rose to greet the tall girl, like a gentleman as he was. But, somehow, when he shook her hand it looked so small in his big one, and her face reminded him so strongly of his dead brother, that he was not satisfied with so cold a welcome, and with a sudden softening of the keen eyes he took her up in his arms, whispering, with a rough cheek against her smooth one,—

"God bless you, child! forgive me if I forgot you for a minute, and be sure that not one of your kins-folk is happier to see you here than Uncle Jem."

That made it all right; and when he set her down, Rose's face was so bright it was evident that some spell had been used to banish the feeling of neglect that had kept her moping behind the curtain so long.

Then every one sat round and heard all about the voyage home,—how the Captain had set his heart on getting there in time to keep Christmas; how every thing had conspired to thwart his plan; and how, at the very last minute, he had managed to do it, and had sent a telegram to Archie, bidding him keep the secret, and be ready for his father at any moment, for the ship got into another port, and he might be late.

Then Archie told how that telegram had burnt in his pocket all dinner-time; how he had to take Phebe into his confidence, and how clever she was to keep the Captain back till the speech was over, and he could come in with effect.

The elders would have sat and talked all the evening, but the young folks were bent on having their usual Christmas frolic; so, after an hour of pleasant chat, they began to get restless, and having consulted together in dumb show, they devised a way to very effectually break up the family council.

Steve vanished, and, sooner than the boys imagined Dandy could get himself up, the skirl of the bag-pipe was heard in the hall, and the bonny piper came to lead Clan Campbell to the revel.

"Draw it mild, Stenie, my man; ye play unco weel, but ye mak a most infernal din," cried Uncle Jem, with his hands over his ears, for this accomplishment was new to him, and "took him all aback," as he expressed it.

So Steve droned out a Highland reel as softly as he could, and the boys danced it to a circle of admiring relations. Captain Jem was a true sailor, however, and could not stand idle while any thing lively was going on; so, when the piper's breath gave out, he cut a splendid pigeon-wing into the middle of the hall, saying, "Who can dance a Fore and After?" and, waiting for no reply, began to whistle the air so invitingly that Mrs. Jessie "set" to him laughing like a girl; Rose and Charlie took their places behind, and away went the four with a spirit and skill that inspired all the rest to "cut in" as fast as they could.

That was a grand beginning, and they had many another dance before any one would own they were tired. Even Fun See distinguished himself with Aunt Plenty, whom he greatly admired as the stoutest lady in the company; plumpness being considered a beauty in his country. The merry old soul professed herself immensely flattered by his admiration, and the boys declared she "set her cap at him," else he would never have dared to catch her under the mistletoe, and, rising on the tips of his own toes, gallantly salute her fat cheek.

How they all laughed at her astonishment, and how Fun's little black eyes twinkled over this exploit! Charlie put him up to it, and Charlie was so bent on catching Rose, that he laid all sorts of pitfalls for her, and bribed the other lads to help him. But Rose was wide-awake, and escaped all his snares, professing great contempt for such foolish customs. Poor Phebe did not fare so well, and Archie was the one who took a base advantage of her as she stood innocently offering tea to Aunt Myra, whom she happened to meet just under the fatal bough. If his father's arrival had not rather upset him, I doubt if the dignified Chief would have done it, for he apologized at once in the handsomest manner, and caught the tray that nearly dropped from Phebe's hands.

Jamie boldly invited *all* the ladies to come and salute him; and as for Uncle Jem, he behaved as if the entire room was a grove of mistletoe. Uncle Alec slyly laid a bit of it on Aunt Peace's cap, and then softly kissed her; which little joke seemed to please her very much, for she liked to have part in all the home pastimes, and Alec was her favorite nephew.

Charlie alone failed to catch his shy bird, and the oftener she escaped the more determined he was to ensnare her. When every other wile had been tried in vain, he got Archie to propose a game with forfeits.

"I understand that dodge," thought Rose, and was on her guard so carefully that not one among the pile soon collected belonged to her.

"Now let us redeem them and play something else," said Will, quite unconscious of the deeply laid plots all about him.

"One more round and then we will," answered the Prince, who had now baited his trap anew.

Just as the question came to Rose, Jamie's voice was heard in the hall crying distressfully, "Oh, come quick, quick!" Rose started up, missed the question, and was greeted with a general cry of "Forfeit! forfeit!" in which the little traitor came to join.

"Now I've got her," thought the young rascal, exulting in his fun-loving soul.

"Now I'm lost," thought Rose, as she gave up her pin-cushion with a sternly defiant look that would have daunted any one but the reckless Prince. In fact, it made even him think twice, and resolve to "let Rose off easy," she had been so clever.

"Here's a very pretty pawn, and what shall be

done to redeem it?" asked Steve, holding the pin-
cushion over Charlie's head, for he had insisted on
being judge, and kept that for the last.

"Fine or superfine?"

"Super."

"Hum, well, she shall take old Mac under the
mistletoe and kiss him prettily. Won't he be mad,
though?"—and this bad boy chuckled over the discomfort he had caused two harmless beings.

There was an impressive pause among the
young folks in their corner, for they all knew that
Mac *would* "be mad," since he hated nonsense of
this sort, and had gone to talk with the elders when
the game began. At this moment he was standing
before the fire, listening to a discussion between
his uncles and his father, looking as wise as a
young owl, and blissfully unconscious of the plot
against him.

Charlie expected that Rose would say, "I
won't!" therefore he was rather astonished, not to
say gratified, when, after a look at the victim, she
laughed suddenly, and, going up to the group of
gentlemen, drew her *uncle* Mac under the mistletoe and surprised him with a hearty kiss.

"Thank you, my dear," said the innocent gentleman, looking much pleased at the unexpected
honor.

"Oh, come; that's not fair," began Charlie. But
Rose cut him short by saying, as she made him a
fine courtesy,—

"You said 'Old Mac,' and though it was very disrespectful, I did it. That was your last chance, sir, and you've lost it."

He certainly had, for, as she spoke, Rose pulled down the mistletoe and threw it into the fire, while the boys jeered at the crest-fallen Prince, and exalted quick-witted Rose to the skies.

"What's the joke?" asked young Mac, waked out of a brown study by the laughter, in which the elders joined.

But there was a regular shout when, the matter having been explained to him, Mac took a meditative stare at Rose through his goggles, and said in a philosophical tone, "Well, I don't think I should have minded much if she *had* done it."

That tickled the lads immensely, and nothing but the appearance of a slight refection would have induced them to stop chaffing the poor Worm, who could not see any thing funny in the beautiful resignation he had shown on this trying occasion.

Soon after this, the discovery of Jamie curled up in the sofa corner, as sound asleep as a dormouse, suggested the propriety of going home, and a general move was made.

They were all standing about the hall lingering over the good-nights, when the sound of a voice softly singing "Sweet Home," made them pause and listen. It was Phebe, poor little Phebe, who never had a home, never knew the love of father or mother, brother or sister; who stood all alone in the wide world, yet was not sad nor afraid, but took her bits of happiness gratefully, and sung over her work without a thought of discontent.

I fancy the happy family standing there together remembered this and felt the beauty of it, for when the solitary voice came to the burden of its song, other voices took it up and finished it so sweetly, that the old house seemed to echo the word "Home" in the ears of both the orphan girls, who had just spent their first Christmas under its hospitable roof.

21

A Scare

"Brother Alec, you surely don't mean to allow that child to go out such a bitter cold day as this," said Mrs. Myra, looking into the study, where the Doctor sat reading his paper, one February morning.

"Why not? If a delicate invalid like yourself can bear it, surely my hearty girl can, especially as *she* is dressed for cold weather," answered Dr. Alec with provoking confidence.

"But you have no idea how sharp the wind is. I am chilled to the very marrow of my bones," answered Aunt Myra, chafing the end of her purple nose with her sombre glove.

"I don't doubt it, ma'am, if you *will* wear crape and silk instead of fur and flannel. Rosy goes out in all weathers, and will be none the worse for an hour's brisk skating."

"Well, I warn you that you are trifling with the child's health, and depending too much on the seeming improvement she has made this year. She is a delicate creature for all that, and will drop away suddenly at the first serious attack, as her poor mother did," croaked Aunt Myra, with a despondent wag of the big bonnet.

"I'll risk it," answered Dr. Alec, knitting his brows, as he always did when any allusion was made to that other Rose.

"Mark my words, you will repent it," and, with that awful prophecy, Aunt Myra departed like a black shadow.

Now it must be confessed that among the Doctor's failings—and he had his share—was a very masculine dislike of advice which was thrust upon him unasked. He always listened with respect to the great-aunts, and often consulted Mrs. Jessie; but the other three ladies tried his patience sorely, by constant warnings, complaints, and counsels. Aunt Myra was an especial trial, and he always turned contrary the moment she began to talk. He could not help it, and often laughed about it with comic frankness. Here now was a sample of it, for he had just been thinking that Rose had better defer her run till the wind went down and the sun was warmer. But Aunt Myra spoke, and he could not resist the temptation to make light of her advice, and let Rose brave the cold. He had no fear of its harming her, for she went out every day, and it was a great satisfaction to him to see her run down the avenue a minute afterward, with her skates on her arm, looking like a rosy-faced Esquimaux in her seal-skin suit, as she smiled at Aunt Myra stalking along as solemnly as a crow.

"I hope the child won't stay out long, for this wind *is* enough to chill the marrow in younger bones than Myra's," thought Dr. Alec, half an hour later, as he drove toward the city to see the few patients he had consented to take for old acquaintance' sake.

The thought returned several times that morning, for it *was* truly a bitter day, and, in spite of his bear-skin coat, the Doctor shivered. But he had great faith in Rose's good sense, and it never occurred to him that she was making a little Casabianca of herself, with the difference of freezing instead of burning at her post.

You see, Mac had made an appointment to meet her at a certain spot, and have a grand skating bout as soon as the few lessons he was allowed were over. She had promised to wait for him, and did so with a faithfulness that cost her dear, because Mac forgot his appointment when the lessons were done, and became absorbed in a chemical experiment, till a general combustion of gases drove him out of his laboratory. Then he suddenly remembered Rose, and would gladly have hurried away to her, but his mother forbade his going out, for the sharp wind would hurt his eyes.

"She will wait and wait, mother, for she always keeps her word, and I told her to hold on till I came," explained Mac, with visions of a shivering little figure watching on the windy hill-top.

"Of course, your uncle won't let her go out such a day as this. If he does, she will have the sense to come here for you, or to go home again when you don't appear," said Aunt Jane, returning to her "Watts on the Mind."

"I wish Steve would just cut up and see if she's there, since I can't go," began Mac, anxiously.

"Steve won't stir a peg, thank you. He's got his own toes to thaw out, and wants his dinner," answered Dandy, just in from school, and wrestling impatiently with his boots.

So Mac resigned himself, and Rose waited dutifully till dinner-time assured her that her waiting was in vain. She had done her best to keep warm, had skated till she was tired and hot, then stood watching others till she was chilled; tried to get up a glow again by trotting up and down the road, but failed to do so, and finally cuddled disconsolately under a pine-tree to wait and watch. When she at length started for home, she was benumbed with the cold, and could hardly make her way against the wind that buffeted the frost-bitten rose most unmercifully.

Dr. Alec was basking in the warmth of the study fire, after his drive, when the sound of a stifled sob made him hurry to the door and look anxiously into the hall. Rose lay in a shivering bunch near the register, with her things half off, wringing her hands, and trying not to cry with the pain returning warmth brought to her half-frozen fingers.

"My darling, what is it?" and Uncle Alec had her in his arms in a minute.

"Mac didn't come—I can't get warm—the fire makes me ache!" and with a long shiver Rose burst out crying, while her teeth chattered, and her poor little nose was so blue, it made one's heart ache to see it.

In less time than it takes to tell it, Dr. Alec had her on the sofa rolled up in the bear-skin coat, with Phebe rubbing her cold feet while he rubbed the aching hands, and Aunt Plenty made a comfortable hot drink, and Aunt Peace sent down her own footwarmer and embroidered blanket "for the dear."

Full of remorseful tenderness, Uncle Alec worked over his new patient till she declared she was all right again. He would not let her get up to dinner, but fed her himself, and then forgot his own while he sat watching her fall into a drowse, for Aunt Plenty's cordial made her sleepy.

She lay so several hours, for the drowse deepened into a heavy sleep, and Uncle Alec, still at his post, saw with growing anxiety that a feverish color began to burn in her cheeks, that her breathing was quick and uneven, and now and then she gave a little moan, as if in pain. Suddenly she woke up with a start, and seeing Aunt Plenty bending over her, put out her arms like a sick child, saying wearily,—

"Please, could I go to bed?"

"The best place for you, deary. Take her right up, Alec; I've got the hot water ready, and after a nice bath, she shall have a cup of my sage tea, and be rolled up in blankets to sleep off her cold," answered the old lady, cheerily, as she bustled away to give orders.

"Are you in pain, darling?" asked Uncle Alec, as he carried her up.

"My side aches when I breathe, and I feel stiff and queer; but it isn't bad, so don't be troubled, uncle," whispered Rose, with a little hot hand against his cheek.

But the poor Doctor did look troubled, and had cause to do so, for just then Rose tried to laugh at Debby charging into the room with a warming-pan, but could not, for the sharp pain that took her breath away, and made her cry out.

"Pleurisy," sighed Aunt Plenty, from the depths of the bath-tub.

"Pewmonia!" groaned Debby, burrowing among the bedclothes with the long-handled pan, as if bent on fishing up that treacherous disease.

"Oh, is it bad?" asked Phebe, nearly dropping a pail of hot water in her dismay, for she knew nothing of sickness, and Debby's suggestion had a peculiarly dreadful sound to her.

"Hush!" ordered the Doctor, in a tone that silenced all further predictions, and made every one work with a will.

"Make her as comfortable as you can, and when she is in her little bed I'll come and say good-night," he added, when the bath was ready and the blankets browning nicely before the fire.

Then he went away to talk quite cheerfully to Aunt Peace about its being "only a chill;" after which he tramped up and down the hall, pulling his beard and knitting his brows, sure signs of great inward perturbation.

"I thought it would be too good luck to get through the year without a downfall. Confound my perversity! why couldn't I take Myra's advice and keep Rose at home. It's not fair that the poor child should suffer for my sinful overconfidence. She shall *not* suffer for it! Pneumonia, indeed! I defy it!" and he shook his fist in the ugly face of an Indian idol that happened to be before him, as if that particularly hideous god had some spite against his own little goddess.

In spite of his defiance his heart sunk when he saw Rose again, for the pain was worse, and the bath and blankets, the warming-pan and piping-hot sage tea, were all in vain. For several hours there was no rest for the poor child, and all manner of gloomy forebodings haunted the minds of those who hovered about her with faces full of the tenderest anxiety.

In the midst of the worst paroxysm Charlie came to leave a message from his mother, and was met by Phebe coming despondently downstairs with a mustard plaster that had brought no relief.

"What the dickens is the matter? You look as dismal as a tombstone," he said, as she held up her hand to stop his lively whistling.

"Miss Rose is dreadful sick."

"The deuce she is!"

"Don't swear, Mr. Charlie; she really is, and it's Mr. Mac's fault," and Phebe told the sad tale in a few sharp words, for she felt at war with the entire race of boys at that moment.

"I'll give it to him, make your mind easy about that," said Charlie, with an ominous doubling up of his fist. "But Rose isn't dangerously ill, is she?" he added anxiously, as Aunt Plenty was seen to trot across the upper hall, shaking a bottle violently as she went.

"Oh, but she is, though. The Doctor don't say much, but he don't call it a 'chill' any more. It's 'pleurisy' now, and I'm *so* afraid it will be *pewmonia* to-morrow," answered Phebe, with a despairing glance at the plaster.

Charlie exploded into a stifled laugh at the new pronunciation of pneumonia, to Phebe's great indignation.

"How can you have the heart to do it, and she in such horrid pain? Hark to that, and then laugh if you darst," she said with a tragic gesture, and her black eyes full of fire.

Charlie listened and heard little moans that went to his heart and made his face as sober as Phebe's. "O uncle, please stop the pain and let me rest a minute! Don't tell the boys I wasn't brave. I try to bear it, but it's so sharp I can't help crying."

Neither could Charlie, when he heard the broken voice say that; but, boy-like, he wouldn't own it, and said pettishly, as he rubbed his sleeve across his eyes,—

"Don't hold that confounded thing right under my nose; the mustard makes my eyes smart."

"Don't see how it can, when it hasn't any more strength in it than meal. The Doctor said so, and

I'm going to get some better," began Phebe, not a bit ashamed of the great tears that were bedewing the condemned plaster.

"I'll go!" and Charlie was off like a shot, glad of an excuse to get out of sight for a few minutes.

When he came back all inconvenient emotion had been disposed of, and, having delivered a box of the hottest mustard procurable for money, he departed to "blow up" Mac, that being his next duty in his opinion. He did it so energetically and thoroughly, that the poor Worm was cast into the depths of remorseful despair, and went to bed that evening feeling that he was an outcast from among men, and bore the mark of Cain upon his brow.

Thanks to the skill of the Doctor, and the devotion of his helpers, Rose grew easier about midnight, and all hoped that the worst was over. Phebe was making tea by the study fire, for the Doctor had forgotten to eat and drink since Rose was ill, and Aunt Plenty insisted on his having a "good, cordial dish of tea" after his exertions. A tap on the window startled Phebe, and, looking up, she saw a face peering in. She was not afraid, for a second look showed her that it was neither ghost nor burglar, but Mac, looking pale and wild in the wintry moonlight.

"Come and let a fellow in," he said in a low tone, and when he stood in the hall he clutched Phebe's arm, whispering gruffly, "How is Rose?"

"Thanks be to goodness, she's better," answered

Phebe, with a smile that was like broad sunshine to the poor lad's anxious heart.

"And she will be all right again to-morrow?"

"Oh, dear, no. Debby says she's sure to have rheumatic fever, if she don't have noo-monia!" answered Phebe, careful to pronounce the word rightly this time.

Down went Mac's face, and remorse began to gnaw at him again as he gave a great sigh and said doubtfully,—

"I suppose I couldn't see her?"

"Of course not at this time of night, when we want her to go to sleep!"

Mac opened his mouth to say something more, when a sneeze came upon him unawares, and a loud "Ah rash hoo!" awoke the echoes of the quiet house.

"Why didn't you stop it?" said Phebe reproachfully. "I dare say you've waked her up."

"Didn't know it was coming. Just my luck!" groaned Mac, turning to go before his unfortunate presence did more harm.

But a voice from the stair-head called softly, "Mac, come up; Rose wants to see you."

Up he went, and found his uncle waiting for him.

"What brings you here, at this hour, my boy?" asked the Doctor in a whisper.

"Charlie said it was all my fault, and if she died I'd killed her. I couldn't sleep, so I came to see how she was, and no one knows it but Steve," he said with such a troubled face and voice that the Doctor had not the heart to blame him.

Before he could say any thing more a feeble voice called "Mac!" and with a hasty "Stay a minute just to please her, and then slip away, for I want her to sleep," the Doctor led him into the room.

The face on the pillow looked very pale and childish, and the smile that welcomed Mac was very faint, for Rose was spent with pain, yet could not rest till she had said a word of comfort to her cousin.

"I knew your funny sneeze, and I guessed that you came to see how I was, though it is very late. Don't be worried. I'm better now, and it is my fault I was ill, not yours; for I needn't have been so silly as to wait in the cold just because I said I would."

Mac hastened to explain, to load himself with reproaches, and to beg her not to die on any account, for Charlie's lecture had made a deep impression on the poor boy's mind.

"I didn't know there was any danger of my dying," and Rose looked up at him with a solemn expression in her great eyes.

"Oh, I hope not; but people do sometimes go suddenly, you know, and I couldn't rest till I'd asked you to forgive me," faltered Mac, thinking that Rose looked very like an angel already, with the golden hair loose on the pillow, and the meekness of suffering on her little white face.

"I don't think I shall die; uncle won't let me; but if I do, remember I forgave you."

She looked at him with a tender light in her eyes, and, seeing how pathetic his dumb grief was, she added softly, drawing his head down: "I wouldn't kiss you under the mistletoe, but I will now, for I want you to be sure I do forgive and love you just the same."

That quite upset poor Mac; he could only murmur his thanks and get out of the room as fast as possible, to grope his way to the couch at the far end of the hall, and lie there till he fell asleep, worn out with trying not to "make a baby" of himself.

22

SOMETHING TO DO

Whatever danger there might have been from the effects of that sudden chill, it was soon over, though of course Aunt Myra refused to believe it, and Dr. Alec cherished his girl with redoubled vigilance and tenderness for months afterward. Rose quite enjoyed being sick, because as soon as the pain ended the fun began, and for a week or two she led the life of a little princess secluded in the Bower, while every one served, amused, and watched over her in the most delightful manner. But the Doctor was called away to see an old friend who was dangerously ill, and then Rose felt like a young bird deprived of its mother's sheltering wing; especially on one afternoon when the aunts were taking their naps, and the house was very still within while snow fell softly without.

"I'll go and hunt up Phebe, she is always nice and busy, and likes to have me help her. If Debby is out of the way we can make caramels and surprise the boys when they come," Rose said to herself, as she threw down her book and felt ready for society of some sort.

She took the precaution to peep through the

slide before she entered the kitchen, for Debby allowed no messing when she was round. But the coast was clear, and no one but Phebe appeared, sitting at the table with her head on her arms apparently asleep. Rose was just about to wake her with a "Boo!" when she lifted her head, dried her wet eyes with her blue apron, and fell to work with a resolute face on something she was evidently much interested in. Rose could not make out what it was, and her curiosity was greatly excited, for Phebe was writing with a sputtering pen on some bits of brown paper, apparently copying something from a little book.

"I *must* know what the dear thing is about, and why she cried, and then set her lips tight and went to work with all her might," thought Rose, forgetting all about the caramels, and, going round to the door, she entered the kitchen, saying pleasantly,—

"Phebe, I want something to do. Can't you let me help you about any thing? or shall I be in the way?"

"Oh, dear, no, miss; I always love to have you round when things are tidy. What would you like to do?" answered Phebe, opening a drawer as if about to sweep her own affairs out of sight; but Rose stopped her, exclaiming, like a curious child,—

"Let me see! What is it? I won't tell if you'd rather not have Debby know."

"I'm only trying to study a bit; but I'm so stupid I don't get on much," answered the girl reluctantly, permitting her little mistress to examine the poor contrivances she was trying to work with.

A broken slate that had blown off the roof, an inch or two of pencil, an old almanac for a reader, several bits of brown or yellow paper ironed smoothly and sewed together for a copy-book, and the copies sundry receipts written in Aunt Plenty's neat hand. These, with a small bottle of ink and a rusty pen, made up Phebe's outfit, and it was little wonder that she did not "get on" in spite of the patient persistence that dried the desponding tears and drove along the sputtering pen with a will.

"You may laugh if you want to, Miss Rose, I know my things are queer, and that's why I hide 'em; but I don't mind since you've found me out, and I ain't a bit ashamed except of being so backward at my age," said Phebe humbly, though her cheeks grew redder as she washed out some crooked capitals with a tear or two not yet dried upon the slate.

"Laugh at you! I feel more like crying to think what a selfish girl I am, to have loads of books and things and never remember to give you some. Why didn't you come and ask me, and not go struggling along alone in this way? It was very wrong of you, Phebe, and I'll never forgive you if you do so again," answered Rose, with one hand on Phebe's shoulder while the other gently turned the leaves of the poor little copy-book.

"I didn't like to ask for any thing more when you are so good to me all the time, miss, dear," began Phebe, looking up with grateful eyes.

"O you proud thing! just as if it wasn't fun to give away, and I had the best of it. Now, see here, I've got a plan and you mustn't say no, or I shall scold. I want something to do, and I'm going to teach you all I know; it won't take long," and Rose laughed as she put her arm around Phebe's neck and patted the smooth dark head with the kind little hand that so loved to give.

"It would be just heavenly!" and Phebe's face shone at the mere idea; but fell again as she added wistfully, "Only I'm afraid I ought not to let you do it, Miss Rose. It will take time, and maybe the Doctor wouldn't like it."

"He didn't want me to study much, but he never said a word about teaching, and I don't believe he will mind a bit. Any way, we can try it till he comes, so pack up your things and go right to my room and we'll begin this very day; I'd truly like to do it, and we'll have nice times, see if we don't!" cried Rose eagerly.

It was a pretty sight to see Phebe bundle her humble outfit into her apron, and spring up as if the desire of her heart had suddenly been made a happy fact to her; it was a still prettier sight to see Rose run gayly on before, smiling like a good fairy as she beckoned to the other, singing as she went,—

"The way into my parlor is up a winding stair,
And many are the curious things I'll show you
when you're there.
Will you, will you walk in, Phebe dear?"

"Oh, won't I!" answered Phebe fervently, adding, as they entered the Bower, "You are the dearest spider that ever was, and I'm the happiest fly."

"I'm going to be very strict, so sit down in that chair and don't say a word till school is ready to open," ordered Rose, delighted with the prospect of such a useful and pleasant "something to do."

So Phebe sat demurely in her place while her new teacher laid forth books and slates, a pretty inkstand and a little globe; hastily tore a bit off her big sponge, sharpened pencils with more energy than skill, and when all was ready gave a prance of satisfaction that set the pupil laughing.

"Now the school is open, and I shall hear you read, so that I may know in which class to put you, Miss Moore," began Rose with great dignity, as she laid a book before her scholar, and sat down in the easy chair with a long rule in her hand.

Phebe did pretty well, only tripping now and then over a hard word, and pronouncing identical "identickle," in a sober way that tickled Rose, though never a smile betrayed her. The spelling lesson which followed was rather discouraging; Phebe's ideas of geography were very vague, and grammar was nowhere, though the pupil protested that she tried so hard to "talk nice like educated folks" that Debby called her "a stuck-up piece who didn't know her place."

"Debby's an old goose, so don't you mind her, for she will say 'nater,' 'vittles,' and 'doos' as long as she lives, and insist that they are right. You do talk very nicely, Phebe, I've observed it, and grammar will help you, and show why some things are right and others ain't,—are not, I mean," added Rose, correcting herself, and feeling that she must mind her own parts of speech if she was to serve as an example for Phebe.

When the arithmetic came the little teacher was surprised to find her scholar quicker in some things than herself, for Phebe had worked away at the columns in the butcher's and baker's books till she could add so quickly and correctly that Rose was amazed, and felt that in this branch the pupil would soon excel the teacher if she kept on at the same pace. Her praise cheered Phebe immensely, and they went bravely on, both getting so interested that time flew unheeded till Aunt Plenty appeared, exclaiming, as she stared at the two heads bent over one slate,—

"Bless my heart, what is going on now?"

"School, auntie. I'm teaching Phebe, and it's great fun!" cried Rose, looking up with a bright face.

But Phebe's was brighter, though she added, with a wistful look,—

"Maybe I ought to have asked leave first; only when Miss Rose proposed this, I was so happy I forgot to. Shall I stop, ma'am?"

"Of course not, child; I'm glad to see you fond of your book, and to find Rose helping you along. My blessed mother used to sit at work with her maids about her, teaching them many a useful thing in the good old fashion that's gone by now. Only don't neglect your work, dear, or let the books interfere with the duties."

As Aunt Plenty spoke, with her kind old face beaming approvingly upon the girls, Phebe glanced at the clock, saw that it pointed to five, knew that Debby would soon be down, expecting to find preparations for supper under way, and, hastily dropping her pencil, she jumped up, saying,—

"Please, can I go? I'll clear up after I've done my chores."

"School is dismissed," answered Rose, and with a grateful "Thank you, heaps and heaps!" Phebe ran away singing the multiplication table as she set the tea ditto.

That was the way it began, and for a week the class of one went on with great pleasure and profit to all concerned; for the pupil proved a bright one, and came to her lessons as to a feast, while the young teacher did her best to be worthy the high opinion held of her, for Phebe firmly believed that Miss Rose knew *every thing* in the way of learning.

Of course the lads found out what was going on, and chaffed the girls about the "Seminary," as they called the new enterprise; but they thought it a good thing on the whole, kindly offered to give lessons in Greek and Latin gratis, and decided among themselves that "Rose was a little trump to give the Phebe-bird such a capital boost."

Rose herself had some doubts as to how it would strike her uncle, and concocted a wheedlesome speech which should at once convince him that it was the most useful, wholesome, and delightful plan ever devised. But she got no chance to deliver her address, for Dr. Alec came upon her so unexpectedly that it went out of her head entirely. She was sitting on the floor in the library, poring over a big book laid open in her lap, and knew nothing of the long-desired arrival till two large, warm hands met under her chin and gently turned her head back, so that some one could kiss her heartily on either cheek, while a fatherly voice said, half reproachfully, "Why is my girl brooding over a dusty Encyclopedia when she ought to be running to meet the old gentleman who couldn't get on another minute without her?"

"O uncle! I'm so glad! and so sorry! Why didn't you let us know what time you'd be here, or call out the minute you came? Haven't I been homesick for you? and now I'm so happy to have you back I could hug your dear old curly head off," cried Rose, as the Encyclopedia went down with a bang, and she up with a spring that carried her into Dr. Alec's arms, to be kept there in the sort of embrace a man gives to the dearest creature the world holds for him.

Presently he was in his easy chair with Rose upon his knee smiling up in his face and talking as fast as her tongue could go, while he watched her with an expression of supreme content, as he stroked the smooth round cheek, or held the little hand in his, rejoicing to see how rosy was the one, how plump and strong the other.

"*Have* you had a good time? *Did* you save the poor lady? *Aren't* you glad to be home again with your girl to torment you?"

"Yes, to all those questions. Now tell me what you've been at, little sinner? Aunty Plen says you want to consult me about some new and remarkable project which you have dared to start in my absence."

"She didn't tell you, I hope?"

"Not a word more except that you were rather doubtful how I'd take it, and so wanted to fess' yourself and get round me as you always try to do, though you don't often succeed. Now, then, own up and take the consequences."

So Rose told about her school in her pretty, earnest way, dwelling on Phebe's hunger for knowledge, and the delight it was to help her, adding, with a wise nod,—

"And it helps me too, uncle, for she is so quick and eager I have to do my best or she will get ahead of me in some things. To-day, now, she had the word 'cotton' in a lesson and asked all about it, and I was ashamed to find I really knew so little that I could only say that it was a plant that grew down South in a kind of a pod, and was made into cloth. That's what I was reading up when you came, and to-morrow I shall tell her all about it, and indigo too. So you see it teaches me also, and is as good as a general review of what I've learned, in a pleasanter way than going over it alone."

"You artful little baggage! that's the way you expect to get round me, is it? That's not studying, I suppose?"

"No, sir, it's teaching; and please, I like it much better than having a good time all by myself. Besides, you know, I adopted Phebe and promised to be a sister to her, so I am bound to keep my word, am I not?" answered Rose, looking both anxious and resolute as she waited for her sentence.

Dr. Alec was evidently already won, for Rose had described the old slate and brown paper copybook with pathetic effect, and the excellent man had not only decided to send Phebe to school long before the story was done, but reproached himself for forgetting his duty to one little girl in his love for another. So when Rose tried to look meek and failed utterly, he laughed and pinched her cheek, and answered in that genial way which adds such warmth and grace to any favor,—

"I haven't the slightest objection in the world. In fact, I was beginning to think I might let you go at your books again, moderately, since you are so well; and this is an excellent way to try your powers. Phebe is a brave, bright lass, and shall have a fair chance in the world, if we can give it to her, so that if she ever finds her friends they need not be ashamed of her."

"I think she has found some already," began Rose eagerly.

"Hey? what? has any one turned up since I've been gone?" asked Dr. Alec quickly, for it was a firm belief in the family that Phebe would prove to be "somebody" sooner or later.

"No, her best friend turned up when *you* came home, uncle," answered Rose with an approving pat, adding gratefully, "I can't half thank you for being so good to my girl, but she will, because I know she is going to make a woman to be proud of, she's so strong and true, and loving."

"Bless your dear heart, I haven't begun to do any thing yet, more shame to me! But I'm going at it now, and as soon as she gets on a bit, she shall go to school as long as she likes. How will that do for a beginning?"

"It will be 'just heavenly,' as Phebe says, for it is the wish of her life to 'get lots of schooling,' and she will be *too* happy when I tell her. May I, please?—it will be so lovely to see the dear thing open her big eyes and clap her hands at the splendid news."

"No one shall have a finger in this nice little pie; you shall do it all yourself, only don't go too fast, or make too many castles in the air, my dear; for time and patience must go into this pie of ours if it is to turn out well."

"Yes, uncle, only when it *is* opened won't 'the birds begin to sing?'" laughed Rose, taking a turn about the room as a vent for the joyful emotions that made her eyes shine. All of a sudden she stopped and asked soberly,—

"If Phebe goes to school who will do her work? I'm willing, if I can."

"Come here and I'll tell you a secret. Debby's 'bones' are getting so troublesome, and her dear old temper so bad, that the aunts have decided to pension her off and let her go and live with her daughter, who has married very well. I saw her this week, and she'd like to have her mother come, so in the spring we shall have a grand change, and get a new cook and chamber-girl if any can be found to suit our honored relatives."

"Oh, me! how can I ever get on without Phebe? Couldn't she stay, just so I could see her? I'd pay her board rather than have her go, I'm *so* fond of her."

How Dr. Alec laughed at that proposal, and how satisfied Rose was when he explained that Phebe was still to be her maid, with no duties except such as she could easily perform between school-hours.

"She is a proud creature, for all her humble ways, and even from us would not take a favor if she did not earn it somehow. So this arrangement makes it all square and comfortable, you see, and she will pay for the schooling by curling these goldilocks a dozen times a day if you let her."

"Your plans are always *so* wise and kind! That's why they work so well, I suppose, and why people let you do what you like with them. I really don't see how other girls get along without an Uncle Alec!" answered Rose, with a sigh of pity for those who had missed so great a blessing.

When Phebe was told the splendid news, she did not "stand on her head with rapture," as Charlie prophesied she would, but took it quietly, because it was such a happy thing she had no words "big and beautiful enough to thank them in," she said; but every hour of her day was brightened by this granted wish, and dedicated to the service of those who gave it.

Her heart was so full of content that it overflowed in music, and the sweet voice singing all about the house gave thanks so blithely that no other words were needed. Her willing feet were never tired of taking steps for those who had smoothed her way; her skilful hands were always busy in some labor of love for them, and on the face fast growing in comeliness there was an almost womanly expression of devotion, which proved how well Phebe had already learned one of life's great lessons,—gratitude.

23

PEACE-MAKING

"Steve, I want you to tell me something," said Rose to Dandy, who was making faces at himself in the glass, while he waited for an answer to the note he brought from his mother to Aunt Plenty.

"P'raps I will, and p'raps I won't. What is it?"

"Haven't Arch and Charlie quarrelled?"

"Dare say; we fellows are always having little rows, you know. I do believe a sty is coming on my starboard eye," and Steve affected to be absorbed in a survey of his yellow lashes.

"No, that won't do; I want to know all about it; for I'm sure something more serious than a 'little row' is the matter. Come, please tell me, Stevie, there's a dear."

"Botheration! you don't want me to turn tell-tale, do you?" growled Steve, pulling his top-knot, as he always did when perplexed.

"Yes, I do," was Rose's decided answer,—for she saw from his manner that she was right, and determined to have the secret out of him if coaxing would do it. "I don't wish you to tell things to every one, of course, but to me you may, and you must, because I have a right to know. You boys need somebody to look after you, and I'm going to do it, for girls are nice peace-makers, and know how to manage people. Uncle said so, and he is never wrong."

Steve was about to indulge in a derisive hoot at the idea of her looking after them, but a sudden thought restrained him, and suggested a way in which he could satisfy Rose, and better himself at the same time.

"What will you give me if I'll tell you every bit about it?" he asked, with a sudden red in his cheeks, and an uneasy look in his eyes, for he was half ashamed of the proposition.

"What do you want?" and Rose looked up rather surprised at his question.

"I'd like to borrow some money. I shouldn't think of asking you, only Mac never has a cent since he's set up his old chemical shop, where he'll blow himself to bits some day, and you and uncle will have the fun of putting him together again," and Steve tried to look as if the idea amused him.

"I'll lend it to you with pleasure, so tell away," said Rose, bound to get at the secret.

Evidently much relieved by the promise, Steve set his top-knot cheerfully erect again, and briefly stated the case.

"As you say, it's all right to tell *you*, but don't let the boys know I blabbed, or Prince will take my head off. You see, Archie don't like some of the fellows Charlie goes with, and cuts 'em. That makes Prince mad, and he holds on just to plague

Arch, so they don't speak to one another, if they can help it, and that's the row."

"Are those boys bad?" asked Rose, anxiously.

"Guess not, only rather wild. They are older than our fellows, but they like Prince, he's such a jolly boy; sings so well, dances jigs and break-downs, you know, and plays any game that's going. He beat Morse at billiards, and that's some-thing to brag of, for Morse thinks he knows every thing. I saw the match, and it was great fun!"

Steve got quite excited over the prowess of Charlie, whom he admired immensely, and tried to imitate. Rose did not know half the danger of such gifts and tastes as Charlie's, but felt instinc-tively that something must be wrong if Archie dis-approved.

"If Prince likes any billiard-playing boy better than Archie, I don't think much of his sense," she said severely.

"Of course he doesn't; but, you see, Charlie and Arch are both as proud as they can be, and won't give in. I suppose Arch *is* right, but I don't blame Charlie a bit for liking to be with the others sometimes, they are such a jolly set," and Steve shook his head morally, even while his eye twin-kled over the memory of some of the exploits of the "jolly set."

"Oh, dear me!" sighed Rose, "I don't see what I can do about it, but I wish the boys would make up, for Prince can't come to any harm with Archie, he's so good and sensible."

"That's the trouble; Arch preaches, and Prince won't stand it. He told Arch he was a prig and a parson, and Arch told him he wasn't a gentleman. My boots! weren't they both mad though! I thought for a minute they'd pitch into one another and have it out. Wish they had, and not gone stalking round stiff and glum ever since. Mac and I settle our rows with a bat or so over the head, and then we are all right."

Rose couldn't help laughing as Steve sparred away at a fat sofa-pillow, to illustrate his meaning; and, having given it several scientific whacks, he pulled down his cuffs and smiled upon her with benign pity for her feminine ignorance of this summary way of settling a quarrel.

"What droll things boys are!" she said, with a mixture of admiration and perplexity in her face, which Steve accepted as a compliment to his sex.

"We are a pretty clever invention, miss, and you can't get on without us," he answered, with his nose in the air. Then, taking a sudden plunge into business, he added, "How about that bit of money you were going to lend me? I've told, now you pay up."

"Of course I will! How much do you want?" and Rose pulled out her purse.

"*Could* you spare five dollars? I want to pay a little debt of honor that is rather pressing," and Steve put on a mannish air that was comical to see.

"Aren't all debts honorable?" asked innocent Rose.

"Yes, of course; but this is a bet I made, and it ought to be settled up at once," began Steve, finding it awkward to explain.

"Oh, don't bet, it's not right, and I know your father wouldn't like it. Promise you won't do so again, please promise!" and Rose held fast the hand into which she had just put the money.

"Well, I won't. It's worried me a good deal, but I was joked into it. Much obliged, cousin, I'm all right now," and Steve departed hastily.

Having decided to be a peace-maker, Rose waited for an opportunity, and very soon it came.

She was spending the day with Aunt Clara, who had been entertaining some young guests, and invited Rose to meet them, for she thought it high time her niece conquered her bashfulness, and saw a little of society. Dinner was over, and every one had gone. Aunt Clara was resting before going out to an evening party, and Rose was waiting for Charlie to come and take her home.

She sat alone in the elegant drawing-room, feeling particularly nice and pretty, for she had her best frock on, a pair of gold bands her aunt had just given her, and a tea-rose bud in her sash, like the beautiful Miss Van Tassel, whom every one admired. She had spread out her little skirts to the best advantage, and, leaning back in a luxurious chair, sat admiring her own feet in new slippers with rosettes almost as big as dahlias. Presently Charlie came lounging in, looking rather sleepy and queer, Rose thought. On seeing her, however, he roused up and said with a smile that ended in a gape,—

"I thought you were with mother, so I took forty winks after I got those girls off. Now, I'm at your service, Rosamunda, whenever you like."

"You look as if your head ached. If it does, don't mind me. I'm not afraid to run home alone, it's so early," answered Rose, observing the flushed cheeks and heavy eyes of her cousin.

"I think I see myself letting you do it. Champagne always makes my head ache, but the air will set me up."

"Why do you drink it, then?" asked Rose, anxiously.

"Can't help it, when I'm host. Now, don't *you* begin to lecture; I've had enough of Archie's old-fashioned notions, and I don't want any more."

Charlie's tone was decidedly cross, and his whole manner so unlike his usual merry good-nature, that Rose felt crushed, and answered meekly,—

"I wasn't going to lecture, only when people like other people, they can't bear to see them suffer pain."

That brought Charlie round at once, for Rose's lips trembled a little, though she tried to hide it by smelling the flower she pulled from her sash.

"I'm a regular bear, and I beg your pardon for being so cross, Rosy," he said in the old frank way that was so winning.

"I wish you'd beg Archie's too, and be good

friends again. You never were cross when *he* was your chum," Rose said, looking up at him as he bent toward her from the low chimney-piece, where he had been leaning his elbows.

In an instant he stood as stiff and straight as a ramrod, and the heavy eyes kindled with an angry spark as he said, in his high and mighty manner,—

"You'd better not meddle with what you don't understand, cousin."

"But I do understand, and it troubles me very much to see you so cold and stiff to one another. You always used to be together, and now you hardly speak. You are so ready to beg my pardon I don't see why you can't beg Archie's, if you are in the wrong."

"I'm not!" this was so short and sharp that Rose started, and Charlie added in a calmer but still very haughty tone: "A gentleman always begs pardon when he has been rude to a lady, but one man doesn't apologize to another man who has insulted him."

"Oh, my heart, what a pepperpot!" thought Rose, and, hoping to make him laugh, she added slyly: "I was not talking about men, but boys, and one of them a Prince, who ought to set a good example to his subjects."

But Charlie would not relent, and tried to turn the subject by saying gravely, as he unfastened the little gold ring from his watch-guard,—

"I've broken my word, so I want to give this back and free you from the bargain. I'm sorry, but

I think it a foolish promise, and don't intend to keep it. Choose a pair of ear-rings to suit yourself, as my forfeit. You have a right to wear them now."

"No, I can only wear one, and that is no use, for Archie will keep *his* word I'm sure!" Rose was so mortified and grieved at this downfall of her hopes that she spoke sharply, and would not take the ring the deserter offered her.

He shrugged his shoulders, and threw it into her lap, trying to look cool and careless, but failing entirely, for he was ashamed of himself, and out of sorts generally. Rose wanted to cry, but pride would not let her, and, being very angry, she relieved herself by talk instead of tears. Looking pale and excited, she rose out of her chair, cast away the ring, and said in a voice that she vainly tried to keep steady,—

"You are not at all the boy I thought you were, and I don't respect you one bit. I've tried to help you be good, but you won't let me, and I shall not try any more. You talk a great deal about being a gentleman, but you are not, for you've broken your word, and I can never trust you again. I don't wish you to go home with me. I'd rather have Mary. Good-night."

And with that last dreadful blow, Rose walked out of the room, leaving Charlie as much astonished as if one of his pet pigeons had flown in his face and pecked at him. She was so seldom angry, that when her temper did get the better of her it made a deep impression on the lads, for it was generally a righteous sort of indignation at some injustice or wrong-doing, not childish passion.

Her little thunder-storm cleared off in a sob or two as she put on her things in the entry-closet, and when she emerged she looked the brighter for the shower. A hasty good-night to Aunt Clara,— now under the hands of the hair-dresser,—and then she crept down to find Mary the maid. But Mary was out, so was the man, and Rose slipped away by the back-door, flattering herself that she had escaped the awkwardness of having Charlie for escort.

There she was mistaken, however, for the gate had hardly closed behind her when a well-known tramp was heard, and the Prince was beside her, saying in a tone of penitent politeness that banished Rose's wrath like magic,—

"You needn't speak to me if you don't choose, but I must see you safely home, cousin."

She turned at once, put out her hand, and answered heartily,—

"*I* was the cross one. Please forgive me, and let's be friends again."

Now that was better than a dozen sermons on the beauty of forgiveness, and did Charlie more good, for it showed him how sweet humility was, and proved that Rose practised as she preached.

He shook the hand warmly, then drew it through his arm and said, as if anxious to recover the good opinion with the loss of which he had been threatened,—

"Look here, Rosy, I've put the ring back, and I'm going to try again. But you don't know how hard it is to stand being laughed at."

"Yes, I do! Ariadne plagues me every time I see her, because I don't wear ear-rings after all the trouble I had getting ready for them."

"Ah, but her twaddle isn't half as bad as the chaffing *I* get. It takes a deal of pluck to hold out when you are told you are tied to an apron-string, and all that sort of thing," sighed Charlie.

"I thought you had a 'deal of pluck,' as you call it. The boys all say you are the bravest of the seven," said Rose.

"So I am about some things, but I *cannot* bear to be laughed at."

"It is hard, but if one is right won't that make it easier?"

"Not to me; it might to a pious parson like Arch."

"Please don't call him names! I guess *he* has what is called moral courage, and *you* physical courage. Uncle explained the difference to me, and moral is the best, though often it doesn't look so," said Rose thoughtfully.

Charlie didn't like that, and answered quickly, "I don't believe he'd stand it any better than I do, if he had those fellows at him."

"Perhaps that's why he keeps out of their way, and wants you to."

Rose had him there, and Charlie felt it, but would not give in just yet, though he was going fast, for somehow, in the dark he seemed to see things clearer than in the light, and found it very easy to be confidential when it was "only Rose."

"If he was my brother, now, he'd have some right to interfere," began Charlie, in an injured tone.

"I wish he was!" cried Rose.

"So do I," answered Charlie, and then they both laughed at his inconsistency.

The laugh did them good, and when Prince spoke again, it was in a different tone,—pensive, not proud nor perverse.

"You see, it's hard upon me that I have no brothers and sisters. The others are better off and needn't go abroad for chums if they don't like. *I* am all alone, and I'd be thankful even for a little sister."

Rose thought that very pathetic, and, overlooking the uncomplimentary word "even" in that last sentence, she said, with a timid sort of earnestness that conquered her cousin at once,—

"Play I was a little sister. I know I'm silly, but perhaps I'm better than nothing, and I'd dearly love to do it."

"So should I! and we will, for you are not silly, my dear, but a very sensible girl, we all think, and I'm proud to have you for a sister. There, now!" and Charlie looked down at the curly head bobbing along beside him, with real affection in his face.

Rose gave a skip of pleasure, and laid one

seal-skin mitten over the other on his arm, as she said happily,—

"That's so nice of you! Now, you needn't be lonely any more, and I'll try to fill Archie's place till he comes back, for I know he will, as soon as you let him."

"Well, I don't mind telling *you* that while he was my mate I never missed brothers and sisters, or wanted any one else; but since he cast me off, I'll be hanged if I don't feel as forlorn as old Crusoe before Friday turned up."

This burst of confidence confirmed Rose in her purpose of winning Charlie's Mentor back to him, but she said no more, contented to have done so well. They parted excellent friends, and Prince went home, wondering why "a fellow didn't mind saying things to a girl or woman which they would die before they'd own to another fellow."

Rose also had some sage reflections upon the subject, and fell asleep thinking that there were a great many curious things in this world, and feeling that she was beginning to find out some of them.

Next day she trudged up the hill to see Archie, and having told him as much as she thought best about her talk with Charlie, begged him to forget and forgive.

"I've been thinking that perhaps I ought to, though I *am* in the right. I'm no end fond of Charlie, and he's the best-hearted lad alive; but he can't say No, and that will play the mischief with him, if he does not take care," said Archie in his grave, kind way. "While father was home, I was very busy with him, so Prince got into a set I don't like. They try to be fast, and think it's manly, and they flatter him, and lead him on to do all sorts of things,— play for money, and bet, and loaf about. I hate to have him do so, and tried to stop it, but went to work the wrong way, so we got into a mess."

"He is all ready to make up if you don't say much, for he owned to me he *was* wrong; but I don't think he will own it to you, in words," began Rose.

"I don't care for that; if he'll just drop those rowdies and come back, I'll hold my tongue and not preach. I wonder if he owes those fellows money, and so doesn't like to break off till he can pay it. I hope not, but don't dare to ask; though, perhaps, Steve knows, he's always after Prince, more's the pity," and Archie looked anxious.

"I think Steve does know, for he talked about debts of honor the day I gave him—" There Rose stopped short and turned scarlet.

But Archie ordered her to "fess," and had the whole story in five minutes, for none dared disobey the Chief. He completed her affliction by putting a five-dollar bill into her pocket by main force, look-ing both indignant and resolute as he said,—

"Never do so, again; but send Steve to me, if he is afraid to go to his father. Charlie had nothing to do with that; *he* wouldn't borrow a penny of a girl, don't think it. But that's the harm he does Steve, who adores him, and tries to be like him in all things. Don't say a word; I'll make it all right, and no one shall blame you."

"Oh, me! I always make trouble by trying to help, and then letting out the wrong thing," sighed Rose, much depressed by her slip of the tongue.

Archie comforted her with the novel remark that it was always best to tell the truth, and made her quite cheerful by promising to heal the breach with Charlie, as soon as possible.

He kept his word so well that the very next afternoon, as Rose looked out of the window, she beheld the joyful spectacle of Archie and Prince coming up the avenue, arm-in-arm, as of old, talking away as if to make up for the unhappy silence of the past weeks.

Rose dropped her work, hurried to the door, and, opening it wide, stood there smiling down upon them so happily, that the faces of the lads brightened as they ran up the steps eager to show that all was well with them.

"Here's our little peace-maker!" said Archie, shaking hands with vigor.

But Charlie added, with a look that made Rose very proud and happy, "And *my* little sister."

"Uncle, I have discovered what girls are made for," said Rose, the day after the reconciliation of Archie and the Prince.

"Well, my dear, what is it?" asked Dr. Alec, who was "planking the deck," as he called his daily promenade up and down the hall.

"To take care of boys," answered Rose, quite beaming with satisfaction as she spoke. "Phebe laughed when I told her, and said she thought girls had better learn to take care of themselves first. But that's because *she* hasn't got seven boy-cousins as I have."

"She is right, nevertheless, Rosy, and so are you, for the two things go together, and in helping seven lads you are unconsciously doing much to improve one lass," said Dr. Alec, stopping to nod and smile at the bright-faced figure resting on the old bamboo chair, after a lively game of battledore and shuttlecock, in place of a run which a storm prevented.

"Am I? I'm glad of that, but really, uncle, I do feel as if I *must* take care of the boys, for they come to me in all sorts of troubles, and ask advice, and I like it *so* much. Only I don't always know what to do, and I'm going to consult you privately and then surprise them with my wisdom."

"All right, my dear; what's the first worry? I see you have something on your little mind, so come and tell uncle."

Rose put her arm in his, and, pacing to and fro, told him all about Charlie, asking what she could do to keep him straight, and be a real sister to him.

"Could you make up your mind to go and stay with Aunt Clara a month?" asked the Doctor, when she ended.

"Yes, sir; but I shouldn't like it. Do you really want me to go?"

"The best cure for Charlie is a daily dose of Rose water, or Rose and water; will you go and see that he takes it?" laughed Dr. Alec.

"You mean that if I'm there and try to make it pleasant, he will stay at home and keep out of mischief?"

"Exactly."

"But *could* I make it pleasant? He would want the boys."

"No danger but he'd have the boys, for they swarm after you like bees after their queen. Haven't you found that out?"

"Aunt Plen often says they never used to be here half so much before I came, but I never thought *I* made the difference, it seemed so natural to have them round."

"Little Modesty doesn't know what a magnet she is; but she will find it out some day," and the Doctor softly stroked the cheek that had grown rosy with pleasure at the thought of being so much loved. "Now, you see, if I move the magnet to Aunt Clara's, the lads will go there as sure as iron to steel, and Charlie will be so happy at home he won't care for these mischievous mates of his; I hope," added the Doctor, well knowing how hard it was to wean a seventeen-year-old boy from his first taste of what is called "seeing life," which, alas! often ends in seeing death.

"I'll go, uncle, right away! Aunt Clara is always asking me, and will be glad to get me. I shall have to dress and dine late, and see lots of company, and be very fashionable, but I'll try not to let it hurt me; and if I get in a puzzle or worried about any thing I can run to you," answered Rose, good-will conquering timidity.

So it was decided, and without saying much about the real reason for this visit, Rose was transplanted to Aunt Clara's, feeling that she had a work to do, and very eager to do it well.

Dr. Alec was right about the bees, for the boys did follow their queen, and astonished Mrs. Clara by their sudden assiduity in making calls, dropping in to dinner, and getting up evening frolics. Charlie was a devoted host, and tried to show his gratitude by being very kind to his "little sister," for he guessed why she came, and his heart was touched by her artless endeavors to "help him be good."

Rose often longed to be back in the old house, with the simpler pleasures and more useful duties of the life there; but, having made up her mind, in spite of Phebe, that "girls were made to take care of boys," her motherly little soul found much to enjoy in the new task she had undertaken.

It was a pretty sight to see the one earnest, sweet-faced girl among the flock of tall lads, trying to understand, to help and please them with a patient affection that worked many a small miracle unperceived. Slang, rough manners, and careless habits were banished or bettered by the presence of a little gentlewoman; and all the manly virtues cropping up were encouraged by the hearty admiration bestowed upon them by one whose good opinion all valued more than they confessed; while Rose tried to imitate the good qualities she praised in them, to put away her girlish vanities and fears, to be strong and just and frank and brave as well as modest, kind, and beautiful.

This trial worked so well that when the month was over, Mac and Steve demanded a visit in their turn, and Rose went, feeling that she would like to hear grim Aunt Jane say, as Aunt Clara did at parting, "I wish I could keep you all my life, dear."

After Mac and Steve had had their turn, Archie and Company bore her away for some weeks; and with them she was so happy, she felt as if she would like to stay for ever, if she could have Uncle Alec also.

Of course, Aunt Myra could not be neglected, and, with secret despair, Rose went to the "Mausoleum," as the boys called her gloomy abode. Fortunately, she was very near home, and Dr. Alec dropped in so often that her visit was far less dismal than she expected. Between them, they actually made Aunt Myra laugh heartily more than once; and Rose did her so much good by letting in the sunshine, singing about the silent house, cooking wholesome messes, and amusing the old lady with funny little lectures on physiology, that she forgot to take her pills and gave up "Mum's Elixir," because she slept so well, after the long walks and drives she was beguiled into taking, that she needed no narcotic.

So the winter flew rapidly away, and it was May before Rose was fairly settled again at home. They called her the "Monthly Rose," because she had spent a month with each of the aunts, and left such pleasant memories of bloom and fragrance behind her, that all wanted the family flower back again.

Dr. Alec rejoiced greatly over his recovered treasure; but as the time drew near when his year of experiment ended, he had many a secret fear that Rose might like to make her home for the next twelvemonth with Aunt Jessie, or even Aunt Clara, for Charlie's sake. He said nothing, but waited with much anxiety for the day when the matter should be decided; and while he waited he did his best to finish as far as possible the task he had begun so well.

Rose was very happy now, being out nearly all day enjoying the beautiful awakening of the world, for spring came bright and early, as if anxious to do its part. The old horse-chestnuts budded round her windows, green things sprung up like magic in the garden under her hands, hardy flowers bloomed as fast as they could, the birds sang blithely overhead, and every day a chorus of pleasant voices cried, "Good morning, cousin, isn't it jolly weather?"

No one remembered the date of the eventful conversation which resulted in the Doctor's experiment (no one but himself at least); so when the aunts were invited to tea one Saturday they came quite unsuspiciously, and were all sitting together having a social chat, when Brother Alec entered with two photographs in his hand.

"Do you remember that?" he said, showing one to Aunt Clara, who happened to be nearest.

"Yes, indeed; it is very like her when she came. Quite her sad, unchildlike expression, and thin little face, with the big dark eyes."

The picture was passed round, and all agreed that "it was very like Rose a year ago." This point being settled, the Doctor showed the second picture, which was received with great approbation, and pronounced a "charming likeness."

It certainly was, and a striking contrast to the

first one, for it was a blooming, smiling face, full of girlish spirit and health, with no sign of melancholy, though the soft eyes were thoughtful, and the lines about the lips betrayed a sensitive nature.

Dr. Alec set both photographs on the chimney-piece, and, falling back a step or two, surveyed them with infinite satisfaction for several minutes, then wheeled round, saying briefly, as he pointed to the two faces,—

"Time is up; how do you think my experiment has succeeded, ladies?"

"Bless me, so it is!" cried Aunt Plenty, dropping a stitch in her surprise.

"Beautifully, dear," answered Aunt Peace, smiling entire approval.

"She certainly *has* improved, but appearances are deceitful, and she had no constitution to build upon," croaked Aunt Myra.

"I am willing to allow that, as far as mere health goes, the experiment *is* a success," graciously observed Aunt Jane, unable to forget Rose's kindness to her Mac.

"So am I; and I'll go farther, for I really do believe Alec has done wonders for the child; she will be a beauty in two or three years," added Aunt Clara, feeling that she could say nothing better than that.

"I always knew he would succeed, and I'm so glad you all allow it, for he deserves more credit than you know, and more praise than he will ever get," cried Aunt Jessie, clapping her hands with an enthusiasm that caused Jamie's little red stocking to wave like a triumphal banner in the air.

Dr. Alec made them a splendid bow, looking much gratified, and then said soberly,—

"Thank you; now the question is, shall I go on?—for this is only the beginning. None of you know the hinderances I've had, the mistakes I've made, the study I've given the case, and the anxiety I've often felt. Sister Myra is right in one thing,—Rose *is* a delicate creature, quick to flourish in the sunshine, and as quick to droop without it. She has no special weakness, but inherits her mother's sensitive nature, and needs the wisest, tenderest care to keep a very ardent little soul from wearing out a finely organized little body. I think I have found the right treatment, and, with you to help me, I believe we may build up a lovely and a noble woman, who will be a pride and comfort to us all."

There Dr. Alec stopped to get his breath, for he had spoken very earnestly, and his voice got a little husky over the last words. A gentle murmur from the aunts seemed to encourage him, and he went on with an engaging smile, for the good man was slyly trying to win all the ladies to vote for him when the time came.

"Now, I don't wish to be selfish or arbitrary, because I am her guardian, and I shall leave Rose free to choose for herself. We all want her, and if she likes to make her home with any of you rather than with me, she shall do so. In fact, I encouraged her visits last winter, that she might see what we can all offer her, and judge where she will be happiest. Is not that the fairest way? Will you agree to abide by her choice, as I do?"

"Yes, we will," said all the aunts, in quite a flutter of excitement, at the prospect of having Rose for a whole year.

"Good! she will be here directly, and then we will settle the question for another year. A most important year, mind you, for she has got a good start, and will blossom rapidly now if all goes well with her. So I beg of you don't undo my work, but deal very wisely and gently with my little girl, for if any harm come to her, I think it would break my heart."

As he spoke, Dr. Alec turned his back abruptly and affected to be examining the pictures again; but the aunts understood how dear the child was to the solitary man who had loved her mother years ago, and who now found his happiness in cherishing the little Rose who was so like her. The good ladies nodded and sighed, and telegraphed to one another that none of them would complain if not chosen, or ever try to rob Brother Alec of his "Heart's Delight," as the boys called Rose.

Just then a pleasant sound of happy voices came up from the garden, and smiles broke out on all serious faces. Dr. Alec turned at once, saying, as he threw back his head, "There she is; now for it!"

The cousins had been a-Maying, and soon came flocking in laden with the spoils.

"Here is our bonny Scotch rose with all her thorns about her," said Dr. Alec, surveying her with unusual pride and tenderness, as she went to show Aunt Peace her basket full of early flowers, fresh leaves, and curious lichens.

"Leave your clutter in the hall, boys, and sit quietly down if you choose to stop here, for we are busy," said Aunt Plenty, shaking her finger at the turbulent clan, who were bubbling over with the jollity born of spring sunshine and healthy exercise.

"Of course, we choose to stay! Wouldn't miss our Saturday high tea for any thing," said the Chief, as he restored order among his men with a nod, a word, and an occasional shake.

"What is up? a court-martial?" asked Charlie, looking at the assembled ladies with affected awe and real curiosity, for their faces betrayed that some interesting business was afloat.

Dr. Alec explained in a few words, which he made as brief and calm as he could; but the effect was exciting, nevertheless, for each of the lads began at once to bribe, entice, and wheedle "our cousin" to choose his home.

"You really ought to come to us for mother's sake, as a relish, you know, for she must be perfectly satiated with boys," began Archie, using the strongest argument he could think of at the moment.

"Oh, do! we'll never slam, or bounce at you or call you 'fraid cat,' if you only will," besought Geordie and Will, distorting their countenances in the attempt to smile with overpowering sweetness.

"And I'll always wash my hands 'fore I touch you, and you shall be my dolly, 'cause Pokey's gone away, and I'll love you *hard*," cried Jamie, clinging to her with his chubby face full of affection.

"Brothers and sisters ought to live together; especially when the brother needs some one to make home pleasant for him," added Charlie, with the wheedlesome tone and look that Rose always found so difficult to resist.

"You had her longest, and it's our turn now; Mac needs her more than you do, Prince, for she's 'the light of his eyes,' he says. Come, Rose, choose us, and I'll never use the musky pomade you hate again as long as I live," said Steve, with his most killing air, as he offered this noble sacrifice.

Mac peered wistfully over his goggles, saying in an unusually wide-awake and earnest way,—

"Do, cousin, then we can study chemistry together. My experiments don't blow up very often now, and the gases aren't at all bad when you get used to them."

Rose meantime had stood quite still, with the flowers dropping from her hands as her eyes went from one eager face to another, while smiles rippled over her own at the various enticements offered her. During the laugh that followed Mac's handsome proposition, she looked at her uncle, whose eyes were fixed on her with an expression of love and longing that went to her heart.

"Ah! yes," she thought, "*he* wants me most! I've

often longed to give him something that he wished for very much, and now I can."

So, when, at a sudden gesture from Aunt Peace, silence fell, Rose said slowly, with a pretty color in her cheeks, and a beseeching look about the room, as if asking pardon of the boys,—

"It's very hard to choose when everybody is so fond of me; therefore I think I'd better go to the one who seems to need me most."

"No, dear, the one you love the best and will be happiest with," said Dr. Alec quickly, as a doleful sniff from Aunt Myra, and a murmur of "My sainted Caroline," made Rose pause and look that way.

"Take time, cousin; don't be in a hurry to make up your mind, and remember, 'Codlin's your friend,' " added Charlie, hopeful still.

"I don't want any time! I *know* who I love best, who I'm happiest with, and I choose uncle. Will he have me?" cried Rose, in a tone that produced a sympathetic thrill among the hearers, it was so full of tender confidence and love.

If she really had any doubt, the look in Dr. Alec's face banished it without a word, as he opened wide his arms, and she ran into them, feeling that home was there.

No one spoke for a minute, but there were signs of emotion among the aunts, which warned the boys to bestir themselves before the water-works began to play. So they took hands and began to prance about uncle and niece, singing, with sudden inspiration, the nursery rhyme,—

"Ring around a Rosy!"

Of course that put an end to all sentiment, and Rose emerged laughing from Dr. Alec's bosom, with the mark of a waistcoat button nicely imprinted on her left cheek. He saw it, and said with a merry kiss that half effaced it, "This is my ewe lamb, and I have set my mark on her, so no one can steal her away."

That tickled the boys, and they set up a shout of

"Uncle had a little lamb!"

But Rose hushed the noise by slipping into the circle, and making them dance prettily,—like lads and lasses round a May-pole; while Phebe, coming in with fresh water for the flowers, began to twitter, chirp, and coo, as if all the birds of the air had come to join in the spring revel of the eight cousins.

LITTLE WOMEN
Louisa May Alcott

The good-natured March girls—Meg, Jo, Beth, and Amy—manage to lead interesting lives despite Father's absence at war and the family's lack of money. Whether they're making plans for putting on a play or forming a secret society, their gaiety is infectious and even Laurie next door is swept up in their enthusiasm. Written from Louisa May Alcott's own experiences, this is a remarkable story.

LITTLE MEN
Louisa May Alcott

With two sons of her own, and twelve rescued orphan boys filling the informal school at Plumfield, Jo March—now Jo Bhaer—couldn't be happier. But despite the warm and affectionate help of the whole March family, boys have a habit of getting into scrapes, and plenty of troubles and adventures are in store.

A LITTLE PRINCESS
Frances Hodgson Burnett

Sara Crewe's world is transformed when her wealthy, adoring father dies, leaving her penniless. She is suddenly forced to work as a servant at the boarding school she once attended. But Sara has a loving heart and a strong spirit, and she knows that she will persevere.

HEIDI
Johanna Spyri

After her parents die, five-year-old Heidi goes to live with her grandfather in his lonely hut high in the Alps. She quickly learns to love her new life. But then her strict aunt decides that Heidi must be sent away again, to live in town. Heidi cannot bear being away from the mountains and is determined to return to the happiness of life with her grandfather.

PUFFIN CLASSICS

POLLYANNA
Eleanor H. Porter

When an orphaned Pollyanna moves in with her maiden aunt, she transforms the lives of everyone she meets with her optimism. She uses the "glad game" her father taught her to appreciate what she has—until one day something so terrible happens that even Pollyanna doesn't know how to feel glad about it.

A TALE OF TWO CITIES
Charles Dickens

Charles Darnay and Sydney Carton are alike in appearance, different in character, and in love with the same woman. In the midst of the French Revolution, Darnay, who has fled to London to escape the cruelty of the French nobility, must return to Paris to rescue his servant from death. But he endangers his own life in the process and is taken into captivity. Carton may be able to help, but will his resemblance be enough to save Darnay's life?

PUFFIN 🐧 **CLASSICS**

AN OLD-FASHIONED GIRL
Louisa May Alcott

Life changes for Polly Milton when she leaves her country home to visit her cousins in the city. Polly's naïveté and her country ways embarrass her sophisticated cousins. She's not like them, and she doesn't know if she wants to be. But will Polly be able to enjoy city life without changing?

FIVE CHILDREN AND IT
E. Nesbit

The last thing Cyril, Anthea, Robert, Jane, and their baby brother expect to find while digging in the sand is a Psammead—an ancient Sand-fairy! Having a Sand-fairy for a pet means having one wish granted each day. But the fivesome doesn't realize all of the trouble wishes-come-true can cause.

THROUGH THE LOOKING GLASS
Lewis Carroll

When Alice steps through the looking glass, she enters a world of chess pieces and nursery rhyme characters who behave very strangely. Humpty Dumpty, Tweedledee and Tweedledum, the dotty White Knight, and the sharp-tempered Red Queen—none of them are what they seem. In fact, through the looking glass, *everything* is distorted.

RIP VAN WINKLE AND OTHER STORIES
Washington Irving

The enchanting tale of Rip Van Winkle in the Kaatskill Mountains; the gruesome story of Ichabod Crane, who met the Headless Horseman of Sleepy Hollow; the mystery of the Spectre Bridegroom—these are just some of the captivating tales in this celebrated collection.

Also by Michael Green
from Thomas Nelson Publishers

Who Is This Jesus?
Explore the mystery and the majesty of the Son of God and find answers to the questions that lead to faith.

Beginning Your New Life in Christ
Help new believers get grounded in their faith with this emphasis on how a relationship with Christ can transform a life.

Evangelism Through the Local Church
Show how the local church can share the gospel in terms that are meaningful for today's secular society.

How Shall WE Reach Them?

Michael Green & Alister McGrath

OLIVER
NELSON

THOMAS NELSON PUBLISHERS
Nashville • Atlanta • London • Vancouver

Published in Nashville, Tennessee, by Thomas Nelson, Inc., Publishers, and distributed in Canada by Word Communications, Ltd., Richmond, British Columbia.

The Bible version used in this publication is THE NEW KING JAMES VERSION. Copyright © 1979, 1980, 1982, 1990, Thomas Nelson, Inc., Publishers.

Green, Michael, 1930–
    How shall we reach them? / Michael Green & Alister McGrath.
        p.   cm.
    Includes bibliographical references (p.   ).
    ISBN 0-7852-8109-6 (pbk.)
    1. Evangelicialism. 2. Christianity and other religions. 3. Apologetics—20th century. 4. Religious pluralism—Christianity. I. McGrath, Alister E., 1953–   . II. Title.
    BR1640.G73 1995
    266—dc20   95-5642
                                                                        CIP

Printed in the United States of America.

2 3 4 5 6 — 00 99 98 97

Contents

Introduction

Almost all books emerge from a stimulus and an occasion. This one certainly does! The stimulus has been a personal friendship between the authors and a profound conviction that the Christian account of the world is not merely relevant, but true. Indeed, we are persuaded that it is only relevant because it is true. The occasion was a conference held at Nottingham in December 1992, which we led jointly. Dr. McGrath had recently published his outstanding book on apologetics, *Intellectuals Don't Need God and Other Modern Myths* (Zondervan). An important conference on the same subject had been organized a little earlier by Bishops Lesslie Newbigin and Hugh Montefiore, entitled "The Gospel and Our Culture," which sought to regain the academic high ground at a period of massive cultural shift and change in our understanding of the nature of human knowledge. Clearly, a new day is dawning, a day of renewed confidence in the truth of the Christian story.

It is, in fact, a fascinating time to be alive. The dogmas of the Enlightenment, which have dominated Western thought for two centuries, are in full retreat. The barrenness of materialism is evident. The hunger for spirituality is very clear. Even if people have yet to discover fully the spirituality of historic Christianity, they are aware that a spiritual dimension to life is not being satisfied.

We are standing at one of the turning points of human thought. At such a time as this, it is vital to understand why so many people in the West are not Christians and how thoughtful, believing Christians can reach out to them in a way that is loving, attractive, and reasonable. That is what we have tried to do in this book. We trust that it will strengthen confidence in the truth of the gospel and give some helpful suggestions as to how we may commend it to others in terms that make sense to them.

We are grateful to our four distinguished contributors for their expert essays on their themes, supplementing our more general approach. And we are very grateful to Victor Oliver, of Oliver-Nelson Books, for his encouragement and support during the writing of this book.

May God make us all more confident, humble, and enthusiastic sharers of the Easter faith. Jesus lives! Alleluia!

Michael Green

Chapter 1

Starting Where People Are

Alister McGrath

One of the greatest changes in the history of the Western church has taken place in the last generation. It was not all that long ago that the churches saw themselves as having chiefly pastoral and prophetic roles. They were concerned with caring for the well-being of their congregations and communities, and standing up for justice and integrity when they were seen to be threatened. Yet now things are changing—fast. Something new has been added to these concerns. It has not displaced them. In fact, it is coming to be seen as underlying the effective continuation of these roles in the future. The new concern is now being seen as essential if the Christian churches are to play a major role in Western society in the third millennium. The name of this concern? *Evangelism.*

Rediscovering Evangelism

Evangelism. How much the associations of that word have changed! Not all that long ago it was associated just with lonely individuals such as the incomparable Billy Graham with his vast crusades. It was seen as the particular concern—indeed, you could say *obsession*—of evangelical groups within Christianity. It was something that the mainstream churches need not worry about. The future seemed secure without emphasis on witnessing to people or proclaiming the gospel. The immediate postwar boom in church attendance and Christian commitment was seen as representing a permanent state of affairs. Many senior church figures denounced evangelism as "Christian imperialism," seeing it as a hangover from the days of colonialism and empire building. It was a quaint and old-fashioned idea, which was out of sync with modern ways. It would never catch on.

That was yesterday. Today, we have seen a dramatic change of mood. The need for evangelism has been conceded all around—as a matter of urgency. The church establishments have realized that the postwar belief boom was a blip, a temporary trend that disguised a growing alienation from Christianity. The situation was not addressed with the seriousness it deserved. The price of that neglect has been depressingly high. In England, the national church busied itself with navel gazing, undertaking a major and lengthy reform of canon law. And while it fiddled, tinkering with its internal regulations, a nation lost its faith.

The crises of the 1960s arrived. *Time* magazine headlined "the death of God." Secularization hit Western society. Church membership began to decline. In 1952, 2 percent of the American population declared itself to be "religious nones." Ten years later, that figure was virtually unaltered. Today, it stands at 12 percent and shows every sign of continuing unchecked. In the 1970s, the mainstream churches began to lose members on a long-term basis. By the late 1980s, the pattern was clear. Those churches committed to evangelism were growing; those that scorned it were declining. In the 1990s, this development is of such importance that it cannot be overlooked. Evangelism must be a normal, regular, and expected aspect of modern church life—for both pastor and congregation.

Looking back on the eccentricities of the 1960s, many were reminded of Hans Christian Andersen's story of the emperor's new clothes. An illusion was shattered by the insistent questioning of a young boy. The churches' illusions of a safe and assured future lay in tatters, shown up as an illusion by the litany of decline to emerge from recent church attendance statistics. "If some of my own clergy who go around to their endless committees and yak and yak and yak away would only get on with the job of trying to convert their own parishioners, I think that we should not be in quite the state of decline that we are." This remark of Mervyn Stockwood, one of the Church of England's most creative radical bishops of the 1960s, bears witness to the new realism that has settled over even the most traditional of mainline churches.

It comes as no surprise to discover that, in the 1990s, evangelism has gone mainstream. It is no longer the prerogative of any religious party or denomination. There is now nothing bizarre, nothing strikingly partisan, about this appreciation of the importance of evangelism. Some still refuse to face up to the grim realities, hoping for a turnaround in their fortunes without any effort on their part. But a new realism has dawned within the churches. They have been jolted out of their complacency.

The embargo on evangelism has been lifted inside the mainline churches throughout the West. The churches have realized that they can maintain an effective pastoral and prophetic role in pluralist Western society only on the basis of a position of merited influence—a position justified on the basis of present numerical strength rather than increasingly vague and fuzzy memories of the past. Resting on the glories of the past cuts no ice with anyone anymore. Nostalgia may be a nice experience, but it does nothing to ensure the presence of an effective caring

Christian voice in an increasingly confused and dislocated society.

A colleague asked me recently if I believed in evangelism. "*Believe* in it?" I retorted. "I *rely* on it!" Evangelism is no longer seen as something undertaken only by cranks or overenthusiastic yet well-meaning college students; it is seen as integral to the life, mission, and well-being of the churches. Evangelism is refreshingly *normal*!

This might seem to suggest that evangelism is just a pragmatic response to a situation in which it has become necessary. In fact, the current situation within the Western churches has led to the *rediscovery*, not the *invention*, of evangelism. In the 1890s, the Student Christian Movement was founded. Its watchword was "the evangelization of the world in this generation." Today, a century later, that vision is being rediscovered.

Without realizing it, Western Christianity had become dependent on the legacy of the Middle Ages in Europe. The idea of Christendom had gained sway—that is, the idea of a defined geopolitical area with a settled Christian worldview. Evangelism was totally unnecessary when Christian assumptions were so deeply built into society. But that situation has changed, especially recently, with wide-scale immigration into Europe from Islamic regions of the world, and the cultural erosion of faith because of the challenges of Marxism and other modern worldviews.

The new situation has prompted Christians to look into their past and realize that evangelism was high on the agenda of the church until the rise of Christendom made it unnecessary—in the apostolic Christianity of the New Testament itself, in the history of the early church, and in the events of the Great Awakening of the eighteenth century. But Christendom is probably on its way out. We cannot rely on its legacy any longer. Christianity must earn its position in society, not rely on the heritage of the Middle Ages. Evangelism is the key to the future of Christianity in the West as it stands poised to enter its third millennium.

We need to be clear about what evangelism is before we can move on to the main theme of this book—apologetics. We begin by trying to give some definitions of evangelism. The English word *evangelism* comes from the Greek word for gospel, and it is probably best translated as "proclaiming good news" or "bearing good news." At the heart of any understanding of evangelism are two ideas: (1) the good news of Jesus Christ, which gladdens the hearts of men and women, and (2) the need for this news to be proclaimed if people are to hear and benefit from it. Note that the term has no overtones of manipulation, imperialism, or authoritarianism. It speaks of the good news of what God has done for weak, mortal, and sinful human beings, and of the responsibility of those who have heard and benefited from this news to pass it on to others.

Evangelism rests on the basic human desire to want to share the good things of life. We do not evangelize to dominate people, to score points off them, or to assert our superiority to them. If those motivations have been there in the past, then the church needs to repent of them. The real reason for evangelism is generosity—the basic human desire to share something precious and satisfying with those who matter to us. It is like one beggar telling another where to find bread. It is an act of sharing, of refusing to keep something so wonderful and satisfying to ourselves. "Taste and see that the LORD is good," wrote the psalmist (Ps. 34:8). Evangelism is like recommending a delicious new recipe to friends or telling them about something wonderful that has happened to you. If something really matters to you, you won't want to keep it to yourself!

A basic part of evangelism is explaining why we are Christians. What is it about the Christian faith that matters to us? How does it make a difference to our lives? These sorts of things, simple though they are, can be of enormous significance in bearing witness to the presence and love of God in the world. At a more sophisticated level, evangelism could be about presenting the full claims of the Christian faith with an invitation to respond to them. But that could be a lot farther down the line. We need to be sensitive to where people are. So important is this point that we need to take it farther by exploring for the first time what is meant by *apologetics*.

Apologetics: A Cinderella Turned Princess

With this new emphasis on the faithful and effective presentation of the Christian faith, a neglected resource has come into its own. That resource is apologetics. Once a Cinderella, it has now claimed its rightful place at the royal ball. Everyone knows that jargon is a nuisance. Too often, it conceals the meaning of words and allows professionals to hide behind a smoke screen of complex terms. *Apologetics* runs the risk of falling into this category. Yet the term can and must be used. It refers to a precise and well-defined area of Christian ministry that is related to evangelism, yet distinct from it. Apologetics is a kind of preevangelism, something that prepares the ground for evangelism at a later stage. Let's explore how.

The Greek word *apologia* literally means "a defense" or "a reason for doing or believing something." The word is used with this general meaning in 1 Peter 3:15, where Christians are urged to give a reason (*apologia*) for the hope that lies within them. Apologetics is about giving reasons for faith. It is about persuading people that Christianity makes sense.

Becoming a Christian does not mean hanging up your brains or kissing good-bye to rational thought. Apologetics aims to deal with barriers to faith, giving reasoned and thoughtful replies that allow our audience to appreciate fully the attraction and coherence of the Christian faith. Once a Cinderella, apologetics has become a princess.

So how does apologetics relate to evangelism? A rough working definition of *evangelism* might be "inviting someone to become a Christian." Apologetics would then be clearing the ground for that invitation so that it is more likely to receive a positive response. Evangelism could be said to be like offering people bread. Apologetics would then be about persuading people that there is bread available and that it is good to eat. Apologetics stresses the reasonableness and attractiveness of the Christian faith; evangelism makes the offer of that faith.

This all sounds rather abstract and could do with a little fleshing out from real life. Here is a scenario, drawn from an experience that an associate of mine—whom we shall call Simon—had recently, that may cast some light on the distinction. Simon had split up with his girlfriend and was rather lonely and miserable. Feeling sorry for him, some female friends threw a dinner party for him. During the course of the evening, they talked about women, life, women, work, and women. As they talked about one of their women friends—whom we shall call Jenny—they detected a noticeable quickening of interest on Simon's part. They extolled Jenny's virtues, what she was like and why they were so fond of her. He began to raise objections. Perhaps she was already in love. Perhaps she wouldn't like him. They reassured him. Finally, they posed the crucial question: Would he like to meet her? He agreed, and a meeting was set up.

Apologetics is just like the commending of Jenny to Simon. It involves setting out the attractiveness of the Christian faith and dealing with some of the difficulties and obstacles that seem to arise. Apologetics, as the analogy suggests, has both positive and negative aspects. Positively, it sets out the attractiveness of the Christian faith; negatively, it tries to neutralize some of the obstacles that seem to come between people and faith in Christ. But in the end, apologetics is about preparation—preparing the way for a relationship, whether that relationship is with Jenny or with the living God. And that is where evangelism comes into its own. Evangelism is about an invitation—an invitation to initiate a relationship. As our homespun analogy suggests, there are parallels between a personal relationship and faith in God.

Another way of understanding the difference between apologetics and evangelism is based on some of the New Testament parables. Jesus often compared the gospel to a banquet or some kind of great party (for example, see Luke 14:15–24). Try to imagine two different approaches to that party. The first approach stresses that there really is a party, explains why it is going to be great fun, and reflects on the great time that everyone is going to have. The second approach issues an invitation to that party. It says, "You're invited." It asks, "Are you going to come?"

Apologetics is about affirming the truth and the attraction of the gospel. Evangelism is about issuing a personal invitation to come to faith and become a Christian. So apologetics is like a kind of preevangelism. It prepares the way for that invitation to be issued by helping people to understand what Christianity is about and why it is so attractive and meaningful. Then the way is clear for the next stage: an invitation or a challenge can be laid down.

The analogies just used bring out a basic distinction between apologetics and evangelism, which is too easily overlooked. Apologetics is nonconfrontational. It is not threatening. Evangelism is. It asks someone to consider whether he or she feels ready to take the step of faith—a step for which apologetics has prepared the way. To make this point clearer, we shall use another analogy, which allows us to explore some points of fundamental importance to the theme of this book.

A Classic Approach: Aristotle

Although the apologetic importance of personal example and witness cannot be ignored, apologetics often takes the form of persuasion through words and argument. It aims to allow the Christian to understand the ways in which people reach decisions in life and to use this knowledge to allow the gospel to be presented in all its wonder and power.

In one sense apologetics is more like rhetoric than logic. Logic is about the kind of neat little arguments that you find in textbooks. Rhetoric is the skill of using human speech to persuade others of the power and rightness of our vision. Logic is about correctness; rhetoric is about changing people's lives.

Most politicians have little interest in logic, often regarding it as little more than hairsplitting. But rhetoric is something else. It has the ability to allow people to share in their visions, to support their causes, and to elect them to office. In the battle for the hearts and minds of people, Christians need to know about rhetoric. So let us explore what the great Greek philosopher Aristotle had to say on this subject. Although what he has to say dates from nearly two and a half thousand years ago, he still has much to say that is of relevance to us today.

According to Aristotle, three factors influence people as they try to make up their minds about issues. We shall use his original Greek words as we analyze them.

1. *Logos.* In the first place, Aristotle stresses the importance of *logos*, or "reason." (Our English word *logic* derives from this Greek term.) There are excellent rational arguments for the Christian faith, and it is important to know them and make use of them. But on their own, they may not be of much use. The mind is only one aspect of the human person; it is necessary to appeal to the heart as well. This brings us to Aristotle's second consideration.

2. *Pathos.* Aristotle refers to the emotional aspects of arguments by which an appeal is made to the heart. The theme of love dominates the New Testament. God loves us. He shows that love in word and deed and supremely through the death of Jesus Christ. In one sense, love is not logical at all. But it is essential to

human life and human relationships. So apologetics must ensure that the relevance of the Christian gospel to the human heart, as well as the human mind, is fully explained and explored.

3. *Ethos.* Finally, Aristotle points out that the situation of the audience needs to be addressed. When you make a public speech, you need to know about the situation of the people you are talking to if you are going to relate to their needs and hopes. This is also true of the apologist. To build effective bridges to faith, you need to know about the possible points of contact for the gospel in the lives and experiences of your audience.

For Aristotle, persuasion involves making an appeal to reason, emotion, and experience. This classic model remains useful today. We must never think of the gospel as simply rational truth; it is something that can and will win people's hearts and change their lives. Aristotle provides both a stimulus and a framework for more effective apologetics.

The Roads to Faith

The French atheist writer Jean-Paul Sartre once wrote a powerful book entitled *The Roads to Freedom.* The image used in that title is helpful. Christianity also offers a road to freedom—but a freedom very different from that explored by Sartre. They say that pictures are worth a thousand words. When dealing with something as rich and complex as the Christian faith, such images can be a lifeline—both to Christians (as they try to deepen their understanding of their faith) and to those outside the Christian faith (as they try to make sense of what it could mean for them). So here is a picture to think about. It is nothing new. In fact, Christians have used this picture for the best part of two thousand years. It may be old and very traditional; nevertheless, it is enormously helpful as we begin to explore the themes of this book.

The picture is that of someone setting out on a long and difficult journey, not quite sure where it is leading or how long it will take. Perhaps we could call this person a pilgrim. Or we might use a Latin term that became popular in the Middle Ages: a *viator*, a "traveler" or "wayfarer." The image has captured the imagination of many novelists, who compare the human search for meaning in life to someone undertaking a journey. For there is something fundamentally restless and dissatisfied about human nature.

One of the saddest questions is, Where am I going? Why is it sad? Because it is all too often asked by someone in despair, someone for whom life has little meaning, or someone who is contemplating ending it all. Questions like this, frequently put in the mouths of heroes of novels and television soap operas, correspond closely to this human worrying about where life is going.

People in secular Western society think more about the meaning of life than many Christians realize. Often a tragedy provokes this thinking by challenging cozy and optimistic views about human nature. The death of a close friend or relative can bring out the deep anxiety that most people have about death and dying. Not only have we lost someone who matters to us. We have also been reminded of the disturbing fact of our own mortality—the harsh fact that we, too, must die. Many people find that a deeply worrying thought because they are very conscious of having no answers or hope in the face of that event. Many secular novels and films express this deep feeling of anxiety and hopelessness in the face of death. True, they have no answers—but at least they make the problem crystal clear.

Others outside the church will have been impressed by the quality of the lifestyle of their Christian friends and secretly wonder whether they could share in their faith and hope. They may slip into church, quietly and unnoticed, to see whether they could recover a faith that they allowed to lapse many years ago. Others may buy a Christian book and read it in the privacy of their homes. There may be obstacles of all kinds in their way. However, they have begun to turn their thoughts in a direction that they might have thought impossible in the past.

Back to the image of a road! Think of each individual as having a personal road that leads to faith. For some, that road may be short and sweet. For others, it may be long and difficult, littered with obstacles. And at the end of that road lies a decision— a decision to come to faith. It may be a decision taken easily, without undue effort. Many Christians come to faith because they were raised in a Christian environment. Perhaps they grew up in a Christian family, attended church regularly, and gradually came to accept and make their own the faith with which they had been surrounded since their youth. For others, the story is very different.

As secularization makes deeper inroads into Western society, it is becoming increasingly common for young people to grow up with little, if any, familiarity with Christianity. Their parents may have no faith of any kind. They may never have attended church. They may have learned nothing of Christianity from their school days. So someone has to explain what Christianity is and why it has exercised such a fascination for so many men and women. Someone will have to listen to the difficulties and hesitations that these people will have. And, finally, someone will have to answer the crucial question: What must I do to become a Christian? The road may be longer; it may take a different form; but in the end, the result is the same. Someone moves to faith. Apologetics aims to clear that road of obstacles to faith. Evangelism provides the opportunity to respond to the Christian gospel in faith.

Becoming a Christian is an enormous step for anyone to make. It involves changes—big changes. Many people need all the help that they can get if they are to become Christians. And the need for help doesn't stop there. They will require support and guidance as they begin the Christian life. To appreciate the importance of apologetics to the tasks of the Christian church, we may explore two aspects of becoming a Christian.

First, *explain what Christianity is all about.* In an increasingly secular culture, fewer and fewer people outside the Christian community have any real understanding of what Christians believe. Half-truths, misconceptions, and caricatures abound. One of the most important tasks of apologetics is explanation. Nothing complicated—just a simple and clear presentation of the basic elements of the gospel.

It doesn't require great skill. It isn't something that only professionals can do. It doesn't require a degree in theology. It just takes a little trouble. In one of his comedies, the French playwright Molière tells of the man who spoke prose without knowing he was doing so. Many Christians will be surprised to discover that they have been doing apologetics without realizing it.

Perhaps you were hindered from coming to faith by misunderstandings about the gospel. Try to remember what they were. How did you feel about them? How did you discover that you had turned your back on a caricature of the real thing? There will probably be people at your church who had very muddled ideas about what Christianity involved. Listen to them. Ask them to tell you about how they discovered the truth and the difference it made. These discussions can be both interesting and helpful. They can be interesting because you learn more about people and discover that they have depths previously hidden from you. And they can be profoundly useful. Someone may describe a problem she had with Christianity and how she resolved it. As you listen, you realize that someone close to you has that same difficulty right now. You listen more intently in the knowledge that this person's experience could well be of real value to someone who matters to you.

That is where many people are right now—disabled by misconceptions and misrepresentations of the Christian faith. Secular culture can be very hostile to the gospel. It may have a vested interest in portraying Christianity in a very negative light. Anything that you can say or do to dispel these false conceptions may be a major step forward in someone's personal journey to faith. You may not be a great debater or a skilled philosopher. But you can tell people of how much your faith means to you, and you can dispel misconceptions—such as the idea that Christianity is a fundamentally boring faith inflicted on people by a vengeful church.

Second, *help them remove barriers to faith.* This is where apologetics comes into its own. Think again of each person's journey to faith as being like a road. That road begins where the person is at present and ends somewhere in the future as he joyfully discovers the wonder of the gospel. In between, there lie a series of barriers, each of which is like a roadblock to faith. For some, there may be many such barriers. For others, there may be only one. Apologetics aims to clear away these barriers.

As will become clear in the next chapter, the barriers may differ in their nature and significance. The strategies for coping with them will vary from one person to another. That is why it is important to listen to people and take them seriously as they explain about their problems in relation to the gospel.

Many Christians, however, are apprehensive about trying to deal with these barriers. How, they wonder, can they cope with them? What can they say that might be helpful to someone with such difficulties? They feel inadequate and useless. Yet you should remember that many people often put their discovery of the gospel down to something that one of their Christian friends did or said, perhaps many years ago. Sometimes that person may have died without knowing that what she said or did would have such effect. She may never know the results of her witness. We need to learn to trust in a God who is able to use our feeble yet faithful efforts.

Let's go back to the image of a personal road to faith, littered with obstacles. Some Christians get very discouraged. They want to be able to say things that will lead to their friends and loved ones coming to faith immediately! And they are saddened and distressed when that doesn't happen. "We have failed!" they cry. But it isn't that simple. They may well have removed one obstacle; yet others remain. But they will have left their friends one step closer to faith. That insight is notable. We may not be able to bring people all the way to faith, but we can leave them closer to that faith than when we first met them. Someone else may have the privilege of removing that final barrier and have the joy of seeing a person discovering the joy of faith.

Starting Where People Are

One of the most important skills in apologetics is the willingness to listen to people. People are at different stages along the road that leads to faith. But how far? And what are the obstacles that they are confronting? The only way to find out is to listen to people and come to know them well. As we saw earlier, one of the most powerful motivations for evangelism is love for others. We want them to share in something that has come to mean so much to us. That probably means we know the people in question well and can gain an idea of what the problems really are.

So listen to people. Try to work out where they are—and start from there. Some may be ready to make a decision for faith at this moment; others may have a long way to go. Be patient! Try to avoid sounding like a tape recorder, which spews out preprogrammed responses to questions. The personal aspect of apologetics is vital. The crucial question we need to ask is not, What kind of things stop people from coming to faith? Rather, it is, What stops this friend of mine from coming to faith? Maybe you are the only person who will be able to answer that question.

A friend of mine told me that she thought she would be lousy at evangelism. "I'm basically a people person," she told me. She meant that her basic concern was for people rather than for ideas. I was delighted, and I told her so. That's why she will be such a good evangelist. She cares about people, and she takes trouble to get alongside them, to know them, and to care for them. In her life, she models God. How? By showing care, compassion, and commitment—just as God showed His love by sending Christ into the world to die for us. By meeting people where they are—just as God entered into this world in the person of Jesus Christ. And by showing how Christianity links up with people's heartfelt concerns—such as loneliness, fear of death, and worry about the future—she will allow people she loves to catch a glimpse of the love of God for them and want to learn more about it.

Evangelism takes place, subtly yet powerfully, every time we talk to our friends about our faith and hope, and try to share what it means for us to be Christians. We may not be able to find the right words or handle all the objections and questions that are raised as we talk. But a powerful and lingering impression is created: individuals matter.

So take people and their problems seriously. Remember that your non-Christian friends may well judge Christianity with reference to you. That's a frightening thought! For them, you are Christianity embodied in a person. But remember that the love you show toward them reflects the love of God for His world. Remember that the seriousness with which you take your friends and their anxieties reflects the way in which God cares for them. Your consideration and compassion may well help them to understand, appreciate, and—finally!—respond to the love of God.

You may not be very good with words or arguments. However, the way you behave toward others is itself a powerful argument. It is a consideration that speaks as loudly as, if not even more loudly than, sophisticated defenses of the faith. Many people who have become Christians put their initial decision to start thinking about Christianity down to the quality of life of their

Christian friends. "I realized that she had something I did not." "There was just something about him that made me wonder." Comments like this are deeply revealing. The way we live can be just as effective in making people pause, think, and reevaluate their outlook on life.

Apologetics, then, has two components, positive and negative. Positively, it is about identifying and setting out clearly the attractiveness of faith. Negatively, it is like clearing away the obstacles on the road to faith. But what kind of obstacles? And how can we deal with them? Michael takes up the story.

Chapter 2

Understanding Why People Are Not Christians

Michael Green

I was given a delightful video called *It's No Good Shouting!* It emerged from a very significant conference by thinking Christians on the gospel and our culture. It picked up, and refuted, characteristic British and American attitudes to foreigners who do not speak the language. If they don't understand, speak slower and shout louder!

This is, of course, as disastrous a way to approach those who do not share our faith as it is to those who do not speak our language. Trying to understand why people are not Christians is essential. Indeed, we shall have little chance of seeing any change until we do. Gone are the days when we could preach the good news louder— and hope they will respond. They may not, for a variety of reasons. We shall look at four of the most common in this chapter.

1. Reasons of the Climate

In every generation, there is a dominant climate of opinion. And in Western lands, once so strongly influenced by Christianity, the climate of opinion is at best apathetic and is frequently hostile to the Christian faith. Why should this be? Why do we not have a flat playing field on which to play our game? For the answer, we shall have to delve, although briefly, into history.

If you had been around in Europe five hundred years ago, you would have lived in a society dominated by Christian associations—if not always by Christian faith and behavior. For a thousand years, since the end of the Roman Empire, the prevailing worldview in Europe was Christian. The most beautiful buildings were Christian. The best art was Christian. Law and justice claimed to be Christian. International relationships operated, theoretically at least, within a Christian framework. The church was the dominant force in society. The pope was more important than any prince. Thought itself was regulated by what the church taught.

You might well have been illiterate, but you would have seen God's handiwork in the fields where you worked each day, and you would have heard His generosity to you in church on Sundays. The parish priest was, along with the squire, the most educated person in the village. You would have learned the catechism. You would have imagined the world to be a three-decker universe—heaven above, the earth in the middle, and the underworld beneath. You would have known many stories of the Scriptures and the lives of the saints. You would have been well aware of the shortness of life; the fear of death and, worse, hell would have often gripped you.

Much the same was true of North America in the seventeenth century where the church played a central role in the lives and thinking of the emerging nation. Indeed, it was a dominant strand in American lifestyle from the days of the founding fathers onward.

Today, that climate has completely disappeared. We live in a society where Christianity seems to be a dwindling force and a minority interest. It seems to have lost any influence in the great cities where most people live. Art, literature, and music are no longer concerned with religious themes. People are, in fact, often extraordinarily ignorant of the barest outlines of what Christianity is. There are no family prayers at home, no instruction in the schools. Few enter full church membership, and those who do may have little idea of Christian teaching and still less conviction of its truth or relevance.

Christianity seems to have nothing to do with relationships at home, in the marketplace, or in international undertakings. We are no longer illiterate—but few read the world's best-seller, the Bible. America boasts a high churchgoing population still, but it is declining; there is more than a tinge of Victorian "churchianity" about it. God and the flag tend to go together on a Sunday. On Monday, it is a very different story. The situation is different superficially in Europe, but the same disease is at work. The churches are often deserted. Ministers are often considered very odd fish. Nobody is quite sure what they are there for.

Our minds are anesthetized to the pain that TV brings in ever-increasing quantities into our homes. We feed those minds with magazines, game shows, soap operas, and thrillers. We are not preoccupied by a fear of death. We never dwell on it, and it is a tremendous shock when it strikes. It has replaced sex as the unmentionable subject. On the whole, for most people most of the time, the real world is so grim and the next world so unreal that we need escape routes that consume us—pop music, TV sports, drugs, and booze—if we are to survive an increasingly long and tedious life span. God never gets a look in.

The climate in Western Europe, North America, and Australasia has become almost totally secularized. It is not that all people have thought about Christianity and rejected it. They have never had cause to think. It doesn't enter into their minds. The climate of the culture makes it seem utterly irrelevant. But if you and I lived in Papua, New Guinea, for example, we would find a totally different cultural climate. Everyone believes in God, and everyone believes in evil spirits. Evangelism is a very different matter there!

What are the causes for this massive about-face over Christianity in Europe, once the heartland of the Christian faith? It is important to ask this question because very much the same causes are at work in the United States, though they are not yet as advanced. The United States is a massive battlefield between ruthless skepticism and the Christian faith. The decline that is evident in Europe threatens America as well.

It is therefore necessary to examine the factors that have contributed to modern unbelief. They are so powerful that they have combined to remove Christianity from the serious consideration of 90 percent of our population: they see no reason to examine it to determine whether it might have any truth or relevance. The most important of these factors during the past five hundred years are probably the following ones:

1. The Renaissance, which occurred during the fourteenth and fifteenth centuries, was crucial. A whole new world of learning was released, springing from the culture of classical Greece and Rome—its art, philosophy, science, and above all its humanism. Humankind, not God, became the measure of all things. This world, not the next, became the center of attention. No longer was the church worldview the only one: the seeds of both pluralism and secularism had been sown.

The Reformation took place during the sixteenth century, spelling a revolution in church and society. The old ecclesiastical stranglehold was broken by the division of Christendom, and the dissemination and power of the Scriptures discredited much of contemporary Catholic teaching. The old "priest" became the new "presbyter." The rise of natural science through men such as

Copernicus and Galileo liberated people from the dogma of church teaching and opened up a spirit of empirical discovery and hard work.

Meanwhile, nationalism was rearing its head. The overarching umbrella of Christendom was ripped apart. Devotion to the nation came to replace old-time devotion to God. Europe was torn to pieces by war. This tendency has continued. The world is fragmenting into ever-smaller entities when its overwhelming need is unity after a half century that has seen the meteoric increase in weapons of mass destruction and has endured the two most terrible wars that have ever devastated the human race.

2. The Enlightenment, headed by thinkers such as Descartes, Hume, and Locke, was an eighteenth-century development of Renaissance principles that has had an incalculable influence on Western thought and attitudes. The Enlightenment was agnostic about God. It wanted to put human reason in His place—reason that would unveil a natural religion common to all humanity; a universal morality in which everyone sought the greatest good of the greatest number; human rights possessed by all people universally; the coherence of society in a social contract (replacing the idea of the Fatherhood of God and the brotherhood of man); and a universe that resembled a great machine, intricate and self-sustaining.

The thinkers of the Enlightenment were for the most part optimists, and they believed in the essential goodness of human nature and in a doctrine of inevitable progress (which became much accentuated under the impact of Darwin's theory of evolution). Although the Enlightenment was responsible for many benefits to humanity, there can be no doubt that its influence has, during the past two centuries, been a major factor in bringing about the common conviction that this world is all that really matters, and that religion is at best empirically unverifiable and socially divisive. It can safely be ignored.

3. Scientific materialism and the associated technological revolution have ushered us into a world utterly beyond the imagination of our forebears. Although science was born in a Christian
worldview among men who, like Bacon, believed that God had
revealed Himself in two books—the book of nature and the book
of Scripture—it was soon seen to be independent of religious
controversies and capable of supporting a totally secular worldview. Married to Enlightenment rationalism and the principle of
radical doubt, it rapidly became a serious threat to Christian
teachings as they were popularly perceived (though not necessarily to the gospel itself!).

Think of some of the big names and the challenges they presented. Copernicus and Galileo, by recognizing the nature of the
solar system, challenged the church's understanding of the earth
as the center of the universe. Newton's discovery of gravity challenged the commonly held idea that divine providence maintained the planets in their courses. And when Newton's follower
Laplace was rebuked by the emperor Napoleon for having left
God out of his scheme of the universe, he replied, "Sire, I have
no need of that hypothesis." Darwin's theory of evolution was at
once perceived to challenge the prevailing idea of God as Creator.

Those challenges continued with Marx and Freud. Both
thinkers have had a decisive effect on the twentieth-century
abandonment of God. Marx replaced Christian teaching by an
atheistic materialism. Instead of Christianity's promised kingdom
of God, Marx offered the idea of a class struggle eventually leading to an economic and social utopia. Freud undercut the whole
Christian worldview by dubbing it, along with all religions, as
sick and illusory. Is it any wonder that these varied streams of opposition to Christian belief and practice have brought about the
climate of opinion in which we live today?

4. A further factor that should be noted is urbanization. The
concentration of people in the cities of the world since the Industrial Revolution is one of the most powerful forces in our society.

Church in city
notes for paper?

It has often had the effect of breaking family ties, uprooting traditional values, and alienating the mass of people from the rhythm of country life, which made belief in God natural. This process of urbanization is proceeding worldwide at a terrifying pace. Crime, the breakdown of relationships, alienation, and disbelief in God are among its side effects. They are increasingly apparent in our societies. The appalling inner-city devastation of cities such as Los Angeles, Miami, and Chicago, coupled with the widespread retreat of the church from these locations, is eloquent testimony to the tendencies that urbanization nourishes, which are extremely hostile to the gospel.

These, then, are some of the reasons that account for the social and intellectual climate of our day. The climate seems to make God an implausible hypothesis, a spent force, a yesteryear's idea. It helps us to see why many scientists, businesspeople, psychiatrists, urban planners—in fact, almost everyone—feel that they can get along without God, if He exists, which seems rather doubtful. And the situation has not been helped by the church's ineffectual response to these developments.

On almost every issue and occasion, the church has hung on to its dogmas and refused to face unwelcome new truths. Think of the fury of the Catholic church against the Reformation. Think of its persecution of Galileo—for which the present pope has only now gotten around to making an apology, 350 years late! Think, on the other hand, of the time-serving liberalism of many of the mainline churches, specifically of Bishop Jack Spong's almost total surrender to the secularist worldview. Think of the way in which many of the churches have consistently opposed the quest for truth, the furtherance of human dignity, and the causes of freedom and justice, which have been among the goals of the Enlightenment. During the Second World War, the Vatican seemed to be on the side of the Nazis. In Latin America, it has been consistently allied to ruling ruthless oligarchies.

As for the cities, the church has never come to terms with the urban masses. Throughout Western society, the churches seem to abandon the city centers and move out to the cozy suburbs. It would be almost though not quite entirely true to say that the church has habitually been reactionary. It has been seen to set its face against the causes of freedom, justice, inquiry, and progress. It has done little to transcend nationalism, to understand the goals of science and democracy, and to reach the industrial workers of our great cities. In the light of this catalog of past failures, is it any wonder that so many people are not Christians? If we are going to change the situation, we must begin by understanding it.

2. Reasons of the Memory

It is not only the climate of opinion that militates against a resurgence of Christian faith in the West today. I recall chatting with a Christian leader in Holland. He is pioneering a completely new type of church because the memories associated with experiences in both the Catholic and the Protestant churches in that country are so unhelpful. And his warm, lively, relevant church (devoted to attractive outreach and demanding every member ministry) is having a great effect, not least in the red-light district of Amsterdam. Or I think of the open-air ministry that I used to attempt in Canada, only to find that the normally quiet and friendly Canadian became abusive and even violent as he passed by and heard me speaking of God and the church. It was because such talk stirred very painful memories in his breast. These people have been deeply wounded by institutional Christianity. They want to have nothing more to do with the church.

Sometimes it is because of the eviction of their family, when they were small children, from property owned by the church.

Sometimes it is because of the banning from Communion after divorce, the designation of marriage after divorce as living in sin, or the refusal to bury Dad in holy ground because he was an unbeliever.

Sometimes it is resentment that a minister was reluctant to baptize a baby in the family where there was no evidence of any commitment to Christianity. Sometimes it was his insistence that the family should come to church for a few weeks before the baptism or that the parents should attend a preparation class. Sometimes the chosen sponsors were rejected because they did not seem to be practicing Christians. The number of hurts and rebuffs, imagined or real, associated with baptism are enormous and probably account for the drop in the number of infant baptisms in Britain to about 20 percent of the population when only decades ago it was virtually universal. In Canada, the fallout from mainline churches is even more acute.

Sometimes the memory harbors resentment against the day when you were thrown out of the church youth club for a couple of weeks to cool your heels. Sometimes it was when the local pastor passed you by as if you didn't exist. Perhaps nobody from the church called to visit when Aunt Agatha was dying. Perhaps nobody even knew. No matter; it is a black mark for the local church, and you are not going to darken its doors again.

Sometimes the resentment is a result of marriage policy. What is all this about some ministers not being prepared to marry you unless you have been baptized? Or if you're pregnant? Or when they stop the photographers from taking pictures in church? Or charge outrageous fees? Or subject you to dreary and uncalled-for marriage preparation? Many noses are put out of joint by the way they feel the church has handled them at the most sensitive time of their lives—when a marriage was in the air.

Sometimes the resentment is against a particular person, who was a member of the church and hurt them deeply in the past. Or against some church official who swindled them in business—a manifest hypocrite. Sometimes . . .

The sources of resentment are endless. And there is a very good reason for it. Christians are human beings. All human beings are likely to make mistakes and are capable of deliberate wickedness. That is the point at which we are all equal. And those who hold resentments against the church need to be shown that they, too, cause pain and provide stumbling blocks to other people. They need to learn the destructive effects of holding grudges. It breeds a cancer in the heart of the one who harbors it.

But the most common of all complaints against the church can be summarized succinctly: "We were forced to go when we were young, and it was deadly dull." Just think of that! Forced to go—why didn't the grown-ups go, too, and make it a family affair? The answer is simple: the grown-ups did not believe or practice the Christian gospel, but they still thought that Christian morals were good (for the kids, anyway). So they sent the children along to Sunday school to get some rough-and-ready ideas of right and wrong into their heads, while Mom and Dad had an extra hour in bed on Sundays t˜ read the paper. That is the escapism, the double standard, the hypocrisy even, underlying the "sent to Sunday school" mentality. It is on the wane now. Parents neither go nor send their kids. But the institution of the Sunday school may have a lot to answer for. Under the pretext of instructing the young, it has separated families and allowed people to think of themselves as Christian by proxy while continuing to be totally untouched by the gospel of Christ to whose representatives they compel their young to go! (This charge cannot, of course, be leveled against the all-age Sunday school, common in many parts of the U.S.)

And think of the second part of that all too common complaint: "We were forced to go when we were young, and it was deadly dull." Deadly dull? How on earth do you make Jesus dull? The most blazing revolutionary who ever lived? The One who revolutionized attitudes to women and outcasts? The One who took on the religious and political establishment single-handedly? The One who lived in poverty and endured with complete composure the most savage and unjustified attacks? The One who died a death of such love and self-sacrifice that it has become the most famous death in history? The one and only person in all the annals of human history to have broken the grip of death? How on earth can you make such a person dull? It is the most phenomenal achievement of theological colleges, theological writers, clergy, and Sunday school teachers that they have managed the unthinkable: they have made Jesus dull. And once people have the idea that Jesus is dull, it is not easy to get them to change their minds.

3. Reasons of the Intellect

Given the climate sketched in the first section of this chapter, we should not be surprised that many people in our society have strong intellectual objections to the Christian faith. I do not think that this is the main cause of contemporary unbelief because (as Freud and Jung have demonstrated) it is perfectly obvious that we are not influenced by considerations of reason in all, or even most, of our lives. But one can be much more down-to-earth than that. Who gets married on the basis of rational grounds alone? Yet although the mind is not the most important gateway to the soul, it remains a very important avenue. Any attempt to draw people to Christianity that evades the challenges posed to the human mind by unbelief will not succeed for long and does not deserve to.

I cannot claim to know all or even most of the reasons that keep people from Jesus Christ. But I do debate, often in the open air, in homes, and in student halls. I love discussing the faith with modern unbelievers. I have noticed that the following nine arguments (all derived from the amalgam of views that have gone to make up modern skepticism) are brought forward more commonly than others. None of them is foolproof.

1. The most basic objection is psychological: religion is a neurosis and does not relate to anything real. This view goes back to Freud's *The Future of an Illusion* in which he predicted the early demise of religion in the light of his theories about the human ego. As it has turned out, however, religion has proved a lot more enduring than Freud's theories. It is demonstrably one of the most powerful forces, for good or ill, in the world today. It is a profoundly rooted human instinct. Is it the only human instinct that relates to nothing?

How are we to explain human society, the world in which we live, the laws of nature, and the hunger of the heart if there is no source greater than ourselves from which we come? To be sure, Freud thought religion neurotic; but that is at least arguably because he lived in an age in which Christianity was the prevailing backdrop to society, and the sick people to whom he ministered had taken that backdrop on board. He seems to have seen nothing of the manifestly nonneurotic and socially constructive activity that was going on in all parts of the world of his day, inspired by the gospel of Christ. In the end, Freud got booted out of Vienna by jackbooted Nazi thugs who had swallowed his theory that religion was an illusion and that might was right.

2. Another common view is phenomenological in character. In other words, it rests on observing the world. This view rests on the immense variety of beliefs sincerely held by pious practitioners all over the world. It concludes that they must all be alternative or complementary routes up the same mountain and are bound to lead to the same destination at the top—namely, God and eternal life.

This is a warming liberal perspective. But as we shall see in a later chapter, it is not one that will withstand too much critical examination. For one thing, this current variation on the doctrine of religious pluralism is rather novel. It is not at all shared by the practitioners themselves. For another, there is no real agreement about what the top of the mountain is and whether or not there is any life to be enjoyed there! For another, the moral dimension of things is totally ignored in this pluralist paradise—the satanists are placed on the same level as Mother Teresa. And—the most basic point of all—most of the people who favor this approach seem to know little about other faiths or even any one faith. They just find pluralism a convenient way of ducking the commitment question.

In any case, there are parallels to consider other than roads up a mountain. What about paths through a maze? There are lots of paths—but only one turns out to lead you safely through to the other side. The rest turn out to be dead ends.

3. Then again, we have a logical objection: "You can't prove that there is a God!" True enough. Neither can you prove that there isn't a God. The only way to logical proof would be to show that there is something greater than God from which His existence could be deduced with certainty. But that is, by definition, impossible. After all, God is the name that we give to the ultimate source of our world, beyond which it is impossible to go.

And if they ask (and they do love to!), "Then who made God?" you can show them that this objection is also flawed. It would indeed be an infinite regress if God were just another cause or effect in a *finite* temporal chain—if He were what the philosophers call contingent. But that is not what we are talking about when we use the name God. We mean a self-existent Being who is the source and origin of the world, as He is of the whole principle of cause and effect. There is no logical argument against an *infinite* personal source for ourselves and our universe.

As a matter of fact, you can offer very good reasons that point in that direction—for example, the fact that there is a world at all, the fact of human personality, the fact of apparent design in our world at every level, the fact of human values, of conscience, and of religious belief. All these are undeniable phenomena, which point clearly in one direction—that there is some kind of God. You can't prove that there is a God any more than you can prove that your mother loves you, but there is plenty of evidence to support the hypothesis!

4. A dying cry may still be heard to this effect: "We are all good people at heart." Why is it dying? Because of the brutal and harsh facts of two world wars, and all the atrocities and suffering that they brought. Yet although it is dying, it remains vocal: "There is no such thing as an evil person—just a socially deprived or psychologically imbalanced or sorely misunderstood person." A great deal of modern educational methods and some legal judgments have proceeded on the basis of that assumption. But it is manifestly false, and few people outside universities still hold to it. Humanists such as H. G. Wells, Bernard Shaw, C. E. M. Joad, and even Bertrand Russell held to this idealistic view of human nature in their time—yet all had to abandon it in the face of the evidence to the contrary.

There is something wicked in the human heart—in all human hearts—and denying it is unrealistic. Another, and in some ways a parallel, illusion is shared by Buddhism and Christian Science: evil is unreal. Try telling that to a husband whose wife has been murdered and daughter raped! Christianity is thoroughly realistic about human nature.

5. There is a widespread conviction these days that truth is relative. You hear it when someone says, "Well, it's true for me. I don't know about you." In a world of so many conflicting ideas and cultures, it seems almost indecent to brand any statement or idea with the label *true* or *false*. Yet that is how it is, and that is what the words mean. We are perfectly happy to apply *true* or *false* to the public world of so-called facts—for example, that the Declaration of Independence dates from 1776, or that Bill

Clinton succeeded George Bush as president of the United States. Yet we squirm when someone has the brazen effrontery to apply the terms to values or ideas.

There is no need to cringe. Important issues are at stake here. Suppose your friend tells you that "all truth is relative; you must not make absolute claims for it." The last thing that this friend will expect is for you to reply, "That statement of yours is relative as well. It may seem okay to you, but it cuts no ice with me." Although your friend has put forward the claim that all truth is relative, it is clear that he is making an *absolute* claim for that statement. Yet, on the basis of his premise, that is impossible! It makes no sense to say that it is absolutely true that all truth is relative. It will do your friends no harm to realize that they have been smuggling an unacknowledged absolute into a world they claim to be totally relative.

6. One of the most common intellectual cop-outs you are likely to hear is that science has killed religion. If you believe in science, you can't believe in God. A moment's thought will show that something is seriously wrong with this objection. The most scientifically advanced nation in the world is the United States of America. It also happens to be one of the world's most overtly Christian nations. In fact, this hackneyed and outdated cliché is little more than a hangover from a nineteenth-century materialist worldview, which saw the world as a great clock. Now scientists see it more as a great mystery.

The feeling that science is opposed to Christian faith is probably also colored by the depressingly bad attempts to defend the faith that Christians have made in the past in the face of scientific advances and truth-claims. Christianity comes across as defensive and reactionary—and nearly always wrong. But of course, we need to remember that natural science was born (and could only have been born) in a culture that valued honest inquiry and believed that no truth could harm you. That is an essentially Christian mind-set.

Many prominent scientists past and present have been deeply committed Christians, seeing no incompatibility between their trust in God as the source, sustainer, and goal of the universe, and their strenuous and persistent inquiries into how it all works. By studying the creation, you come to learn more about the wonder of the Creator. Science is the enemy of obscurantism, not of Christianity.

7. Science, in showing the rational cause of so many things that were once thought to be inexplicable, has made most people suspicious of the idea of miracle. That is all to the good! Christianity has no investment in credulity. The word and the whole concept of *miracle* need more careful definition and study than we have time for at this point. However, I do not see how you can be a Christian without belief in two miracles: the incarnation and resurrection of Jesus of Nazareth. It is totally against the normal run of experienced uniformities in our world for its Creator to enter into it, within the womb of an unmarried girl. And it is no less surprising and unprecedented for this same Jesus to be raised from the clutches of death after His very public and bloody execution. That is the minimum claim that Christians can make for miracles.

There is nothing irrational or superstitious about this. The claim is indeed *miraculum*—a "wonder"—but it is attested by such a wealth of evidence, positive and negative, historical and circumstantial, that it is much harder to refute than to accept. We do not suppress our reason when we examine claims to the miraculous; we rightly use our reason to assess the strength of the evidence on which those claims are made. We also recognize that there is a power greater than our reason whose activities may well be beyond our intelligence but will not run counter to it. On the basis of purely rational grounds, nobody is in any position to deny miracles. We need an openness of attitude and a careful scrutiny by our reason to weigh up the truth-claims presented.

8. Many questions center on the founder of Christianity Himself. These are usually either historical or theological in nature.

The historical questions usually take forms such as the following: Did Jesus ever exist? Was it all written down centuries later? Can we trust the New Testament? and Is there any unbiased reporting about Jesus? Every pastor will have come across variations on these basic themes.

The answer is quite simple: not only did Jesus exist, but the whole of history is dated from Him. The question itself is an evasion; the questioner would love it to be the case that Jesus never existed. Then nobody need bother about Him. But that attitude will not withstand scrutiny. Secular and Jewish, as well as Christian, authors attest His life and death and continued impact. It would be impossible to explain the rise of the Christian church in the first century A.D. had Jesus never existed. His death was very public, and the Roman historian Tacitus noted it.

And no, the evidence about Jesus is not late and unreliable. The Gospels were not dreamed up in the second or third century. The textual tradition of the Gospels is far stronger than for any other book in antiquity. The gap between the original text and our first extant copy is far shorter than for any other ancient book. The spread of translations and versions throughout antiquity makes it fruitless to doubt the integrity of the text. We have copies of the text of all four Gospels as early as A.D. 160, and a fragment of John's gospel is even earlier, A.D. 100–125. Indeed, what is almost certainly a small fragment of Mark's gospel has been found in Cave 7 at Qumran, dating before the destruction of that community by the Romans in A.D. 68.

The Gospels have been subjected to a degree of scrutiny never applied to any other books before in history. They have emerged with their heads held high. Written between A.D. 60 and 90, their picture of Jesus fits in brilliantly with that of the apostle Paul, who wrote ten years or more before the earliest gospel. It is not the reliability of the New Testament that is at issue; it is whether we can face up to the challenge of the person displayed there. Skepticism arises not from the unreliability of the material but from the stark challenge of the Jesus who meets us in its pages.

And what about the charge that the Evangelists were biased in their reporting about Jesus? In fact, there is no such thing as unbiased reporting. Everyone writes from a particular perspective. But there is certainly plenty of evidence from sources that were biased *against* Jesus and His church. The most well-known and easily accessible are the references to Jesus in Tacitus *Annals* 15.44; Suetonius *Nero* 16 and *Claudius* 25; Josephus *Antiquities* 18.3; and Pliny *Epistles* 10.96, 97. These references, along with certain inscriptions and other archaeological finds, go a long way not only to giving independent attestation to the existence of Jesus but also to presenting a picture of Him very like that of the Gospels.

The theological question about Jesus is simple: Was He just a great man, a wonderful teacher, a matchless guru? Or did He share the nature of God as no other person ever has, and is therefore uniquely empowered to speak in His name?

This is not the place to go into the divinity of Christ. But the evidence is cumulative and persuasive. Moreover, it comes from people who were not at all predisposed to believe it. It was anathema to a Jew to suppose that any human being could embody the divine presence. Many Jews preferred to die rather than accord even tongue-in-cheek divine honors to the Roman emperor. Yet many of the first Christians were drawn from those same Jews, who became convinced that Jesus was no less divine than He was human. You would not have found a more unpromising soil anywhere in the world in which to plant such an idea. Yet those intensely critical people were convinced by a number of factors, all pointing in the same direction.

His *teaching* was more than merely human. Nobody had ever heard anything to touch it for profundity, clarity, breadth of appeal, and authority.

His *influence* was greater than that of any warrior, king, or wise man. It touched all types of people. Had the Evangelists lived a little longer, they would have seen it touch all nations.

His *behavior* was impeccable. Nobody could throw mud at Him and make it stick. He had all the virtues known to men and women, yet none of the vices. The ideal had lived in history.

His *fulfillment of prophecy* was unique. His conception, birthplace, teaching in parables, wisdom, salvation, triumphal entry into Jerusalem, His suffering, His ultimate vindication and victory after a shameful death, and His burial in a rich man's tomb—all these were predicted centuries earlier. It all came to pass in this one Man's life. That was unique.

His *miracles* lent powerful evidential attestation to His claims.

His *claims*—to forgive sins, to accept worship, to be the final judge of all—must have persuaded His followers. Their truth was self-evident.

Jesus' *death* clearly had an enormous impact on His followers. They saw it as something He did for the whole of humanity—something utterly without parallel.

And the *resurrection* of Jesus and His return to His heavenly Father, followed by the gift of His unseen Spirit, which galvanized the infant church into action—that was the coping stone of their conviction that the Jesus they had walked with through the dusty fields of Palestine was the Lord of heaven and earth.

These evidences are just as powerful today. They point calmly and strongly to a Jesus who is no great teacher, no famous guru, no wonder worker only, but the embodiment in human flesh of the living God.

9. The ninth intellectual stick used to beat the Christian with is human and existential. It is something that all of us share in at some time or other—suffering. How, it is asked, could a good God, if He is as great as Christians say He is, allow all the suffering in the world?

There is no knockdown answer to that objection in Christian theology or in any other worldview whatsoever. Suffering is one of the ultimate mysteries of life for Christians as well as everyone else. But Christians must not be embarrassed by the question. We have a better answer than anyone else. We will want to maintain that the loving and powerful God does indeed will our happiness and wholeness. But His goodwill is hindered by various factors, including human rebelliousness, which always involves suffering; the nature of the physical world, where pain is inevitable unless the laws of the universe are to be defied; the existence of a powerful force opposed to God, the devil, which is bent on maximizing pain and evil; and the interdependence of the cosmos and all who live in it.

Anyway, we do not worship some cold and abstract God who set this world going with faceless laws and then left it on its own. We are dealing with a God who suffers, a God who cares for us so much that He has intervened in person and allowed the worst of human suffering to sweep over His person. He has personally shouldered its basic ingredient, human wickedness, through what He achieved on the cross. What is more, Jesus rose triumphant over suffering, sin, and death—which is pledge enough of the eternal destiny awaiting those who ally themselves with Him. No anti-Christian objection leads more easily than the problem of pain into relating the central message of our gospel to a bleeding world.

4. Reasons of the Heart

We have spent a good deal of time looking, however briefly, at nine of the most common intellectual objections that people bring against the Christian position. None of them is ultimately compelling, although each of them has some initial appeal. Yet many people who make such objections often turn out not to have thought about them very much. They rest content with their superficial attraction, only to discover that this can be punctured by rigorous discussion.

These people are comparatively easy to bring to Christian faith. Once you show them that their objections are not sufficient to keep them from the loving arms of their Creator and Redeemer, they often take that step of commitment to Him and may become some of the most thoughtful and courageous Christian advocates in the church.

But some who profess these very same objections are not doing so because they are genuine stumbling blocks in the path of faith. They are doing so to evade the challenge of faith. The situation is made more complicated by the fact that they may not realize it.

But it remains true, as Blaise Pascal observed long ago, that "the heart has its reasons." Sometimes they are dark reasons. It may be some attitude, long ago held on to, which Christian commitment would change. It may be some illicit relationship, long cherished, which the gospel might bring to an end. It may be some guilty secret, long hidden, which Christ would bring to light. In short, what seems to be an intellectual reason for rejecting the gospel may actually be a moral reason—not "I can't believe," but "I won't believe." It is not a *reason* but an *excuse* for rejecting Christ.

This situation needs careful handling. If you answer a reason, it will smooth the way for genuine progress. If you answer an excuse, it will immediately be followed by another excuse. Great delicacy is needed. Often something like "you can't prove God" will turn out to be a genuine intellectual difficulty. Sometimes, however, it cloaks a deep-seated dread that the living God may invade my life and clean up the mess He finds there. That would be a very painful experience. And so it is important that God should not be real.

I have found that one of the best ways of differentiating between a genuine difficulty and a moral smoke screen is to ask gently, "Is this really the problem? If I could answer this to your satisfaction, would the way then be clear for you to entrust yourself to Jesus Christ and become one of His followers?" If the answer is no, then I decline to answer the question. You can't play games with the living God. Volition is as important as cognition in getting past these intellectual barriers.

Yes, sometimes the heart's reasons are dark ones, evil ones. We are not willing for the shambles there to be uncovered. But sometimes the reasons of the heart have a different cause. They are hurts inflicted on us by others in the past, and they inhibit our response to the gracious approach of Jesus.

Many people these days have a very low self-image. They have been made to feel that they are no good, that they will never make it. We have very good news indeed for such people. We can assure them on the most solid grounds that God values them so greatly that He came to earth to find them. He rates them so highly that He was prepared to die in order to win their love and allegiance.

Others—it would seem an increasing number—have been abused in childhood and are overcome with shame. We have good news for them, too—the Jesus who removes shame, whether real or imagined, in the warmth of His total and free acceptance, and then washes the dirt out of those deep wounds by the indwelling power of His Holy Spirit.

Others have never experienced love without strings attached. It has always depended on their performance and achievements. They know nothing of having been loved for themselves alone, warts and all. But that is the love showered upon us all by Jesus, who knows the worst about us but loves us just the same. Unconditional love like that can be a lifesaver to the earnest but unhappy achiever.

Others refuse to respond to the Christian offer because they know themselves to be defeated—defeated by habits that they cannot break or by a lifestyle that they do not like but are powerless to change. We have highly relevant good news for them, too. In Jesus of Nazareth they encounter One who can break every fetter and set them free. He is very experienced at it. He has been doing it all over the world for centuries.

As we approach such people with tender understanding and gentle explanation of the aspect of the gospel that speaks to their condition, they realize that Jesus is willing to take failures like them on board. Hope is born, and new life is begun.

Chapter 3

The Art of Building Bridges

Alister McGrath

In opening this book, we noted that apologetics has both negative and positive aspects. Negatively, apologetics concerns understanding and, where possible, neutralizing the difficulties that prevent some people from coming to faith. The good apologist can explain how these difficulties can be resolved or set to one side. The previous chapter explored a series of barriers to Christian faith and indicated how they can be overcome in sensitive and helpful ways. But there is also a positive aspect to apologetics—the identification and exploration of the attractiveness of Christianity. That is the concern in the present chapter.

To begin with, however, let us make a crucial point. The pressures of modern culture mean that many people have little time to listen to you at length. You need to think how you can present the gospel crisply, clearly, and effectively in a very short time space—perhaps as little as thirty seconds. In what follows, we shall explore the challenges and opportunities that this raises.

Summarizing the Gospel in Thirty Seconds

Every now and then, you are going to be asked this question: "What's Christianity all about then?" And you realize that you have about thirty seconds to answer! Having a thumbnail sketch of the gospel in mind enables you to give a helpful reply even in such a brief time.

So how do you condense material to make the best possible use of time? Here is a technique that I was taught many years ago by a colleague from the British Broadcasting Corporation. I will set out the basic method in what follows. You may want to do this with a friend, who will help you assess your performance and suggest improvements.

1. Allow yourself five minutes to say what you think needs to be said. Write your reply to the question "What's Christianity all about then?" When you are satisfied with your reply, read it aloud, and establish how long it took you to say it. And don't cheat: you must speak at your normal rate.
2. Now ask yourself how effective your answer was. In particular, try to identify the core of your reply—the things that were absolutely essential. Did you really need five minutes to say that? Or can you see ways of keeping that core while reducing the time needed to say it? To find out, you must condense that reply.
3. Allow yourself two minutes. Can you retain the content while cutting down on the words needed? You will be surprised to discover how easy it is to get rid of redundant words.
4. Now allow yourself one minute.
5. And now thirty seconds.

Obviously, you cannot say all that you would like to say in such a brief time. But by effective and thoughtful use of biblical material or your own experience, you can pave the way for a longer discussion later. A word of warning, however: if you are using biblical material, you should avoid pulling out a Bible from your pocket and consulting it in public. This creates a very negative impression and may result in your friend deciding that you are an unthinking Bible-thumper. You ought to know your Bible well enough to be able to quote from it briefly without having the text open in front of you. Here are some suggestions for possible approaches.

Parables

Take a parable, such as the parable of the prodigal son (see Luke 15:11–32), which makes the point that a loving God is always waiting for His wayward children to come home. Can you see how this could be the basis of an effective summary of the gospel? See if you can write a thirty-second summary of the gospel on the basis of this parable. You could open your reply like this: "Jesus told a parable that sums up the gospel very nicely. It's about. . . ." There is no need to give the exact reference; just explain what it's all about.

Brief Biblical Passages

Try using brief biblical passages as summaries of the gospel. Especially suitable passages include the following: John 3:3 (which introduces the idea of being born again); John 3:16 (which stresses the love of God); 1 Peter 1:3–4 (which brings out the hope of faith); John 6:51 (which points to the life-giving quality of the gospel); and Romans 5:6 (which identifies the sinfulness of humanity and the remedy offered in the gospel).

Remember that you cannot hope to say everything you would like to in so brief a space. Your reply could take the form: "Jesus once described Himself as the bread of life. Well, I realized that I was hungry, looking for something that would give meaning and purpose to my life. And I found in Jesus someone who could satisfy that hunger and give me new life. And I've never looked back."

Paul's Theological Terms

In his letters, Paul uses a number of theological terms that can be invaluable summaries of the gospel. Terms such as *salvation*, *adoption*, and *reconciliation* can allow you to explain the basic elements of the gospel. These terms will be explored later in this book. Your reply could take the following form: "In one of his letters, Paul talks about being reconciled to God in Christ. That's a great summary of what the gospel is all about. It's about being restored to friendship with God. It's about Jesus making possible a new relationship with God that makes life worth living. And that's just what I found. . . ."

Personal Experience

If you find it difficult to condense biblical material in the way suggested above, you can always talk about your experience. Thirty seconds gives you enough time to tell your friends that Christianity is the best thing that ever happened to you—and why.

With these points in mind, we may move on to consider the attraction of the gospel and our responsibility to ensure that its full attraction is properly conveyed to the listening world.

The Attractiveness of Christianity

As we have seen, a central task of evangelism is to make Christianity credible in the modern world. Traditionally, the area of Christian thought that has dealt with this matter has been apologetics. In the past, apologetics has been a significant aspect of the ongoing mission of the church. Evangelism has been able to build on the achievements of apologetics. I can still remember evangelistic sermons at Oxford in the early 1970s that made extensive use of arguments for the existence of God.

But today, things have changed. The Enlightenment is over. We live in a post-Enlightenment world. The rise of the movement usually called postmodernism in Western society is a telling sign of the loss of confidence in reason and "modern" ideas and values. For many folk, a concern with truth is something of an irrelevance. The first question people tend to ask these days is not, "Is this right?" but, "What will this do for me?" The rise of the New Age movement is widely regarded by cultural analysts as a protest against the spiritual barrenness of the Enlightenment. The Enlightenment emphasis on pure reason seemed boring and irrelevant.

There is another side to this. In some quarters, an obsession with truth has come to have decidedly nasty overtones within the pluralist culture of the modern West. Claims to possess the truth are no longer seen as a positive. They have become a negative. Declaring that you are telling the truth is now seen by many people as something arrogant and triumphalist, which implies that everyone else is wrong. In the strongly pluralist culture in which most of us have to live, truth-claims are often seen as a kind of intellectual fascism. Allan Bloom forcibly pointed this out in his influential book *The Closing of the American Mind*.

The way things have developed over the last quarter of a century, people who talk about truth have come to be viewed as narrow-minded, petty, and authoritarian. People like that are perceived to get in the way of an open society, which both recognizes and takes delight in the variety of viewpoints available. At the academic level, this pluralist outlook finds its expression in postmodernism, with its vigorous rejection of universal truth-claims and commitment to open-endedness. We'll explore the idea of postmodernism in more detail a little later when we look at the importance of being a culture watcher. But at this stage, we need to look at its implications.

So how can we cope with this development? Many old-fashioned American apologists try to deal with the New Age movement by writing massive learned tomes, studded with footnotes, pointing out the logical and philosophical deficiencies of pantheism (the doctrine that everything is divine) and panentheism (the doctrine that God is present equally in all things). And sure, there are problems with the religious outlooks of the New Age movement. The approach adopted by these apologists has the enormous advantage of intellectual sophistication and theological integrity. Nevertheless, it cuts no ice with the intended audience. It has strictly limited potential in public debate. It often casts the Christian apologist as boring, pedantic, and petty against the openness of the New Ager.

For the argument is taking place not in university seminar rooms, between pipe-smoking academics swapping stories about Kant and Hegel, but in the public arena—on television talk shows, in popular magazines, and in supermarket checkout lines. And the vast majority of the public is not interested in conceptual sophistication and finely honed technical arguments. It is interested in quickly grasped and easily understood points. And above all, it is interested in the bottom line: "What's in it for me?"

But we do not need to throw away Christianity's claims to truth in the light of this cultural development. We just need to realize that it's now bad tactics to major on the truth question if it makes people think we are intellectual fascists. The situation demands that we rediscover the *attractiveness* of the gospel. That doesn't mean we sideline the truth of the gospel as if it doesn't matter. Rather, that means we finally have to face up to the fact that if we are going to get a hearing in today's culture, we need to be able to show that Christianity has something relevant and attractive to offer. The bonus is that this is securely grounded in God's self-revelation, not cooked up yesterday in an effort to get a hearing in the marketplace.

We may commend the attractiveness of Christianity—being secure in the knowledge of its truth. The attractiveness of a belief is too often inversely proportional to its truth. The Christian, in enthusing about the attractiveness of the gospel and its enormous potential to transform human life, can be assured that the gospel rests on the bedrock of revealed truth and that acceptance of the gospel glorifies God as well as transforms human life.

I am not in any way suggesting that we alter the gospel to make it more attractive. That is the supreme error of liberalism—the restatement of the gospel in terms that will prove to be easily acceptable to modern culture without due regard to the violence done to the gospel itself in consequence. The issue is that of ensuring that the gospel is preached faithfully for all it is worth without any misrepresentations or misunderstandings, which are the cause of offense to so many.

As Kenneth S. Kantzer puts it:

> We are certainly not interested in shaping evangelical Christianity, and certainly not biblical Christianity, into a form that will prove palatable to the sinful hearts and minds of all humans. We are not trying to remove the "offense of the cross." That offense is an inherent part of biblical and evangelical identity. It would be an irresponsible denial of our deepest faith to remove it. Yet we are deeply concerned also to remove false obstacles to the gospel. We do not want anyone to reject a perversion or misunderstanding of the gospel.[1]

Responsible evangelism, by seeking to remain faithful to the gospel, ensures that its proper and inherent attraction—rather than something spurious and fabricated—is presented to the world. We do not need to *make* the gospel attractive by dressing it up in modern clothes. The gospel already *is* attractive. It is up to us to bring out this attraction as clearly as possible, grounded in the situation of people we talk to. Above all, we need to take the trouble to relate the message to its audience, making sure that it scratches where people itch.

David F. Wells, one of evangelicalism's most significant and respected contemporary exponents, comments thus on the task facing responsible evangelical theology:

It is the task of theology, then, to discover what God has said in and through Scripture and to clothe that in a conceptuality which is native to our own age. Scripture, at its *terminus a quo*, needs to be de-contextualized in order to grasp its trans-cultural content, and it needs to be re-contextualized in order that its content may be meshed with the cognitive assumptions and social patterns of our own time.[2]

The approach adopted is classic: identify what Scripture is saying, and apply it to new contexts. As the context changes, there is a need to ensure that the gospel proclamation is related to that context. And that means making sure we do not use sermon illustrations designed to work in working-class London of the nineteenth century to congregations of upwardly mobile professionals in southern California on the eve of the twenty-first century.

Another way of putting this same vital point was developed by the German philosopher Martin Heidegger. He spoke of a "fusion of horizons," meaning that there was a need to bridge the horizon of the New Testament with that of our culture. If this bridging is not done, they will not connect up. Apologists and evangelists are thus bridge builders, who allow the dynamism of the New Testament to be channeled into our culture.

All of this points to the simple fact that our presentation of the gospel proclamation today must be *receptor oriented* (to lapse into jargon for a moment). In other words, it must be addressed to individual needs and opportunities. In this chapter, we shall be exploring this matter in some detail.

The Art of Building Bridges

The image of building bridges has been carefully chosen. It suggests a number of ideas, each of which is helpful to the task of apologetics.

First, it suggests the idea of bridging a chasm or gulf. It evokes the image of towns and communities that had previously been isolated from each other but are now connected up. A link has been established. Apologetics aims to build bridges between the Christian faith and the broader culture. It aims to make connections between the gospel and human experience—experience such as hopes, fears, and joys. The task of apologetics is to show how the Christian faith is able to make sense of human experience.

Second, the image of building bridges suggests more than establishing contact; it points to individuals being able to cross a gulf, passing from unbelief or indifference to faith. Building bridges is about establishing contact with the non-Christian world, understanding it, and eventually providing a way in which people can cross to faith.

This might seem to suggest, however, that the task of building bridges is something we have to do—starting from nothing. That would be an enormous task! However, the truth of the matter is much more exciting. God has already begun to build bridges for us. There are points of contact for the Christian faith already in the world and in human culture. It is up to us to notice them and make the most of them.

What sort of points of contact? And how do they arise? The Christian doctrine of creation declares that God made humanity in His image and likeness. We are made with an inbuilt ability to relate to God. Sin is fundamentally to do with the disruption of this relationship. As a result, we experience a sense of emptiness, which reflects an absence of God. As Blaise Pascal put it, there is a "God-shaped gap" within us—a gap that really exists and that nothing except the living God Himself can fill. We have all watched children playing with a toy that involves placing pegs into holes. Only the square peg fits the square hole. And only God will fit this God-shaped gap.

This well-documented feeling of dissatisfaction is one of the most important points of contact for the gospel proclamation. In the first place, that proclamation interprets this vague and un-shaped feeling as a longing for God. And in the second, it offers to fulfill it. There is a sense of divine dissatisfaction—not dissatis-faction with God, but dissatisfaction with all that is not God—which arises from God and which ultimately leads to God. This sense of emptiness resonates throughout much secular literature. The Christian faith is able to relate to this experience, to interpret it and, finally, to transform it.

In the first chapter of this book, we pointed out the impor-tance of discovering and respecting individual needs. Good apolo-getics is person based. It rests on knowing the needs, concerns, and worries of individual people, and showing how the Christian gospel interlocks with these needs and anxieties.

Good apologetics rests on two premises: (1) that you know something about your friends, and (2) that you know something about Christianity. The first poses relatively few problems for any-one; the second may, in some cases, cause one or two difficulties. Far too many Christians know too little about Christianity! Both your friends and your Christian faith matter profoundly. Take time to get to know them better.

One of the most exciting consequences of the new emphasis on evangelism within the churches is that it has encouraged Christians to find out more about their faith. It is much easier to explain something if you have thought about it yourself. A solid understanding of Christianity can bring new quality and depth to your discussions with your friends. But there is a major fringe benefit.

I gave a lecture on making sense of the Cross to a church group in Geneva, Switzerland. I pointed out how some of the ideas I was exploring would enable members of the audience to explain Christianity far more effectively to their friends. Someone came up to me afterward. "I don't know whether what you told us will help me evangelize folks," he told me. "But it sure helped me to see things clearer!" One of the spin-offs of taking trouble to get to know more about Christianity is that our own faith is enriched and deepened as a result. Paradoxically, evangelism doesn't just bring people to faith—it deepens the faith of those who already believe. It is a two-edged sword.

Let's look at an example to bring out this point—such as the meaning of the Cross, the topic of my lectures in Switzerland just mentioned. What is the cross of Christ all about? What did Christ achieve by dying on the cross? A basic understanding of the benefits of Christ is of enormous assistance in trying to build bridges between the Christian faith and the lives and experiences of ordinary people.

The death of Christ on the cross is enormously rich in its meaning and includes the following five elements. Each of them will have a particular attraction to different people. It is up to us to ensure that the full attraction and wonder of the gospel proclamation are identified in the case of the person or persons to whom we are speaking. In what follows, we shall try to identify the key elements of an understanding of the Cross and ground it in some of the concerns of human life.

1. *Losers turned winners.* Christ has gained a victory over sin, death, and evil through His cross and resurrection. Through faith, believers may share in that victory and claim it as their own. Many people are deeply anxious about death and find the thought of it unbearable. Christianity is able to interlock with this human feeling and relate directly to it. The New Testament stresses that Christ died so that we might be liberated from the fear of death (see Heb. 2:14–15). Socrates may have taught us to die with dignity. Jesus Christ makes it possible for us to die in hope.

2. *Forgiveness and more—righteousness.* Through His obedience on the cross, Christ has obtained forgiveness and pardon for sinners. Those who are guilty can be washed clean of their sin and be justified in the sight of God. They are acquitted of punishment and given the status of being righteous before God. Someone

who is conscious of a deep sense of moral guilt, which prevents her from drawing near to God, will find the proclamation of forgiveness deeply attractive and meaningful. Knowing that her sins really have been forgiven could transform her life.

3. *Coming home to God.* As sinners, we are alienated from God. God was in Christ reconciling the world to Himself as He made a new relationship possible and available. Just as an alienated man and woman can draw together again through forgiveness and reconciliation, so we who are far from God can draw close to Him through the death of Christ.

Many people have a sense of being far from God. Christianity declares that God has drawn close to them and offers them the hand of friendship. Again, many people are conscious of having lapsed from a faith they once possessed. They wonder if they could ever come back to that faith. Would God have them back? The parable of the prodigal son (see Luke 15:11–32) makes it abundantly clear that God delights in the return of those who have sojourned in the far country—wherever that may have been, and for however long it lasted. Like the waiting father, God is eagerly anticipating the return of His wandering children A celebratory feast awaits them!

4. *True liberty.* People who are imprisoned by the oppressive forces of evil, sin, and the fear of death can be liberated by the gospel of the cross of Christ. Just as Christ broke free from the prison of death, so believers can, by faith, break free from the bonds of sin and come to life in all its fullness. A surprisingly large number of people sense that they are trapped in their situations—trapped by their own powerlessness, their enslavement to secret sins or forces beyond their control. The cross and resurrection of Christ offer the hope of liberation, for both individuals and peoples—spiritual and political freedom.

The exploration of these themes can be profoundly helpful. There have been many remarkable spin-offs of evangelistic ministry in the United States and the Far East. One of them is that some people hooked on narcotics find they can finally kick the habit after conversion to Christianity, especially in its more charismatic forms. *Jesus spells freedom!* is no rhetoric but a neat summary of the impact of the death and resurrection of Jesus Christ on human life.

5. *Healing and wholeness.* People who are wounded because of sin can be made whole again through the ministrations of the wounded Physician of Calvary. Through His cross and resurrection, Christ is able to bind up our wounds and heal us, restoring us to wholeness and spiritual health. Opponents of Christianity often point out how the churches attract many of the weaker and more hopeless members of society. And so they do. And why? Because these people appreciate that Christianity has something to offer them—something that nobody else seems able to offer. Many Christian writers have compared the church to a hospital —a group of people who need healing and are finding it in the midst of a loving and caring community.

Notice carefully that this approach does not reduce the word of the Cross to a single idea. Instead, it aims to identify the different ideas and images already in the gospel message. One or more of them may prove to be of decisive importance or attractiveness to someone who is hearing the gospel for the first time. But that does not mean the message of the Cross has been *reduced* to that theme. That means we take trouble to find out what our resources are so that we can connect up as effectively as possible with the needs of the individuals to whom we are ministering.

Although every aspect of the message of the Cross is relevant to the human situation in general, individual human beings will have different specific needs. The gospel must be *particularized* in terms of the individual situations. We need to be able to point out how the Christian faith relates to their situations. The theme of victory over the fear of death may well be profoundly important to one person. That of healing may be directly relevant to another. In trying to explain the attractiveness of Christianity to someone, we need to ask the following question: What aspect of the Christian faith would be of special relevance to this person? Asking that question forces us to attempt to understand both the person and the resources the gospel has to offer.

So how does this work out? Let's suppose that you are talking to a friend. Perhaps you have just been to a colleague's funeral together or have been discussing how widespread AIDS has become. As you talk, you realize that she is frightened of dying. It would be entirely appropriate for you to explain why death doesn't frighten you as much as it once did. You would not be imposing on your friend or exploiting her any more than if you were to offer her an analgesic for a headache or tell her about a book you enjoyed reading recently.

You would explain how your faith enabled you to cope with the thought of death. You don't need to ask her to share your faith or put her under any pressure to do so. In effect, you are telling her something about yourself and something about Christianity at one and the same time. (In our secular culture, surprisingly few people know why Christians celebrate Easter; this conversation would thus be educationally useful!) By picking up the great theme of resurrection and hope, you are helping her to understand more about Christianity. The long-term outcome may be that she will decide to make this faith her own.

Does that mean *reducing* the gospel to the hope of eternal life? No. It recognizes that as a point of contact for the gospel for this person.

The component of the message of the Cross that addresses this fear of death is like the thin end of a wedge—it secures a point of entry. It is an emphasis within the message, not reduction of the message to a single point. It is but a starting point—a highly relevant starting point, to be sure. It is a Trojan horse, which enters the camp of unbelief, before throwing open its gates to the full resources of the gospel. The rest can, and will, follow in its wake.

The rest of the Christian faith remains to be experienced by that person. She has discovered it in part; its fullness will gradually break in on her in the glorious process of exploration that attends good Christian discipline. The aspect of the gospel that attracts someone to faith is often overshadowed in later Christian life as another aspect of the gospel comes to be understood and its attraction appreciated fully. You've got to start somewhere; it's up to you to work out where the best starting point for your friends might be.

We need to ensure that the relevance and power of the gospel for each specific situation are fully brought out. We cannot leave the gospel proclamation unfocused and generalized on a kind of "to whom it may concern" basis. The gospel concerns individual people and situations; our job is to make the connections, grounding the gospel in the specifics and particularities of those we talk to. We must be prepared to identify the attraction of the gospel for others and make its attraction for us visible in our lives.

The worshiping church community is, and ought to be, one of the most important forums of evangelism as Christians express, in music and praise, their love of and delight in their faith. As many surveys demonstrate, most people do not come to faith through logical arguments or rational proofs for faith. They are drawn because of the obvious attraction of the gospel for people they love and a deep-rooted feeling that they themselves lack something significant. Apologetics has to learn to take these considerations into account. Otherwise, it will get nowhere—fast.

But how can we do this? How can we make sure that we do justice to our faith? We owe it to ourselves and to God to explain the Christian faith for all it's worth. The following four suggestions may well prove useful.

1. *Read some books.* The Bibliography section at the end of this book identifies books that are likely to be helpful as you try to follow through some ideas and issues. But books are not of use just to you. You can lend them—perhaps even give them—to your friends in the hope that they may prove helpful.

2. *Listen to sermons* on key issues of relevance to apologetics and evangelism. If your local pastors don't preach on these themes, ask them to do so. It is an area of major importance to the future of the Christian church, and pastors are under an obligation to be of assistance to the people under their care. They can always invite visiting preachers. If all else fails, use the tape li braries of churches with long-standing preaching ministries in these areas. Most big cities have churches where the regular preaching diet includes coverage of these key issues.

3. *Join study groups.* Many local churches set up study groups that provide a forum for discussion of these issues. Call your church office for details. If there isn't one, think about establishing one, perhaps with the assistance and guidance of some friends. You can discuss books or other materials of relevance to these issues. You can describe your experiences of trying to share the Christian faith in the everyday world. You can use existing study material, whether in the form of books, audiocassettes, or videos.

4. *Attend conferences* on these themes. Many centers throughout the Western world offer regular courses, study days, or summer schools on the themes of this book. Ask to be put on their mailing lists. Many Christian seminaries have extension courses for the benefit of those wishing to increase their understanding of Christianity while holding down a full-time job. Write for details. And remember that attending these courses will do far more than educate you. You will meet other like-minded people, hear the top people in the field speaking on the issues of the moment, and have the chance to ask questions and raise your special concerns in plenary sessions or workshops.

Becoming a Postmodern Culture Watcher

If you want to build bridges to any culture, you need to be an observer of it. That means being inside it. As the history of

Christian missions makes clear, the best apologist to a culture is someone who belongs to that culture, not someone imported into it.

Most Westerners, whether they are aware of it or not, are part of a postmodern culture. They may not agree with the general outlook of that culture, but they cannot avoid the fact that they are immersed in it and have to proclaim the gospel within it. To come to terms with this fact is not in any way to declare that the ideas of postmodernism are correct or true; in fact, they are rather shallow and unconvincing and can easily be shown to be so. But our immediate task is not to overturn a culture; it is to gain a favorable hearing for the gospel within that culture.

So what is *postmodernism*? The term is notoriously vague, and it means all kinds of different things to different people. The word was first used in the 1930s by Frederico de Onis to refer to a new approach to architecture that reacted against modernism. Neither the approach nor the term really caught on. The term was used again in the 1960s by stylish New Yorkers, that time to refer to an artistic movement focusing on common culture rather than aiming to get noticed by academics and museums. By the 1970s, the term had come to mean an eclectic style of architecture in which a building would be designed in such a way as to highlight the diversity of its styles and textures. This idea of eclecticism has remained characteristic of the movement since then. Whereas modernism, basing itself on the ideas of the Enlightenment, argued that a universally valid set of truths could be uncovered by human reason, postmodernism argues that human creativity and individuality really matter. Truth is individual, personal, and eclectic, and it can be seen from an infinite variety of perspectives.

The image of shopping is perhaps the most helpful way of making sense of the postmodern outlook. The postmodern approach to life is rather like a shopping mall in which the individual postmodernist will select items she or he likes and build them into the worldview. It does not matter what the origins may be, or that different ideas are drawn from mutually exclusive origins. Just as a hostess might prepare a meal of Native American, Thai, Cantonese, and Vietnamese dishes, so the postmodern worldview is happily composed of Christian, Buddhist, Confucian, and Native American ideas, mixed together according to the individual's personal taste. The very diversity of the mixture is, in the postmodernist view, its crowning glory.

So how do we respond to this situation? Being a culture watcher is useful in developing ways of presenting the gospel that will either avoid cultural no-go zones or maximize the potential of fault lines. The following points are meaningful in a postmodern context.

First, observing a culture closely will allow you to identify its fault lines. Most cultures are vulnerable at points. They are like vast land masses held together by a mixture of inertia and temporary stability. But cracks can easily open up, sending shock waves throughout the culture. Fault lines are there in modern culture, just as the San Andreas fault is a simple fact of life for anyone living in western California. They represent points at which a culture is aware that it is based on ideas and values that cannot be sustained. And these fault lines represent vital weak points at which a hearing may be gained for the gospel.

What sort of fault lines? Modern Western culture offers many examples, which are presented in different ways by TV programs, movies, and literature. The suppression and sanitization of death are excellent examples. Hospitals prefer to speak of "negative patient care outcome" rather than openly state that a patient has died. Western culture prefers to deny the inevitability of death and avoids open discussion of it. What does this point to? It points to a culture profoundly uneasy about death because of the threat it poses to values and ideas. Much of modern Western culture is founded on the frankly untenable assumption that people are nice, really, and that they all want to get along together. It therefore finds it very difficult to cope with mindless and gratuitous violence, vicious oppression, and ruthless exploitation because they so blatantly contradict this modern optimistic myth.

These fault lines are present, in different ways and to different extents, and can easily become the subject of conversations that will allow the inherent realism of the gospel to be appreciated. The gospel is about the hope of eternal life in the face of death; it is about the reality of sin, and the joy of forgiveness and renewal. We are increasingly living in a runaway world, which cannot control its own development and which cannot cope with this insight.

Second, being a culture watcher allows insights into how best to contextualize the gospel. For example, our postmodern culture is image oriented—a phenomenon that Jacques Ellul brilliantly characterized in the phrase "the humiliation of the word." That is, we must give consideration to developing image-based approaches to apologetics and evangelism instead of relying totally on traditional word-based approaches. (In making this point, I am not for one moment suggesting that Christianity should abandon or modify its emphasis on Scripture and preaching! I am making the point that to reach out to people who are currently outside the church, it is necessary to be sensitive to their situation. It is the gospel that is to be proclaimed, not the superiority of the cultural niche of its preacher.)

Third, there is a new interest in spirituality and the supernatural within postmodernism. With the collapse of the Enlightenment, belief in the supernatural is back on the cultural agenda in a big way. "In the twilight of the gods, men came forth like giants. In the twilight of the men, all the gods came back again," declared Rob Draper.

Yet this interest in spirituality is not institution oriented. The church does not figure in the postmodern rediscovery of the supernatural and the spiritual. So be careful! Your task is to commend the supernatural and spiritual richness of the gospel, not to sell the church as an institution. The characteristic evangelical emphasis on the gospel, rather than the church, is of major importance in this context. The importance of vibrant worship, built on a strong sense of the transcendence of God and the immanence of our experience of the Holy Spirit, is a powerful evangelistic tool.

Fourth, postmodernism does not like the idea of a metanarrative—that is, a universally valid account of all reality. But it is very open to personal narratives—that is, the narratives that give meaning to individual lives. So be prepared to tell your story—the story of how you became a Christian and all that it means to you.

Fifth, postmodernism is strongly pluralist. You will have problems trying to persuade postmodernists that Christianity is the *only* serious option. But you can persuade them that it is a very attractive option. Once they become interested and start to take things farther, you will be in a much stronger position to talk about the uniqueness of the Christian gospel and the claims of Jesus Christ.

The ways in which an orthodox Christian gospel can be made more relevant to modern society are illustrated by a series of experiments in the Western world, which have sought to break down the acceptability barrier of the gospel by eliminating all alienating factors not essential to the gospel itself. For example, a well-established fact is that many people are initially alienated from Christianity by the strangeness of traditional Christian worship. The attractiveness of Christian ideas must not be compromised by cultural turnoffs. Why turn people off Christianity with Tudor church music, an eighteenth-century liturgy, or pastors dressed in the style of seventeenth-century New England? For some inside the churches, they are important and precious symbols of historical continuity; for most outside the church, they are evidence of an outdated and irrelevant gospel. And so the gospel is rejected or spurned because of the cultural unacceptability of nonessential, perhaps even marginal, aspects of Christian worship.

Willow Creek Community Church has pioneered an approach that breaks down these incidental barriers. The church auditorium has none of the traditional ecclesiastical trappings. There are no pulpit, no organ, no hymnals, and no traditional clergy vestments. Yet the gospel is proclaimed effectively. National religious magazine *Guideposts* named Willow Creek 1989 Church of the Year for "presenting timeless truth in a contemporary way." This approach has its critics and its detractors. The Easter 1990 Sunday supplement of *USA Today* described Willow Creek as "McChurch," implying it was the religious equivalent of fast-food chain McDonald's. But there is no doubt that this church, located in Chicago, and an increasing number of imitators throughout the Western world are getting a hearing for the gospel among those who would regard a traditional church setting as a no-go zone. Culture watching allows us to develop new approaches of this kind that aim to fuse the horizons of gospel and its audience, and build effective bridges to them.

In the next two chapters, our attention shifts to specific groups of people to whom bridges need to be built.

Chapter 4

Building Bridges to . . .

Alister McGrath

As we have just seen, good apologetics is about relating the gospel to specific needs and situations. This chapter aims to provide some guidance about how to relate the gospel to a series of groups of people. Each section is more a series of hints than an exhaustive treatment of the subject in question.

Apathetic Materialists

Apathy rules! Or so it seems as we cast our eyes over modern Western society where any interest in the spiritual side of life is overshadowed, if not eclipsed, by a preoccupation with material things. But a deep sense of unease has descended on many hitherto apathetic materialists, who have up to now been cushioned from some of the harsher facts of life through the economic prosperity and "feel good factor" of the 1980s. The belief that materialism satisfies now seems to many to be a publicly discredited myth. Marxism, perhaps the only worldview to actively promote a purely materialist worldview, has died in front of our eyes. Economic recession has led many to question whether anyone can put faith in material prosperity. The easygoing days of the late 1980s seem very far away at the moment.

And in the midst of this loss of faith in materialism, Christians can gain a renewed hearing for the gospel. There are still many apathetic materialists around us, but there are also many disenchanted materialists surveying the wreckage of careers and visions and wondering if they could find something more satisfying and enduring. Materialism is deeply vulnerable at the moment— a window of opportunity that those concerned for renewal must make the most of.

It is perhaps no accident that periods of growth in the church often seem to be linked with economic decline. The proclamation of the gospel today meets with a sympathy that would have been unimaginable at the height of the economic boom of less than a decade ago. Is it an accident that the Decade of Evangelism coincides with a period of economic depression? Or may we see a hand of God's good providence, preparing the hearts and minds of hitherto apathetic materialists to hear the good news of the gospel? Or to learn of the Bread of Life, which endures and satisfies when material prosperity and business confidence seem to be failing?

In what follows, I want to identify one point of contact through which Christians can gain a sympathetic hearing for the gospel. This is a sense of emptiness or dissatisfaction. There are many others, such as an awareness of mortality in the face of death or a deep sense of alienation. The point of contact that I wish to explore here will illustrate the kind of openings available to Christians in talking to those who are, to all outward appearances, content with a materialist standpoint. But I use that phrase "to all outward appearances" advisedly. Many apathetic materialists are deeply unhappy, yet will not admit to this for fear of losing face. Beneath an apathetic or contented facade, there may lie hidden a very miserable and discontented person who is looking for something in life that will satisfy him or her.

Awareness of such a sense of emptiness resonates throughout secular culture. One thinks of Boris Becker, the noted tennis player, who came close to taking his own life through being overwhelmed by this sense of hopelessness and emptiness. Even though he was enormously successful, something was missing. He said, "I had won Wimbledon twice before, once as the youngest player. I was rich. I had all the material possessions I needed: money, cars, women, everything. . . . I know that this is a cliché. It's the old song of the movie and pop stars who commit suicide. They have everything, and yet they are so unhappy. . . . I had no inner peace." Or one thinks of Jack Higgins, a highly successful thriller writer at the top of his profession, author of bestselling novels such as *The Eagle Has Landed*. He is reported to have been asked what he now knew that he would liked to have known when he was a boy. In a newspaper interview, he said: "That when you get to the top, there's nothing there."

Becker and Higgins are excellent witnesses from the world of secular culture to this vital point of contact with even the most hardened apathetic materialists. Most people are aware that something is missing from their lives, even if they may not be able to put a name to it. They may not be able to do anything about it. But the Christian gospel is able to interpret this sense of longing, this feeling of unfulfillment, as an awareness of the absence of God and thus to prepare the way for its fulfillment. Once we realize that we are incomplete, that we lack something, we begin to wonder if that spiritual emptiness could be filled.

This kind of feeling underlies the famous words of Augustine of Hippo, an early Christian writer: "You have made us for yourself, and our hearts are restless until they rest in you." The Christian doctrines of creation and redemption combine to interpret this sense of dissatisfaction and lack of fulfillment as a loss—a loss of fellowship with God—that can be restored. They yield a picture of a broken human nature, which still possesses an ability to be aware of its loss and to hope that it might be restored. Here is a natural point of contact for the gospel, grounded in the frustration of human nature to satisfy itself by its own devices.

This sense of dissatisfaction is explored further by one of the twentieth century's finest apologists, C. S. Lewis. Lewis was an Oxford don who discovered Christianity (much to his surprise!) toward the middle of his life and devoted the rest of it to writing and speaking about the coherence and credibility of faith. Although Lewis is best known for his *Narnia* books, such as *The Lion, The Witch, and the Wardrobe*, he was also one of the most widely read and respected apologists of the modern period. In his sermon, "The Weight of Glory," Lewis wrote of "a desire which no natural happiness will satisfy, . . . a desire, still wandering and uncertain of its object and still largely unable to see that object in the direction where it really lies."

Lewis pointed out that there is something self-defeating about human desire. Why? Because when we achieve the things that we long for, they somehow seem to leave us unsatisfied. The paradox of hedonism—the fact that pleasure cannot satisfy so that the pursuit of pleasure is ultimately self-defeating—is a good example of this curious phenomenon. Even in our contentment, we feel the need for something that is missing, but whose absence seems only too real. There is a "divine dissatisfaction" within human experience. This naturally prompts us to ask whether anything may satisfy the human quest to fulfill the desires of the human heart.

Lewis declared that there is. Hunger, he suggested, is an excellent example of a human sensation that corresponds to a real physical need. This need points to the existence of food by which it may be met. Any human longing, he argued, points to a genuine human need, which in turn points to a real object corresponding to that need. And so, Lewis stated, it is reasonable to suggest that the deep human sense of infinite yearning that cannot be satisfied by any physical or finite object or person must point to a real human need that can, in some way, be met. Lewis argued that this sense of longing points to its origin and its fulfillment in God Himself.

In all that, Lewis echoed a great theme of traditional Christian thinking about the origin and goal of human nature. We are made by God, and we experience a deep sense of longing for Him, which only He can satisfy. Here, then, is a God-given point of entry for the gospel. We can talk to people about our faith, knowing that beneath the confident or apathetic exterior of our materialist neighbors there may well lurk a deeply unhappy person, who is looking for a pearl of great price, for the Bread of Life—that is, for something that is worth having and that satisfies. So let us commend the deep sense of satisfaction and fulfillment that the gospel brings to our lives in the knowledge that some, overhearing our comments, will begin to consider the claims of the Savior who is able to bring such richness and joy to this poor and hope-starved world.

University and High School Students

College students are a prime category of people to whom bridges need to be built. The great nineteenth-century Cambridge preacher Charles Simeon knew that. Whenever an undergraduate came into his church, he would say to himself: "There's another six hundred people!" In terms of their future influence, they can be of immense importance. Today's college student is tomorrow's social, political, and religious leader. Students are also often open to considering the Christian faith at this stage in their lives. All of us engaged in student ministry know how exciting and demanding it can be.

So how do we build bridges to such students? I write as one who discovered Christianity as a student. Maybe my experience can be helpful to others. I went to Oxford University in 1971 as a committed atheist. Like many young people of the time, I had been deeply influenced by Marxism, and I had rejected Christianity as the "opiate of the people." I was capable of standing on my own two feet. I didn't need a crutch to support me. In any case, Christianity was just a means of delaying the revolution. Such views were fashionable in those days. But if I were being entirely honest, I think I would have to admit that I had rejected a caricature of Christianity rather than the real thing.

On arriving at Oxford, I met some Christian students. Like many people of my age (I was eighteen), I was determined to keep an open mind about things. I decided to give Christianity another chance. And gradually, I noticed things. I noticed that my Christian friends had a quality of life that I envied. I also went to some Christian meetings and discovered that Christianity did not seem to say the things I thought it did. In fact, it said a lot of things that made sense. I came to the point where I decided that I wanted to accept Christianity and make it my own.

That's not a very interesting story (although it matters a lot to me!). Nevertheless, it illustrates some noteworthy points. First, many college students have open minds. They may well have rejected Christianity in their youth. Increasingly, however, social trends mean that many young people know nothing about Christianity at all. As a result, they have not been disillusioned by it or prejudiced against it as a result of overenthusiastic Christian schooling (how many people have been turned off Christianity for life by compulsory school chapel?). Nor have they reacted against Christianity as part of the adolescent program of rebelling against parental authority.

Once, Christianity represented the Establishment against which it was "proper" to rebel. To reject parental authority was to reject the Christian faith. Now, that same gospel is often seen as an exciting new cause, something to discover as part of growing up independent of parental constraints. I've met many American college students who have become Christians, whose parents were baby boomer hippies. While working among students in Australia, I was deeply impressed by the number of students who were the first Christians in their families in living memory; they had come in from the cold entirely on their own, without any parental support or influence.

So the first point is simple. Explaining what Christianity is all about can be news to many young people. We cannot take it for granted that they have rejected Christianity; they may not even know what it is. One of the best forms of apologetics is the clear and patient explanation of Christianity and its attractions. Very often, there is no need to defend the Christian faith—there are no prejudices to defend it against! The good news is indeed *news* to many young people in our increasingly secular Western cultures.

A second point concerns the public image of Christianity in schools and colleges. Students are often concerned about their public image—about how they are perceived by their fellow students. To be a Christian is often to be seen as a freak. In part, this image is fostered and nourished by people in positions of authority within the educational establishment. Let me explain what I have in mind.

I grew up during the 1960s. It was a fascinating time to be young. It seemed as if a new age were about to dawn. In the United States, the civil rights movement blossomed, there were mass protests against the Vietnam War, and tens of thousands packed into the tiny town of Woodstock to hear the music of the coming generation. In Paris, students rioted, protesting against the Establishment. Something new and irresistible seemed about to happen. And it was generally agreed that the future held no place for religion. John Lennon asked us to imagine a "world without religion"—a sort of paradise on earth.

In the end, it all came to nothing. Religion has made a powerful comeback, and it is widely recognized as one of the most potent factors in modern international politics. But many who grew up in the 1960s cherished the vision of a world without religion. *And many of them are today in senior positions in high schools and universities.* The result? High school and university students are often put under the authority of men and women who have a deep-rooted hostility toward any religion.

One recent survey suggested that 30 percent of American college professors had no religious commitment of any kind. Students are vulnerable. They need help and support if their faith is to survive in such a negative environment. Religion is all too often presented to them as something outdated and discredited. And that puts Christian students on the defensive—against their teachers and against their peers. I have seen the same pattern in the problems faced by university students in the United States and Australia, by high school students in the United Kingdom, and by international school students in Switzerland. It is tough being a Christian on campus.

Yet much can be done. For example, students are often reassured when they see that intelligent and approachable people can be Christians as well. The work of national and international student Christian organizations—such as Campus Crusade, the Inter-Varsity Fellowship (IVF) in North America, the University and Colleges Christian Fellowship (UCCF) in the United Kingdom, the Australian Fellowship of Evangelical Students (AFES)—is vital. The organizations encourage students, provide fellowship for them, and above all set before them credible and encouraging role models—that is, people with high credibility in student circles, who have no hesitation in affirming and proclaiming their faith. The reinforcement of a positive image for Christianity in high schools and universities is of central importance apologetically.

A third point also concerns the public image of Christianity. Many non-Christians still think that, for example, Christian worship is all about little old ladies listening to an old man dressed in black speaking old-fashioned English, littered with *Thous* and

Thees, to the accompaniment of deadly dull sixteenth-century music. That remains the popular stereotype of Christian praise! Could anything be more alienating to young people? This perception can easily be changed by inviting such skeptics to a service at a lively local church catering especially to young people. Their prejudices may well be swept away in the first blast of rock music harnessed to the proclamation of the good news of Jesus Christ.

A fourth point relates to the specific needs of young people. Western society is fragmenting, often causing considerable emotional damage to college students from broken homes with permanently absent fathers. A powerful bridge that can be built to college students is friendship. This fact will appall some people. "Surely apologetics is all about arguments!" some will protest. Arguments have their proper place. However, one of the most effective arguments for a loving God is not philosophizing about the problem of suffering; it is showing love, care, and compassion to others. Young people need to be loved, accepted, and cared for. And in our behaving in that way toward them, we are opening a window through which the love of God may be seen.

In helping college students to understand and appreciate the Christian faith, you need to bear in mind two anxieties that trouble some of them. First, some students worry about the long-term future of Christianity. They are young; they want to be sure that they are committing themselves to something that will still be around and still be relevant in their old age. That is understandable. After all, many of my student contemporaries in the 1970s were Marxists. I haven't met one of them since then who retains that worldview. Might not Christianity go the same way?

Several things need to be said here. Marxism is a human invention, a political philosophy reflecting the social situation in Germany of the 1830s. No wonder it has proved utterly incapable of relating to the global situation of the 1990s! Christianity is a universal faith, dealing with the universal human predicament of sin and mortality. But more than that, Christianity is a response to a loving and living God. As Paul reminded the Christians at Corinth (see 1 Cor. 2:1–5), their faith rested not on human wisdom but on the power of God. We are dealing not with some throwaway package but with something that is here until kingdom come! And this is where older Christians have a real role to play. They are able to demonstrate that Christianity has long-term potential by virtue of their being—and continuing to be!—Christians.

The second difficulty concerns saving face. Although it is probably an issue for many people thinking about becoming Christians, it is especially acute for college students. Their public image matters to them. Becoming a Christian often results in public humiliation. So how can we be of use here? A major contribution to solving this problem has been provided by the Harvard Negotiation Project. Based at Harvard University and developed by leading academics such as Roger Fisher, Willison Professor of Law, this project has concentrated on ways of resolving difficulties without losing face or compromising personal integrity. Here are the basic principles that should be applied: (1) separate the problem from the people, and (2) make it easy for them to change their minds.

1. Separate the Problem from the People

Why do people get locked into their situations in an argument? I've lost count of situations in which people get locked into their belief system. They feel that their personal integrity totally depends on never admitting that they are wrong. Becoming a Christian amounts to admitting that they are wrong—which amounts to a shocking loss of face. The basic strategy is as simple as it is effective: separate the people from the ideas. Help the people to see that there is no necessary connection between personal identities and the ideas they hold at the moment.

Does this mean that we are using unacceptable means of explaining the gospel? Are we using highly pressurized sales methods to put people under an obligation to accept the gospel? Certainly not. It means taking the trouble to work out why people have difficulties in accepting the gospel. Anyway, we aren't trying to sell anything; we're trying to give something away.

2. Make It Easy for Them to Change Their Minds

People find it difficult to change their minds if they are made to feel it is a win-or-lose situation. Bad apologetics creates the impression that changing your mind is equivalent to losing an argument. And nobody likes losing arguments—especially in public.

Roger Fisher and William Ury, explaining how the principles of the Harvard Negotiation Project may be applied, make this point as follows in their study, "Getting to Yes":

> Often in a negotiation people will continue to hold out not because the proposal on the table is inherently unacceptable, but simply because they want to avoid the feeling or the appearance of backing down to the other side. If the substance can be phrased or conceptualized differently so that it seems a fair outcome, they will then accept it. . . . Face-saving involves reconciling an agreement with principle and with the self-image of the negotiators. Its importance should not be underestimated.

So how can this basic principle be applied? Through two major strategies. First, do not force your conversation partner to enter into a win-or-lose situation. Do not present Christianity as being right (which immediately implies that your conversation partner is wrong and thus provokes a confrontation). Instead, present Christianity as being attractive, and explain why. Christianity gives you hope in the face of death, a sense of peace in the presence of God, a new perception of personal dignity, and a revitalized sense of purpose (to name but a few of the many attractions of the gospel).

What perception does this create for your dialogue partner? That you are concerned to offer him something that you have found valuable and exciting. You are not telling him that he is wrong; you are offering him something of value. The negative impression you avoid creating is that of defeating your colleague in an argument. The positive impression you succeed in creating is that of caring for your colleague. And is this not one of the fundamental impulses underlying all good apologetics—a sense of love and compassion for our friends?

Second, use yourself as an example of someone whose mind has changed. Clearly, this approach depends upon your having once been a non-Christian and subsequently changing your mind. If that is the case, you can help whomever you are talking with to see that personal identity and ideas are separable. You could say something like this: "I used to think that Christianity was something of an irrelevance. But I had the courage to change my mind. And I'm glad I did." Acknowledge the problem, indicate that facing and resolving it is a matter of courage, and bring home that the outcome of that decision was positive. The instinct to save face is thus outweighed by the greater human instinct—to do something courageous that is seen to be courageous. Little things often matter a lot in apologetics; too often, they get overlooked.

Wounded Religionists

There is nothing like a negative experience of religion to keep agnosticism in business. I had very negative experiences of Christianity from my school days at a very religious boarding school in Northern Ireland. By the end of my time there, I was a convinced atheist. Yet as I look back on those days, it seems to me that my youthful atheism was not actually the result of any real intellectual difficulties with Christianity. I was simply nauseated with compulsory chapel services. I was looking for faith; I was forced to accept religion. It was hardly surprising that I rejected it!

Many people are outside the churches precisely because they had such bad experiences inside them. In an earlier chapter, Michael Green noted some of the powerful reasons of the memory that dispose people against Christianity. So how can we build bridges to them?

In the first place, we need to be honest about this: Christianity has acquired a bad odor for many people, with much justification. Some Christian churches are insensitive to people's needs. Many Christians find their faith faltering because of the arrogance of a pastor, the thoughtlessness of other members of the congregation, or the appalling public image presented by some publicity-seeking church leaders. All of this is true. Yet it needs to be pointed out that Christ came to call sinners. Christians are sinners: forgiven sinners, sinners who are trying to mend their ways by the grace of God, but sinners nonetheless. They make mistakes, and they need forgiveness. Try to explain to your friends that they must not judge the gospel by its weak and fallible human representatives. After all, think how much worse they might be if they were not Christians.

In the second place, explain the difference between faith and religion. Faith is a trusting human response to the love of God. Religion is a human invention, something that human beings have constructed and thought up. Religion is all too often about little more than outward observance of ritual. It majors on external appearances and outward observance. Faith, on the other hand, is about our turning to God in trust and joy. It does not involve any rituals—just accepting thankfully all that God offers.

"I can't stand religious people!" a friend once told me. Your friends have probably been turned off Christianity by religion. Try to help them discover faith. Point out how the New Testament, and especially the teaching of Jesus, is refreshingly free of religious stipulations. For some people, discovering the distinction between religion and faith is one of the most liberating things that ever happened to them. Help them to discover the love of God and discard oppressive human rituals and stifling petty obsessions.

But there remains another category of people. They have become involved with Christianity in one of its high-pressure forms, usually of an evangelical or charismatic variety. They have found its emotional demands too much to cope with. They have suffered from burnout, and they have been left reeling from their experiences.

These people need space to recover and freedom to regain their strength. The last thing that they need is to be placed under any kind of pressure. Help them to talk about their experiences; try to understand how they feel about them. The more relaxed and less demanding atmosphere of most mainstream churches may provide them with exactly the climate they need to recover and begin to rebuild their faith.

Chapter 5

Building Bridges to Other Religions

INTRODUCTION
by Alister McGrath

Western society is becoming increasingly multicultural. Building bridges to people of other faiths is becoming of increasing importance. So how can this be done? In this chapter, four experts will share their wisdom on building bridges to four specific religious groupings of significance in modern Western culture. The following general principles may be helpful before moving on to deal with this more detailed discussion.

First, people of other religions will probably share with Christians a concern for the spiritual side of life. They are likely to be as critical of the typical Western obsession with materialism as Christians are. This is a vital observation because it establishes common ground.

Second, remember that there is considerable respect for Jesus Christ among members of other religions—especially Muslims. A discussion can center on these questions: Who is Jesus, and why is He so important? Be prepared to talk about the Resurrection. What actually happened on Easter Day? What does it tell us about the identity of Jesus? And what's in it for us? This immediately shifts the discussion away from the rather vague idea of Christianity and other religions and focuses it directly on a question of history: What happened to Jesus?

Third, appreciate that many non-Christians have negative feelings about Christianity for historical reasons. Some Muslims, for example, still feel intensely resentful against Christianity because of the Crusades of the Middle Ages. They view the Crusades as an attempt by Christians to impose their faith on countries of the Middle East. It is important—and entirely correct—to disown these past events. Christianity is not to be spread at the point of a sword. It commends itself because of its intrinsic merits, truth, and attractiveness.

Fourth, be aware of a deep fear of many people that becoming a Christian means bidding farewell to their own cultures, including many of their most cherished features. Thomas Aquinas, one of the most remarkable Christian writers of the Middle Ages, spoke of "grace perfecting, not abolishing, nature." He meant that the gospel brings things to perfection. It does not destroy or deny what is good; it allows that goodness to be brought to its fulfillment. At its best, Christianity seeks to honor and preserve what is good in other religions—such as the genuine search for truth and a passionate quest for true knowledge of God.

The manner in which Christianity relates to the Old Testament law is an excellent example of this point. Christ declared that He had come not to abolish that law but to fulfill it—in other words, to bring it to its intended perfection. People who come to Christian faith from other religious backgrounds often speak of a sense of joy or delight at discovering how they can retain many of their finest and deepest hopes through realizing that these reach their climax and fulfillment in Christ.

Finally, the very act of showing friendship to people of other religions is itself a vital witness. It mirrors the love and care of God for all His people. By taking the trouble to relate to such people, we are conveying the message that there are no barriers to the saving love of God. A failure to do so might be taken to suggest that God does not care for them or that they lie outside the sphere of His grace. Personal friendship always matters, but it matters especially in this context.

These are some general approaches to building bridges to other religions. But those who are working with specific groups of people will want more specific guidance than that provided here. In the following sections, four acknowledged experts will share their wisdom on building bridges to the New Age movement, Eastern religions, Judaism, and Islam. Particularly detailed and up-to-date information is provided in the case of the New Age, which is often misunderstood by evangelicals. Each section is fully complete in itself and includes suggestions for further reading.

THE NEW AGE MOVEMENT
by Linda Christensen

Introduction

My purpose is to provide the reader with the big picture about the New Age movement. Instead of focusing on the intricacies of New Age beliefs, I am seeking to provide a general framework for understanding this movement.

The New Age movement (NAM) is not your typical new religious movement or cult. Most religious movements revolve around the teachings and experiences of a charismatic founder, which then become institutionalized. The end result is a particular religious organization with identifiable leaders and a specific body of teachings and practices. This then presents a number of boundaries at the outset, affording a description of the movement in a relatively simple and straightforward manner.

That is not the case with the NAM. It has no founder. It has no authoritative, hierarchical leadership. It has not developed the traditional forms of social institutions commonly found with religious movements. And it does not have a clearly defined and systematized body of teachings or a scriptural text. Rather, this movement encompasses innumerable spokespersons or leaders, groups and organizations, teachings and beliefs, and it functions as a loosely structured, decentralized network. All that makes the movement far more complex and difficult to define and understand. Accordingly, it has been sorely misinterpreted by people in all camps—New Agers, Christians, the popular press, and academics alike.

Central to understanding this movement is that its impetus lies in the counterculture of the sixties, which vocalized a rejection of mainstream values, lifestyles, and institutions and launched a quest for alternatives. The NAM is very much a grassroots movement, which has sprung up representing a profound disillusionment by people of most, if not all, sectors in society with the secular modernist paradigm of reality. As religious movements revolve around the vision of their charismatic founder, the NAM revolves around a critique of Western mainstream culture and a vision of a new culture rooted in a new paradigm of reality. Therefore, this movement is sociocultural as well as religious in nature.

Furthermore, the new paradigm of reality offered in this movement has been (or more exactly, is still in the process of being) forged by highly qualified academics and researchers in numerous disciplines. Such makes this new religious movement one of the most sophisticated and articulate movements in existence. It is also a highly literary type of movement. Its scriptures are the writings not only of channelers, metaphysical teachers, and

Eastern gurus, but of those engaged in the leading frontiers of research in physics, cosmology, psychology, consciousness research, the paranormal, and biomedicine/health that appear to support New Age metaphysical speculations.

Our response to this movement as Christians must involve more in-depth research and understanding than are usually given to a new religious movement. What we are dealing with here is not a passing fad or fly-by-night cult. The NAM represents a visible manifestation on a more popular level of a deeper, more serious paradigm shift and questioning of modern Western culture. A desacralized vision of reality is deemed unacceptable by increasing numbers of people who are on a quest for discovering their souls and the sacred in life. They do not consider Christianity a viable alternative because it sold out too much to secular culture on the one hand (i.e., the liberals), and it is too unadaptable and irrelevant to modern times and issues on the other (i.e., the conservatives).[2]

The Rise of the New Age Movement

One could regard the NAM as a response to a type of existential crisis in the West, which is occurring on two levels. On an intellectual level, many feel the need for a new vision for Western society, one that will replace the secular humanist/modernist vision in providing new values to direct our culture. On an experiential level, many are on a spiritual quest—a quest to "reenchant the world," making it more humane, spiritual, and meaningful. In practical terms, they search for new ways of being, experiencing, and relating to themselves, others, and life at large. It is a quest for a new vision and way of life that will affect both inner and outer worlds, a transformation of both self and society.

The counterculture represented such a quest for a new vision. It rejected and rebelled against the Establishment and all conventional values and institutions, being a movement of protest. All the while it was groping for, and experimenting with, alternatives. Yet "no comprehensive alternative model was articulated, at least not one around which the counterculture coalesced."[3]

Nevertheless, an alternative vision eventually did begin to emerge in a somewhat cohesive way in the late seventies and became known as the NAM by the eighties. The NAM drew from various sources for inspiration. First of all, it stands in kinship with a long-standing tradition, which Robert S. Ellwood has termed an "alternative reality tradition" that has roots going back to the Gnosticism, Neoplatonism, and Hellenistic mystery religions of the beginning of the common era.[4] This alternative reality tradition with its monistic and gnostic tendencies was generally confined to the underground for centuries until it found new expression through being revived during and after the Renaissance by various occultists and occult societies.

This leads to the second source. In the nineteenth century, numerous factors came into play that led to the establishment of what could be called an alternative *religious* tradition in North America, which provided the NAM some sources to work with in its quest for an alternative vision. Mesmerism was brought to New England in the 1830s, which led to an experimentation with hypnosis and paranormal diagnoses of illnesses as well as procuring healings through the power of suggestion. The New Thought movement ensued, which taught that mind is the basis of reality as we experience it—if one changes a perception or thought, one effects a change in reality. Positive thinking and affirmative prayer were influential contributions to American spirituality coming from this movement.[5] We have the rise of Spiritualism as a movement beginning with the purported claims of contacting the dead by the Fox sisters in 1848 and with the Swedenborgian Andrew Jackson Davis who provided a theological interpretation of such phenomena.[6] A highly influential metaphysical group birthed at the time was the Theosophical Society founded by Madame H. P. Blavatsky and Colonel H. S. Olcott in

1875 in New York. The Theosophists provided a grand synthesis of Eastern religious thought with Western occultism and the science of the time, which was enamored with Darwin's theory of evolution.

Another source of inspiration was the romanticists and transcendentalists of New England, notably Ralph Waldo Emerson. They likewise were very much disenchanted with traditional religion and the rationalist approach to reality of the modernists, and they sought an alternative vision, looking to both the East and Neoplatonism. They also sought to bring about a synthetic vision of East and West, and reason and mysticism. The quest for a unified and comprehensive vision of reality that can account for all religions and all disciplines of knowledge, harmonizing religion, science, the paranormal, Eastern and Western thought, is very much a part of the New Age quest.

Another factor from the nineteenth century was the increased accessibility to Eastern thought in North America. Many of the scriptures from the East were translated and made available for the first time to the Western populace, thereby providing fuel for an alternative religious orientation. That was then supplemented with an influx of missionaries from the East into North America at the turn of the century. Most notably, Swami Vivekananda addressed the World Parliament of Religions in Chicago in 1893, later establishing several Vedanta Societies in the West (with which Aldous Huxley was associated). Paramahansa Yogananda made an address to the International Congress of Religious Liberals in Boston in 1920, and then he founded the Self-Realization Fellowship. The Soto Zen Mission was established in Los Angeles in 1922, soon followed by various Zen centers in other cities.

The interest in Eastern spirituality only intensified in the postwar period. The work of Daisetz T. Suzuki popularized Zen Buddhism with the former clergyman Alan Watts becoming one of its chief spokespersons in America. Then in 1965, the Oriental

Exclusion Act was rescinded in the U.S., which led to an "Asian invasion." Numerous teachers from the East migrated to America, motivated by a new missionary zeal, which led to the rise of many new religious movements.[7]

By the time we come to the sixties and the counterculture, we find numerous organizations and teachers, as well as a bounty of literature, available in America offering an alternative religious conception of reality. The student protest against the Establishment and the conventional outlook of the West led to experimentation with alternative values, lifestyles, religions, philosophies, and politics. An important factor in making an Eastern/metaphysical outlook viable and popular was the coming of the drug culture and the related explorations of altered states of consciousness (as exemplified by Harvard psychologists Timothy Leary and Richard Alpert, the latter now known as the New Age guru Ram Dass). As Harvey Cox (among others) has noted, people's "drug experience sharply undercut the credibility of any form of 'Western' faith-vision and made some sort of 'Eastern' religious worldview the only credible one."[8] Young people began to "turn East" in significant numbers.

This revolt against conventional values and institutions was initially of a more radical and political nature, becoming more subdued and cultural in focus by the end of the sixties. Many of the student protesters involved in the radical Left became disillusioned with politics and began to direct their search inward. The result was, according to sociologist Steven Tipton, two kinds of revolution taking place, one political, revolving around the value of equality, and the other cultural, concerning itself over "the *quality* of personal and social life in itself . . . [and] . . . the redefinition of what was good. The guiding value of the second revolution was the central cultural and personal value of self-realization and self-fulfillment."[9]

The counterculture seemed to disappear as quickly as it appeared. It has been noted, however, that the Vietnam War "effectively triggered what had been a much more latent disenchantment with the status quo in American life."[10] When the war came to an end, so did the open rebellion. However, the total disappearance of the counterculture is an illusion—the quiet revolution, the active search for alternatives, continued but was largely directed toward self-transformation.[11] This is where the human potential movement has played a decisive role in defining the nature of self-transformation, in both theoretical and practical terms.

Furthermore, as more intellectuals were influenced by the developments coming out of the counterculture (many having been involved as students), new areas of research were explored such as paranormal phenomena and altered states of consciousness, biofeedback and the body-mind connection, alternative therapies such as acupuncture and therapeutic touch, the effects of meditation, and the like. Also, numerous physicists and other scientists began to publish their speculations on the implications of the findings in modern physics related to quantum theory, possible relationships between the hologram and the workings of the human brain, as well as the implications of systems theory for the planet as a living organism (the Gaia hypothesis).[12] Increasingly, the movement became less identified with strictly metaphysical/occult and Eastern teachings. More and more the spokespersons on the New Age circuit were American intellectuals, whereas in the sixties and seventies, they were predominantly gurus and occultists.

People on the vanguard of these trends began to notice that a social/spiritual movement of great significance was emerging. Marilyn Ferguson, a leading New Ager, appears to have written one of the earliest and most widely read comprehensive accounts of this movement in 1980.[13] Her book *The Aquarian Conspiracy: Personal and Social Transformation in the 1980s* has had, and continues to have, a large audience and influence. By 1988, it had sold over 500,000 copies in North America and was translated into ten languages and published in eight countries.[14] Robert Ellwood comments that books like *The Aquarian Conspiracy* "have a way of not only describing what they are about but also becoming a part of it—even of helping to make it happen."[15]

Two years later came another work that likewise helped "to make it happen"—*The Turning Point: Science, Society, and the Rising Culture* by physicist Fritjof Capra. His central thesis is that the innumerable crises facing modern society (e.g., high inflation, unemployment, energy consumption, crime, violence, pollution, ecology, and health care) are but "different facets of one and the same crisis . . . , a crisis of perception"—the attempt to apply "the concepts of an outdated worldview—the mechanistic worldview of Cartesian-Newtonian science—to a reality that can no longer be understood in terms of these concepts."[16] He argues that we need "a new 'paradigm'—a new vision of reality; a fundamental change in our thoughts, perceptions, and values."[17]

Capra then refers to how the counterculture has "generated a whole series of social movements that all seem to go in the same direction, emphasizing different aspects of the new vision of reality."[18] His purpose in writing this book was "to provide a coherent conceptual framework that will help them recognize the communality of their aims," and he believes that the coalescing of these movements will "form a powerful force for social change . . . [which] is likely to result in a transformation of unprecedented dimensions, a turning point for the planet as a whole."[19]

As Capra foresaw, these various movements and trends came to form the numerous strands of which the NAM is comprised. The NAM essentially is a network of these various groups that united into a common social/religious movement through their sharing a common vision of reality. These movements began to coalesce and network in the early seventies, largely as a result of the publication of numerous periodicals (e.g., *East-West Journal, New Age, New Realities, New Directions, New Age Journal, Yoga Journal*). National directories began to be published (e.g., *Year One Catalog, Spiritual Community Guide*), and in many cities (now most, if not all), local papers were published regularly, such as *Common Ground*, which provide a directory of local New Age activities and services.[20]

The New Age Network

The New Age network of groups seems to encompass five thematic categories. These categories illustrate the various strands that historically, through their coalescence, have given birth to this movement.

Social, Political, Ecological

First, there are groups of a social, political, and/or ecological orientation. The counterculture began with a focus on social transformation. There soon arose numerous movements and groups promoting one or another cause, such as the rights of minorities and women, world peace and nuclear disarmament, and the protection of the environment.

Alternative Spiritual

The second, and perhaps largest, category of groups consists of the new religious movements that became so prolific during the sixties and seventies. By the end of the sixties, many people became disillusioned with their attempts at transforming society and began to seek self-transformation. Many joined one of the numerous unconventional or alternative religious groups that became established in North America, such traditions as Zen and Tibetan Buddhism, Vedanta philosophy, Yoga, Sufism, and those groups led by an assortment of gurus. However, increasingly, shamanism, Native American Indian traditions, and wicca/neopaganism are capturing people's interest. People are not as enamored with the Eastern spiritual traditions as they were in the sixties but seem to be looking at more indigenous traditions.

Personal Growth

Third, the personal growth and development groups have largely arisen out of the human potential movement of the seventies. This movement spawned numerous groups and a deluge of literature, seminars, and therapists and the "pop psychology" that is now prolific. The human potential movement, the work of Abraham Maslow, and humanistic psychology as a whole, along with its offspring of transpersonal psychology, have contributed the pivotal strand of the NAM where a generic form of spirituality is offered in more neutral psychological terms.

The Esalen Institute in California quickly became the center for this movement, offering a variety of psychospiritual techniques at the hands of a new Western guru—the enlightened psychotherapist. Here, to actualize one's fullest potential as a human being entails *spiritual* awareness and actualization as well, and many of the techniques for this are derived largely from Eastern spiritual traditions. The human potential movement took many of the spiritual techniques and practices of the "new religions" prolific in the sixties and seventies and decontextualized them (i.e., removed them from their religious contexts) and psychologized them by replacing native religious language with psychological jargon. This birthed a distinctive culture of consciousness exploration in the name of personal growth and self-actualization, which are largely what the New Age is about.

Metaphysical

The seventies also witnessed an unprecedented popularization of the occult, which provides the fourth type of group making up the New Age network. Literature, workshops, and societies offer to awaken one's latent psychic powers, to discover one's past (reincarnated) lives through hypnotic regression, to teach one how to contact one's spirit guides and become a channeler and how to use crystals to enhance life in every way, to cite a few examples.

Holistic Health

The holistic health movement can be regarded as a fifth category in the New Age network. Holistic health practitioners seek to supplement established medical practices, which primarily are focused on crisis intervention in terms of surgical removal or repair of damaged or diseased organs. It is generally held that the underlying causes of much ill health and disease are not addressed by conventional medicine in that it fails to embrace a holistic approach.

As designated by the term *holistic*, the belief is that the human being consists of body, mind, and spirit, which together make up an interconnected whole. Therefore, all need to be taken into account in the diagnosis and treatment of the patient. This entails an openness to explore and employ alternative forms of therapy and health care that conventional medicine generally rejects as being unscientific, such as the use of guided imagery, meditation, reflexology, psychic healing, acupuncture, shamanistic rituals, and the like. However, such alternative therapies are increasingly being incorporated into mainstream health care. I have found that many who become New Agers do so as a result of a search for healing and physical well-being after having been frustrated with mainstream approaches to health care.

In summary, none of these groups alone fully represents or can be equated with the NAM per se. Rather, the movement exists as a network of such diverse groups. There is a strong tendency for these groups to have in common with each other a particular view of reality, although they may differ on the details. That links them together into a common movement.

New Age Beliefs

There is such an eclecticism and tolerant diversity of beliefs associated with this movement that it is difficult, if not outright impossible, to present a comprehensive discussion of them. I have found it useful to keep in mind that there are a few key, universal, nonnegotiable tenets in the movement and then a plethora of diverse beliefs that are more negotiable that tend to be associated with certain factions.[21] First, I will comment on some beliefs and general orientations commonly held within the movement.

The universally held tenets of a metaphysical nature in this movement are basically two: (1) a belief in the interconnectedness of reality, a call for a holistic vision of the cosmos and the self, and (2) a belief in the sacred being primarily (but not exclusively) located as immanent in the cosmos, divinity being the essential nature of all of life. To rephrase this in the overly simplistic cliché (which tends to belittle these ideas without addressing their potential sophistication), "all is one and all is God." This should not be taken as a form of monistic pantheism; rather, the New Age conception is more in line with panentheism. Deity is understood to be immanent, somehow manifest in and through the world, while also being transcendent and ultimately beyond the world. Furthermore, God is related to in both personal and impersonal terms in the New Age, although there is a tendency to reject any kind of anthropomorphism.[22]

The New Age emphasizes holistic ways of knowing. The use of intuition, imagination, creativity, and right- versus left-brain ways of perception to follow one's heart and connect with one's inner guidance is regularly, if not adamantly, encouraged. The New Age also emphasizes internal conviction and personal experience as being criteria more important than external sources or rational argument for determining what is true. Pragmatism is prevalent here; "if it works, use it" is a common motto.

These alternative ways of knowing are contended to be central to the achievement of the New Age vision of reality. The New Age can give the impression of being against the use of reason (and at the more popular level many embrace this as a means of escaping issues that challenge their beliefs). However, it is really calling for an epistemology that seeks to overcome an exclusively rationalistic/positivistic approach, which tends to reduce reality to only what is immediately present to the senses in an empirical way.

The movement is also very much characterized by a belief in the "perennial philosophy" popularized by Aldous Huxley.[23] It is maintained that all religions in their primal, essential forms teach the same basic principles as summarized below:

> The everyday world and our personal consciousness are manifestations of an underlying divine reality. . . . Human beings can realize the existence of the Divine Ground "by a direct intuition, superior to discursive reasoning." . . . We possess a hidden higher self, the spark of divinity within the soul, which reflects this transcendental reality in our lives. . . . This awakening . . . is the goal or purpose of human life.[24]

This claim of all religions being essentially one can be sustained only through a process of selective abstraction, where the particularities that differentiate religions are removed and their teachings are largely taken out of their contexts. What regularly happens in the New Age's treatment of not only other religions but also various belief systems is a threefold process of decontextualization, syncretization, and universalization. An item of belief, symbol, theme, practice, or what have you is taken out of its native context, then syncretized with other elements, and then claimed to represent a universal and ancient truth. In this way New Age beliefs acquire a universality that legitimates the movement, undermining any idea that the New Age is "new," just a current fad. Rather, it is held to embody truths long forgotten as a result of suppression by our modernist culture.

I have discovered that the movement encompasses four levels or types of orientation.[25] I will discuss some of the more specific beliefs in the NAM as they are associated with these different sectors. Noting these distinctions has proven to be useful; however, they overlap a great deal.

New Age Consumerism

The most superficial level of the movement could be identified as New Age consumerism. The label of New Age is used to sell trendy products to a particular clientele. The demand for various New Age products and services is reflected in the spending of an estimated $400 million on such in 1986 and the publishing of the first New Age Yellow Pages in 1987.

The New Age has become big business on numerous fronts. The book publishing industry has taken advantage of the increasing interest in spirituality and New Age–related topics. In 1987, the New Age Publishers and Retailers Association was established by representatives in the publishing industry to promote this new market. In the same year, the estimate was that in the United States, the annual retail sales of books in the New Age category totaled $100 million.[26]

In 1987, the first New Age Grammy Award was given in music, reflecting the growth of the New Age music industry. The adaptation of New Age philosophy and techniques in the workplace has also been a growth industry with an estimated $4 billion spent by American corporations to improve employee performance and increase profits.

New Age Cults and Occultism

Then there are various New Age cults and a more diffuse form of New Age occultism, which together comprise groups of an esoteric type that tend to be preoccupied with rather apocalyptic and millenarian visions and whose teachings are drawn from occult/metaphysical schools of thought. Here I would categorize the numerous channelers as forming potential religious cults in that they usually have a substantial following of adherents committed to their teachings.

Channelers and New Age metaphysical groups in general teach that the problem with humanity is a loss of identity. We have forgotten who we are and why we are here. A common cliché in these circles is that "we are spiritual beings having a human experience," having chosen to undergo an adventurous "experiment in consciousness." We willingly entered this realm of illusion, the "Earth School," to grow through an experience of unity and love while in a state of apparent separation from our divine origins and source. The problem is that we have so forgotten from where and why we came that we have come "under the spell of matter" and have become enslaved by our egos, fear, and guilt, all based on illusory perceptions. We have given this illusory world, a construct of consciousness to begin with, a power over us by seeing it as a reality on its own terms. Fear, guilt, and suffering have arisen as a result. We need to wake up to who we are, to see the illusions for what they are, and to complete the task we set out to do so that we can return "Home" enriched by our experimentation on the earth plane.

There also is much talk about raising the vibrational level of the physical plane, including that of the human body, to a higher, more subtle vibration, allowing for a shift to occur from the physical to the spiritual plane. That will occur when enough individuals have raised their vibrational levels to achieve a "critical mass" in terms of numbers to cause a shift in the collective consciousness of humanity to "tip the scale" from the physical plane to the spiritual.[27] When this is effected, a New Age will dawn. However, it seems likely that global disasters will precede this as necessary birth pangs leading to the transformation. Some channelers foretell many disasters and plagues that will serve as a "cleansing of Mother Earth" of unwilling and hindering consciousnesses, calling for the death of millions of souls. They are seen as being analogous to cancer cells that threaten to destroy the whole organism (planet earth) unless they are removed.[28]

A belief in karma and reincarnation is predominant in the movement as a whole, but particularly so in New Age occultism. Karma refers to the Eastern belief in a cosmic moral law of retribution, that is, what happens to a person in this life is the just reward (positive or negative) for actions committed in a past life. However, the New Age understanding emphasizes that it serves an educational role in that the experiences in one's life are an outworking of karma designed to encourage needed growth and development, furthering one's evolution. One lives innumerable lives as the soul continually reincarnates, taking on a new bodily form after the death of a previous form as the soul progresses in its evolutionary journey.

In this metaphysical wing of the New Age, the thrust is that this world is illusory in nature; it is a creation of thought/consciousness (a form of idealism), and people are called to transcend the physical realm in order to enter the spiritual, which is the truly real. This way of thinking tends to entail a form of escapism, the undermining of the value of our physical existence. This orientation is seriously in conflict with mainstream New Age thought, as described in the next two levels.

However, in these first two levels, the term *New Age* is used most often. It may be for this reason that they are usually taken to be representative of the NAM as a whole by the public and the media. Yet most New Agers I have encountered, both in field research and in the literature, disdain such an identification, and for that reason they tend to want to disown the New Age label for themselves.[29] To focus on such groups with the assumption that they are representative and essential to the movement would be a mistake and is one that is commonly made.

New Age as Social/Cultural Transformation

The third level or sector of this movement could be described as the New Age as social/cultural transformation. Here the focus is a call for a new vision of reality to direct Western culture. The argument is that the modernist vision of reality is insufficient in ensuring the resolution of numerous modern crises and the future well-being of our planet. Generally, New Agers hold that the human dilemma arises out of a lack of recognition of the interconnectedness and sacredness of life. The consequences of this are seen to be catastrophic. New Agers maintain that a dualistic perspective (as espoused in Western mainstream culture), where subject-object distinctions are regarded as objectively real, is the source and cause of the ills of modern society.

The argument basically goes like this. Because we do not see that we are one with other peoples of the world and, instead, see them as separate from ourselves and, hence, as potential enemies, we have military buildup and eventual war. Because we do not regard the earth as sacred and ourselves as interconnected with it, we feel free to abuse it. Because we believe that our religion is *the* truth and the others are false, we have holy wars. Therefore, the old way of viewing life (in terms of a Cartesian-Newtonian model of reality) must be eradicated for the sake of both human and planetary survival. Individuals and society at large need to undergo a major transformation in their understanding of reality and to embrace a philosophy of unity/wholeness to ensure world peace, social justice, ecological well-being, and religious tolerance.

Such a call to transform Western culture legitimates the movement with respect to the modern situation. To become a New Ager is to be supportive of attempts to ensure the well-being of our planet and humanity instead of remaining apathetic at best or, worse, supportive of the old structures that have brought us to the place of such unhindered exploitation.

New Age Spirituality

The fourth level could be identified as New Age spirituality. This spirituality is expressed in the movement's quest for well-being, healing, wholeness, and an all-around enhancement of the quality of life, beginning with oneself and then encompassing all of humanity as well as the planet. Along with this quest for healing/wholeness is a call to resacralize life. Here the New Age signifies a new consciousness that results in the experience of the sacramental nature of everyday life, the experience of self and life as both sacred and holistic. This represents a practical expression of the third level, and these two levels are closely related and intertwined, making up mainstream New Age thought.

For example, the editors of the *New Age Journal* have put forth a volume depicting what the NAM is about. They never use the term *New Age* at all; instead, they refer to it as an "emergence of a new spirituality." Central to this new spirituality is an overcoming of all dualisms. The primary dualism is that between the sacred and the profane. Such dualisms have been supported by

> most religions East and West, [where] God is separate from the Earth; spirit and matter coexist as partners with irreconcilable differences, and people devalue the body, sexuality, the emotions, and the natural world. Because it separates the divine from nature, this worldview unknowingly sanctions the exploitation of nature, which it considers to exist only to serve humankind, and contributes to our current ecological dilemmas.[30]

The orientation to reality that I have encountered in the mainstream camp of the New Age is quite different from that in the occult camp and is the one that I think truly represents what the New Age movement is about. It is more akin to Taoism, Zen and Tibetan Buddhism, and a Native Indian orientation to reality. The emphasis is on seeing the sacred in the mundane, the extraordinary in the ordinary, and on embodying the spiritual in the physical, here and now. It is a very earthy type of spirituality, focused on living out one's spirituality in one's everyday life and activities. It calls for a vision that sees "the world of matter as divine and as worthy of love as the immaterial spiritual realm," and "it acknowledges the sacredness of the body, sexuality, the emotions, and the natural world."[31]

Relying on other entities that are channeled is seen as a form of disempowerment, a looking to an authority outside yourself to give you the answers. This cultivates a codependency and is not an empowering spirituality. This, one respondent said, is akin to what the Enlightenment sought to get away from concerning medieval Christianity—the idea of divine revelations being authoritative and demanding people's allegiance—and so some, he said, are basically running around like "New Age popes."

Also, a number have said that the apocalypticism in the occult camp is potentially dangerous. There is not enough value placed on this world and our physicality, which is not separate from our spirituality. Hence, there is not the needed philosophical basis for protecting the environment. There also is seen to be a "copping out of our responsibility to care for the planet" if we are to wait for these "higher, cosmic forces" to bring in this "new age" that will save us. Furthermore, those of the apocalyptic camp often regard themselves as among the chosen to be spared during the coming catastrophes, which leads to a dangerous "we'll be saved because we're holy" attitude, according to one respondent.

What has struck me as probably *the* predominant feature in New Age activities is a focus on defining and expressing the self along the lines of a new paradigm, one that moves away from the conventional emphasis on the self as a strictly material being that expresses itself purely in cognitive terms (i.e., verbally and rationally). Many of the New Age workshops revolve around the use of drumming/chanting, movement/dance, music/sound, color/art, meditation/guided visualization, and the like in encouraging people to explore ways of being, aspects of the self, that are not strictly tied to the verbal, rational domain, which is our culture's prevalent mode of self-expression. In this regard the New Age calls for a more holistic conception and expression of the self. There is little teaching in New Age group activities; rather, the focus is on experiencing such new dimensions of the self or beyond.[32]

This new paradigm of the self that seems to be rather universal revolves around the understanding of the self as spirit, mind, and body.

Spirit. It is stated again and again that people need to connect with their true, or "higher," self, which lies within. This inner self is also referred to as source, God, spirit, or the heart (versus the ego or the head). The nature of this inner self is peace, love, wisdom, bliss, immortality, in sum, all the characteristics regularly ascribed to divinity. In fact, one's soul or essential self is divinity. Furthermore, it is held that this inherent divinity is the essential nature of all things; all of reality is one interconnected whole, interrelated by a life force, an intelligence, that can be referred to as God. As you live and act out of your source, you will achieve harmony in life because you will be acting in congruence with the source present in all things, including your life's circumstances. That is why you are to always ask what the universe is trying to teach you in any situation, especially a problematic one, because it has a divine purpose. The sooner that it is aligned with, the sooner you can move beyond that circumstance.

Much of the teaching and practice in the New Age is focused on guiding people into a conscious awareness of, and connection with, this inner divinity. People are to live more in the present moment and place more emphasis on being than doing. Our culture is seen to be suffering from living too much in the head, that is, the ego's or analytical mind's focus on the future, in terms of accomplishing goals, which leads to a utilitarian approach to life and an emphasis on doing. The New Age teaches people how to live in the now, how to find their purpose and, above all, their selves. So much of what I have seen in terms of field research revolves around people attempting to define and relate to their inner, essential selves, which transcend their public, social roles and could be identified, therefore, with soul or spirit.

Mind. It is maintained that to fully manifest our true nature, we need to be freed from the constraints placed on personhood by the events of our biographical past and social mores. Consequently, the New Age highlights personal growth work. This encompasses group therapy, inner child work, psychotherapy, past life regression therapy, rebirthing, neurolinguistic programming, and various other methods that seek to bring into one's conscious awareness the various patterns or mental scripts that are directing one's thoughts and behaviors. There is much focus on accessing one's subconscious through dreamwork, guided imagery, and regression therapy. It is commonly held that the conscious rational mind blocks and suppresses a great deal, stifling one's personal growth and fuller self-actualization. Furthermore, the realm of spirit is held to be more closely associated with the subconscious than the conscious, predominantly analytical, mind.

The overall goal is to no longer be held victim to various unconscious forces that have been put in place by culture, family, or personal biographical incidents that disempower individuals from being in control of their lives and their personhoods. There is much talk among New Agers of becoming self-empowered and taking responsibility for their lives. This is one area where the New Age dictum "we create our reality" comes in. Much of what is going on here could be regarded as people attempting to deconstruct their old selves and old perceptual realities in order to construct new selves and new experiential realities. Some describe this process as blatantly as that. Much in this area would not conflict with mainstream psychology, for much that is available in pop psychology is here relied upon by the movement.

Body. The New Age model radically diverges from the established medical model of the human body. First of all, the New Age model is in stark disagreement with the standard body-mind dualism that sees body and mind as separate and independent entities. Second, it rejects the established model of the body as a strictly biochemical, material entity. Third, it disagrees with conventional subject-object dualism that sees the human subject/body as a self-contained entity, separate and distinct from the environment.

Rather, the New Age paradigm embraces the idea that body and mind are very much interconnected and influence each other (for better or worse). There also is an interconnection between the subject/body and the environment, with there likewise existing influences both ways. The human body is not primarily a material entity but one of energy and intelligence/information, thereby allowing a place for what we could call spirit.

The New Age holistic model of the human being in terms of spirit, mind, and body as interconnected allows for the possibility of the mind affecting the body because it is held that consciousness is not confined to the brain but is present in every cell through neuropeptides. A New Age cliché is "where awareness goes, energy flows." As one brings one's awareness to a particular part of the body that is in discomfort or needs healing, one can direct the flow of bodily energy to the place that will quicken the needed healing or stimulate a flow of energy blocked in that area.

This holistic model also allows for the potential viability of much supposed paranormal phenomena in terms of the subject influencing, or being influenced by, the environment, such as telekinesis, or other people in the form of healing through therapeutic touch.[33]

The Christian Response

Among North American evangelicals, a rather predominant interpretation of the NAM is that it is satanically inspired. It is considered the grand deception of the last days before Christ's return and the means by which the Antichrist will establish his world order. To sanction such an interpretation, there has been a great deal of bias in the selection of New Age sources to have them fit with such a biblical apocalypticism. The group that provided the most fuel for such an interpretation of the New Age is former theosophist Alice Bailey's Arcane School. Bailey channeled numerous works from 1920 until her death in 1949, which outlined "The Plan" for establishing a new world order headed by the spiritual heirarchy. Benjamin Creme, a more recent promoter of these teachings, has been declaring that the Ascended Master, Maitreya the Christ, has materialized on our physical plane and is ready to lead the world into a utopian New Age.

Although New Agers generally tend to espouse some form of globalism and often regard themselves as planetary citizens (implying an allegiance to the human race and the planet that supersedes nationalism), they do not support the idea of a one-world government nor do they herald the coming of a messianic world leader to head up such a rule. New Agers are very much opposed to authoritarian structures, and they emphasize that people need to individually and collectively take responsibility for improving the world instead of looking to authority figures to solve the problems for us.[34] The mistake made by a number of evangelical interpreters is that they have taken Bailey's and Creme's teachings and adherents (which in terms of numbers and influence are rather insignificant compared to others) as representative of the NAM as a whole instead of recognizing them as esoteric offshoots associated with a larger movement.

Another issue that I see as problematic is how the focus on much of Christian apologetics with respect to the New Age (and other issues, for that matter) revolves around illustrating the heretical nature of the movement. This is commonly done by juxtaposing New Age beliefs with biblical doctrines to point out how the two conflict. The assumption seems to be that if one illustrates how unbiblical the New Age is, that settles the issue, and it has been properly dealt with. A serious consequence of such a protectionistic, purely defensive approach is that there is a lack of understanding with any depth concerning extremely important issues of our time. Much of our understanding is more of a Christian projection where we tend to create our own straw men and then attack them, totally missing the real issues and remaining ineffective in dealing with them.

Besides the above example of such a faulty construct of what the New Age is about (as setting the stage for the Antichrist), another would be the common assumption in evangelical critiques of New Age thought that it is monistic or pantheistic in character. That would be an easy conclusion to reach from a superficial reading of New Age literature because there clearly is much talk of "God being within," that we are all "one" and we are all "gods." Pantheism easily lends itself to severe criticism, and identifying New Age thought with it can be a convenient way of attempting to discredit the movement. However, as we study it more deeply, we soon realize that New Age thought is more complex, more ambiguous, and not as clearly defined as many Christians would like to think. Rather, if it can be categorized at all, it would be as panentheism, where divinity is posited as both transcendent to and immanent in nature. The rather simplistic critiques often given of New Age thought seem to address caricatures of the movement. It is easy to discredit an ideology by caricaturing its teachings. However, New Agers fall guilty of this as well in how they often employ New Age clichés.

There is indeed weirdness associated with the movement. To debunk it and think that one has discredited the movement as a whole is a big mistake. Much of a serious intellectual challenge in this movement needs to be carefully considered and addressed. As a movement, it represents a popular religious expression of a more profound and serious challenge to a modernism defined by Newtonian science, Cartesian dualism, and the Enlightenment's rationalism. It is a type of spirituality that is seeking to establish a postmodern paradigm for its context. In my opinion, Christians must recognize what is valid within this movement and affirm that. It is calling for a return of the spiritual dimension in life and in our vision of reality as a culture. Such demands a new paradigm to allow for that.

Theologically, much in this movement could be regarded as being in line with what theologians would call general revelation. To quite a degree, the movement is a human response to the divine call, as are all religious quests, and this fact needs to be recognized and affirmed. However, on the specifics of the nature of God, especially the special revelation we have in the person and work of Christ, we can give New Agers a clearer and more specific understanding of the God of love that they want to believe in and that they intuit must exist. For it is in the gospel that we have a concrete historical expression of the empirical reality of this God and that He is indeed a God of love who desires a personal relationship with us—and one that will surpass any relationship that a spirit guide can give. Talk about God in terms of dogma to be believed in will not win over the New Ager.

Persons involved in a movement as experientially oriented as the New Age need to encounter the reality of the God behind

Christian doctrine in the lives (and in the churches) of those who represent Him. Rather than seeing the New Age as a movement inspired by Satan, as many evangelicals do, I would call for seeing it as a response to God's call and a harvest that is ripe for an evangelism that would seek to work with the NAM in a more constructive way than simply condemning it.

Many former New Agers became Christians as a result of their ongoing quest for God and spirituality. Their conversion is frequently a consequence of some significant spiritual experience that convinces them of the truth of Christianity. In practical terms, then, the role of the Christian as evangelist is one that does not necessarily have to focus on rational argumentation. Rather, we should seek to invite and encourage an experiential encounter between the New Ager and our Lord Jesus, the risen Christ. Doing this involves being in relationship with New Agers. Instead of being fearful and defensive of them, Christians should go to New Age gatherings and cultivate an authentic friendship with some of them. They are for the most part a wonderful group of people—very open and warm, and eager to talk about spiritual things.

You could advertise your church ministry or some special outreach designed for New Agers in the local New Age paper, or you could start up a New Age blues phone line. Enter into an ongoing, relaxed dialogue with them. Listen to what they have to say and be respectful of their beliefs, but thoughtfully raise issues and problems. Above all, share with them how you have come to know and experience God through Christ (ease into this in a natural and authentic way, without coming across as though your primary agenda is to convert/preach to them; seek to be an authentic friend). Emphasize the message of love, healing, forgiveness, and liberty that Christianity is all about. New Agers, like most non-Christians, have a negative stereotypical image of Christianity in mind, expecting Christians to be intolerant, legalistic, narrow-minded, and hypocritical, being very religious but not very spiritual. Such images need to be countered and can be dissipated only if New Agers meet and get to know Christians who are deeply spiritual, authentic, caring, and thoughtful people.

In evangelizing a New Ager (or ultimately anyone for that matter), who you are is more important than whatever clever arguments or Scripture quotations you can recite. Our calling is to be Christlike; people need to see the person of Jesus in our lives and our very being.

For Further Reading

Because this movement is quite recent, there is not as much material available as there would be on other movements. Besides the works cited in this chapter, I strongly recommend the following secular, academic works that are invaluable: the two works by J. Gordon Melton, Jerome Clark, and Aidan A. Kelly, *The New Age Encyclopedia* (Detroit: Gale Research, 1990) and *New Age Almanac* (Detroit: Gale Research, 1991); James R. Lewis and J. Gordon Melton, eds., *Perspectives on the New Age* (Albany: State University of New York, 1992); and Mary Farrell Bednarowski, *New Religions and the Theological Imagination in America* (Indianapolis: Indiana University Press, 1989).

Unfortunately, good works on the New Age by evangelicals are rather limited. The following represents some of the better ones: Russell Chandler, *Understanding the New Age* (Dallas: Word, 1988); Ted Peters, *The Cosmic Self: A Penetrating Look at Today's New Age Movements* (San Francisco: Harper, 1991); Elliot Miller, *A Crash Course on the New Age Movement: Describing and Evaluating a Growing Social Force* (Grand Rapids: Baker, 1989); Karen Hoyt and J. Isamu Yamamoto, eds., *The New Age Rage: A Probing Analysis of the Newest Religious Craze* (Old Tappan, N.J.: Revell, 1987); the works by Douglas R. Groothius, *Unmasking the New Age: Is There a*

New Religious Movement Trying to Transform Society? (Downers Grove, Ill.: IVP, 1986), *Confronting the New Age: How to Resist a Growing Religious Movement* (Downers Grove, Ill.: IVP, 1988), *Revealing the New Age Jesus: Challenges to Orthodox Views of Christ* (Downers Grove, Ill.: IVP, 1990); and two earlier works that are among the better discussions of this movement are Os Guiness, *The Dust of Death: A Critique of the Counterculture* (Downers Grove, Ill.: IVP, 1973), and the chapter on "the New Consciousness" in James W. Sire, *The Universe Next Door: A Basic Worldview Catalogue* (Downers Grove, Ill.: IVP, 1976).

In regard to the historical roots of the New Age movement in terms of the alternative religious tradition in America, I recommend the following: Robert C. Fuller, *Mesmerism and the American Cure of Souls* (Philadelphia: University of Pennsylvania Press, 1982); J. Stillson Judah, *The History and Philosophy of Metaphysical Groups in America* (Philadelphia: Westminster Press, 1967); Charles S. Braden, *Spirits in Rebellion: The Rise and Development of New Thought* (Dallas: Southern Methodist University, 1963); Robert S. Ellwood, *Alternative Altars: Unconventional and Eastern Spirituality in America* (Chicago: University of Chicago Press, 1979); Geoffrey K. Nelson, *Spiritualism and Society* (London: Routledge and Kegan Paul, 1969); Howard Kerr and Charles L. Crow, eds., *The Occult in America: New Historical Perspectives* (Chicago: University of Illinois Press, 1983); Bruce F. Campbell, *Ancient Wisdom Revived: A History of the Theosophical Movement* (Berkeley: University of California Press, 1980); and Carl T. Jackson, *The Oriental Religions and American Thought: Nineteenth Century Explorations* (Westport, Conn.: Greenwood Press, 1981).

With respect to the new areas of research and theorizing coming out of the counterculture and the attempts to articulate a new paradigm of reality, the following provides only a few examples of such works. Explorations regarding human nature: Charles T. Tart's *Altered States of Consciousness* (as editor), *Transpersonal Psychologies* (as editor), and *PSI: Scientific Studies of the Psychic Realm*; Kenneth Pelletier's *Mind as Healer, Mind as Slayer* and *Toward a Science of Consciousness*; Herbert Benson's *The Mind/Body Effect*; Bernie Segal's *Love, Medicine and Miracles* and *Peace, Love and Healing*; Deepak Chopra's *Quantum Healing: Exploring the Frontiers of Mind/Body Medicine* and *Ageless Body, Timeless Mind: The Quantum Alternative to Growing Old*; Stanislov Grof's *The Adventure of Self-Discovery*; Ken Wilber's *The Atman Project* and *Spectrum of Consciousness*; and Jean Houston's *The Possible Human* and *The Search for the Beloved: Journeys in Sacred Psychology*. Explorations regarding the nature of reality: Karl Pribram's holographic model in *The Languages of the Brain*; David Bohm's *Wholeness and the Implicate Order*; Ken Wilber's *The Holographic Paradigm and Other Paradoxes: Exploring the Leading Edge of Science* (as editor); Fritjof Capra's *The Tao of Physics*; and Michael Talbot's *Beyond the Quantum: How the Secrets of the New Physics Are Bridging the Chasm Between Science and Faith*. With respect to the "Gaia hypothesis," see James Lovejoy's *Gaia: A New Look at Life on Earth*; Peter Russell's *The Awakening Earth: The Global Brain*; and Lawrence E. Joseph's *Gaia: The Growth of an Idea*.

On the New Age as a growth industry see the following: Richard Blow, "Moronic Convergence: The Moral and Spiritual Emptiness of New Age," *The New Republic*, Jan. 25, 1988; Allene Symons, "Marketing the New Age," *Publisher's Weekly*, Sept. 25, 1987; Jeffrey A. Trachtenberg, ed., "Mainstream Metaphysics," *Forbes*, June 1, 1987; and Annetta Miller and Pamela Abramson, "Corporate Mind Control: New Age Gurus Want to Change Employee Thinking," *Newsweek*, May 4, 1987.

EASTERN RELIGIONS
by Michael Griffiths

In this section, my purpose is to expound these religions not as a set of static, separate, and independent belief systems, but as a dynamic continuum of related beliefs, interreacting with each other and constantly mutating and metamorphosing, traveling eastward in history, encountering the differing cultural environments of China, Korea, and Japan.

It is self-evident that all human religious belief systems have diverse origins: they usually include a mixture of local animistic folk religion; possibly some natural revelation truly from God (see Rom. 1:20); some original human speculations from significant religious teachers; and sometimes by imitation, osmosis, and syncretism absorbing ideas deriving from other belief systems—from Zoroastrianism, Islam, or even Christianity. Nowhere is this complex mix of ingredients more evident than in India.

General Comments

These are admittedly generalizations, but nonetheless in spite of inevitable exceptions, they give a general outline of the overall worldview.

First of all, the three great monotheistic faiths—Judaism, Christianity, and Islam—are pluralistic, believing that God has created beings distinct from Himself with a measure of dependent autonomy. By contrast, Eastern religions are monistic. The Hindu-Buddhist worldview teaches that all things are one thing: every particular in the world is part of one universal divine principle, called by Hindus Brahman, by Buddhists Busshin, or by the Chinese the Tao.

Second, Christians choose to believe that other people actually exist and have some objective reference, each with real experience. In Eastern religions, while there is inevitably some accommodation to apparent reality, this world—and everything in it—is believed to be an illusion. In this sense, Christians are realists, and monists may be called idealists.

This point is well illustrated by the famous story of the rajah who introduced an untamed elephant to his garden as his guru walked up the drive, and he was most gratified to see his worthy instructor in an undignified scramble to climb a tree to escape. After the beast was driven off, the rajah welcomed his guru, rubbing his hands with ill-concealed glee and saying, "I see that the master did not hold to the truth that the elephant was only part of the world of illusion." His teacher replied with withering scorn: "I see that you are still lost in a fog of ignorance. What you thought that you saw was an illusory guru, being chased by an illusory elephant up an illusory tree."

Monists believe that one's own consciousness is all there is, a most subjective reality, lacking any true objectivity. This belief reaches its logical conclusion in the Zen sect of Buddhism.

Third, monistic religions are essentially deterministic. Things that happen, such as sinful actions, are not so much things that we do, for which we are directly responsible, but things that happen to us. There is no real distinction between good and evil (monism implies that all things are one thing); therefore, ethics is part of the unreal world of accommodation.

There are apparent similarities between Christianity and Eastern religions. Killing, stealing, and adultery are seen as ethically wrong, but for entirely different reasons. According to monistic religions, we should not kill, steal, or commit adultery because things and people have no objective existence. Christians, on the other hand, must not offend God in these ways because our neighbors have objective existence and we are commanded to love and help them. Monists find it difficult to understand why Christians believe we are responsible for sin.

Fourth, reincarnation, or the transmigration of souls, is the underlying assumption of the whole worldview of Eastern religions.

Whether people prosper or suffer, are rich, high caste or poor, outcaste people, depends on a cause in a previous life, having an inevitable effect in this one. That is what *karma* means. Thus, each human being who is born is carrying a set of inherited baggage, or credit-debit accounts built up during previous existences. This gives a credible explanation for success and suffering, for riches and misfortune: it is all due to actions good and bad in previous existences, resulting in inevitable effects in this one. This belief also gives religious sanction to perpetuating the rigid class structure.

Fifth, salvation is escape from the endless succession of pointless births (one year of Brahma lasts twelve million human years, during which you might live up to three hundred thousand times) and rebirths and countless pointless suffering lives, all the result of remorseless karma. The temporary phenomenal existence as a moral entity becomes absorbed into the permanent reality of Brahman, as water existing temporarily as a raindrop is again united with the ocean. Enlightenment (nirvana) opens the eyes to perceive the true nature of human experience and reality and the oneness that exists among all apparently separate entities.

Our story begins around 2000 B.C. when warlike nomadic tribes who called themselves Aryans, from Sanskrit "the noble ones," swept through northern Iran and on to India. They seem to have overrun the Indus Valley civilization, bringing with them the horse, the chariot, and the Sanskrit language. Being nomads, they carried no images and built no temples. Their imagery was drawn from sun, rain, wind, and storm, and it centered on the household fire as the place for offerings. They were polytheistic, but their gods were abstract qualities like Mitra (covenant), Varuna (true speech), and Aryaman (hospitality). Those were the beliefs of the light-skinned Aryan people who conquered India and whose hymns of sacrifice, the Vedas, were known only to their priests, who became the Brahmins of India.

Hinduism

Though what I described under "General Comments" is the underlying philosophical basis of what we call Hinduism, Hinduism is not a single logical belief system like Judaism or Christianity. Rather, it is a collage made up of all the religious beliefs of the Indian subcontinent. The word derives from the Persian word for Indian used by the Muslims when they first arrived in India around A.D. 1200 to describe the religion of the inhabitants. *Hindu* originally meant the region watered by the river Indus. This gives us a vivid illustration for Hinduism, likening it to a long ancient river into which many tributaries flowed for more than three thousand years, a river that has frequently changed its channels and finishes in a huge delta splitting up into many streams. Indians call it *sanatana dharma* (eternal law).

This is not a creedal religion based on revelation; it is based on speculation with an infinite capacity for accommodating to each new set of religious beliefs that arrived in India and syncretizing with them. Today, it varies from the extreme subtleties of philosophical Hinduism to the naive animism and crude idolatry of village Hinduism. It exists in polytheistic, pantheistic, monotheistic, and atheistic forms. It is based on the Vedic hymns and sacrifices of the light-skinned Aryans with their pantheon of gods, who came sweeping into India from the north, mixed together with some of the beliefs of the Indus Valley civilization and the religion of the dark-skinned Dravidians in the south. Doubtless there was some syncretistic identification of one set of introduced gods with those already part of indigenous belief. It thus illustrates the kind of religious mixture described in the opening paragraph.

The Aryan priests established themselves as the uppermost Brahmin class, custodians of the rituals and the sacred scriptures, the Vedas. Neither women nor members of the lowest class (Sudras) were permitted to hear the sacred Vedas. The Rig-Veda is claimed by some Hindus to be the oldest human religious document in existence (1000 B.C.). The conquered Dravidian people of the south became the lowest Sudra castes: *varna*, the word for caste, means literally "color." The Aryan warrior aristocracy and the merchant-tradesmen formed the two Kshatriya and Vaisya middle-caste classes. Members of the three higher classes saw their lives in four stages—first, the student; second, the married householder begetting sons; third, the middle-aged man retreating to the forest for meditation; and fourth, the wandering holy man. The third stage was often ignored, and the fourth was not mandatory.

Essentially three different routes to salvation are recognized in Hinduism:

1. *Jnana marga*, the way of knowledge, including Yoga, open to those who can understand the truth of the Vedas, and especially the more philosophical part of them, the Upanishads. Sapphir Athyal described it as "the most sophisticated system of thought ever devised by man."

2. *Karma marga*, the way of duties, obedience, good deeds, and correct rituals that enables the Hindu to climb up the social ladder (over thousands of rebirths) until reborn as a Brahmin male and perhaps ultimately achieving salvation.

3. *Bhakti marga*, the way of devotion and love to a personal god (mainly Vishnu or Shiva). In such forms of pseudomonotheistic Hinduism, there may be a kind of salvation by the grace of God. Thus, Ramanuja (A.D. 1017–1137) taught the need for total surrender to God and the necessity of kitten salvation (the tigress carries her helpless cubs) rather than monkey salvation (the baby has to hang on to mother like grim death). Did these ideas originate perhaps from osmosis with Nestorian or Syrian Christianity in south India? It is controversial whether they did or not, but they provide words to explain salvation by faith in God's grace.

The Hindu pantheon contains gods mentioned in the Rig-Veda like the old sky god Dyaus (cognate with the Greek Zeus) and the wise god Varuna, guardian of the cosmic order (cognate with Uranus), suggesting some continuity with the gods of Europe and Iran. The other Aryan gods include Indra, god of war and rain; Mitra, the god of friendship and covenant; Agni, the god of the sacrificial fire; and Surya, god of the sun. The Vedic god Rudra becomes identified with Shiva, traces of whom may be found in the Indus Valley civilization at Harappa.

Theologically, all Hindu gods may be seen as personifications of the impersonal Brahman. The Trimurti (the one with three forms, not in any way to be confused with the Christian Trinity) of Brahma the creator, Vishnu the preserver, and Shiva the destroyer never seems to have caught on, though bhakti sects of personal devotion to Vishnu or Shiva dominate the Indian peninsula. Vishnu had ten incarnations, of which Rama and Krishna were the most famous. There is potential confusion here if Jesus is seen only as an incarnation of the Father. The female consorts of the Trimurti have been worshiped—Sarasvati, consort of Brahma, goddess of wisdom; Laksmi, consort of Vishnu (she has incarnations in parallel with her spouse); and Parvati, consort of Shiva. The worshipers of Shakti, the active power of the godhead conceived in feminine terms as a mother goddess, form the third great bhakti sect.

A Historical Outline of Hinduism in India

I. The Vedic Period, 2000–600 B.C.

     A synthesis between polytheistic sacrificial Aryan religion and pantheistic monism of the Upanishads.

II. The Pantheistic Period, 600 B.C.–A.D. 300

     Anticlerical reaction (Jainism and Buddhism) and Hindu renaissance (the Bhagavad Gita).

III. The Monotheistic Puranic Period, A.D. 300–1200

The arrival of Syrian (Nestorian) Christianity in the south and the development of Shivaistic and Vaishnavistic bhakti movements.

IV. The Medieval Period, A.D. 1200–1750

Mogul emperors (Muslims) in Delhi and strong monotheistic influence. The attempted syncretism of Kabir and Guru Nanak (Sikhism).

V. The Modern Period, A.D. 1750 to the present

The rise and fall of the British Empire, and the varied responses to Christianity of refusal (the Arya Samaj), syncretism (the Brahmo Samaj), and counterattack, represented by the following men.

Ramakrishna (1836–86) studied world religions in turn, reading their scriptures, praying their prayers, and he concluded that all are virtually identical.

Vivekenanda (1863–1902) carried this idea to the West and initiated the idea of the spiritual East and the materialistic West.

Mohandas Karamchand Gandhi (1869–1948) is deservedly seen as a great human being and man of the people, but he was influenced as much by John Ruskin, William Morris, and Leo Tolstoy as by the Sermon on the Mount. Gandhi-ji attacked the caste system and rehabilitated the Untouchables as Harijan, "the people of God." His violent assassination was a blow to the doctrine of karma, "for if all misfortune is the fruit of ancient deeds, then such a violent death should be evidence of a gravely sinful past," according to Stephen Neill.

Sarvepalli Radhakrishnan (1888–1975), a former professor of Eastern religions and ethics at Oxford and then president of India, was bitterly opposed to Christianity, according to Stephen Neill. He classified religions in reverse order—beginning with primitive animistic religions that use idols, including much popular Hinduism, at the bottom. Then a slight improvement were religions believing in incarnations (Vaishnavism and Christianity!); then there were religions believing in a personal God (Judaism and Islam); but the topmost and most superior religion was that in which God was an impersonal force—spiritual Hinduism. The philosophical Hindu may be a formidable opponent for the Christian apologist. Radhakrishnan suggested that karma did not mean total fatalistic determinism. Though past cause determined the hand of cards you were dealt in the game of life, skillful play even with such a hand might achieve great things.

Jainism

Mahavira (540–468 B.C.), a Kshatriya, claimed to be the twenty-fourth Tirthankara (or "Fordmaker" across the river of transmigration). He repudiated the Vedas, the Hindu gods, all images, sacrifices, and caste in favor of an atheistic religion of salvation by passionless detachment. He retained the concept of transmigration and saw karma as an almost physical encrustation, like barnacles on a ship's hull.

Renouncing of family life is followed by renouncing of all possessions (including clothes!). *Ahimsa*, the nonkilling of animals, requires straining all drink and wearing a cloth over the mouth to avoid swallowing insects, and it excludes Jains from farming, for plowing might inadvertently kill insects. Vegetables are also deemed to be living beings with souls (but possessing only one of the five senses), so the ultimate renunciation is of all food and final death by self-starvation. Jains may still be found in Gujerat.

Buddhism

Siddhartha Gautama (563–483 B.C.) was an aristocrat Kshatriya, born in Nepal. After marriage and parenthood, he left home around 531 B.C. in what is called the Great Renunciation and began a regimen of extreme asceticism, of the kind taught by his contemporary Kshatriya Mahavira. Finally through meditation, he came to the Great Enlightenment, an experience of nirvana, and so became a Buddha (enlightened one).

His teaching on salvation is summed up in his Four Noble Truths:

1. Life is characterized by suffering or unsatisfactoriness.
2. Suffering (or the unsatisfactoriness of life) is caused by desire.
3. If desire can be eliminated, then suffering will be eliminated.
4. The Eightfold Path describes the necessary steps to eliminate desire.

Gautama described his teaching as the Middle Way, between extreme Jain asceticism and more traditional Hinduism.

To understand the sociohistorical significance of Gautama is to see him initiating an anticlerical movement against Hinduism, teaching nonviolence, or nonkilling, which he learned from the Jains. At one stroke, he made Brahmins redundant because nonkilling meant abolishing sacrifices! It was a master stroke, liberating people from caste bondage, from dependence on the Brahmins, while preserving the underlying monistic presuppositions: belief in reincarnation and karma.

The Hindus ultimately counterattacked in a brilliant anti-Buddhist tract called the Bhagavad Gita, in which Arjuna the warrior prince influenced by Buddhist teaching about nonkilling is reasoned with by his charioteer, who is actually Krishna, an incarnation of Vishnu in disguise. He learns that his enemies are an illusion, and that if he kills them, they will forthwith be reincarnated again, so he should fulfill his caste duties as a warrior. This secondary Hindu scripture Smirti (what is remembered), written about 200 B.C., effectively drove Buddhism out of India, where it is no longer a significant religious force, though it spread to Persia (now Iran), Sri Lanka, Indochina, and the Far East.

Theravada. The original teaching of Gautama, called Theravada (teaching of the elders), is enshrined in the Buddhist canon written in the Pali language about four hundred years after Gautama's death. Gautama is seen as a gifted human teacher who propounded the Four Noble Truths and pioneered the Eightfold Path to enlightenment (but was only one of twenty-eight such enlightened human beings, or Buddhas). Religious professionals (somewhat like monks) live in monasteries, where they share the sustenance provided for them by the wider Buddhist community. This form of Buddhism (much syncretized with underlying animistic folk beliefs) is the dominant religion and social force in Sri Lanka, Burma, Thailand, and Indochina.

Mahayana. The ability of monistic religion to mutate and metamorphose freely is demonstrated by this fresh development. Subsequently, this original Buddhism, which had broken away from Hinduism, all but resyncretizes with the Hindu pantheon. Thus, Gautama Buddha himself is deified as a god to be worshiped, along with a new pantheon of godlike figures called Bodhisattvas, beings who, having achieved the borders of nirvana, remain brimming with merit and grace in order to assist humans to nirvana.

Whereas Theravada offered nirvana only to religious professionals belonging to the monastic community, the new popular forms of theistic Buddhism offered salvation to laypeople as well. Nirvana was within immediate reach of all who sought the grace of Buddha and the Bodhisattvas. Some of this development took place in Persia and in the Hellenistic kingdom of Gandhara (conquered by Alexander the Great, in present-day Pakistan), so that early statues of Buddha and the Bodhisattvas show marked Hellenistic influence. They called this *Mahayana*, the "greater vehicle" that would carry many to salvation, compared with Theravada, derisively described as *Hinayana*, or the "lesser vehicle" that could save only a few human beings.

It should be understood, however, that these two great branches of Buddhist teaching are not mutually exclusive or irreconcilable. They may be found coexisting side by side or even mixing together in the same countries, much as Calvinism and Arminianism coexist side by side in Protestant Christian countries.

Tibetan Tantric Buddhism. Such Buddhism involves occult, magic, and mystical elements, and erotic elements from Shaktism (Shakti was the Hindu mother goddess). Under Chinese Communist rule, the number of monks has decreased significantly.

Within Mahayana Buddhism, several streams evolved as it traveled from Persia (where it was in contact with Nestorian Christianity) across central Asia to China, where it encountered formidable ideological barriers.

Considerable mutation and metamorphosis were necessary to make Buddhism acceptable in China. The notions of renouncing family and childless celibacy seemed irresponsible and impossible for the Chinese. Renunciation was untenable, for though a man might desert his family, he could never escape society. Buddhists severed ties with parents but then organized themselves in spiritual families of teachers and pupils; they seemed to be cowardly escapists in Chinese eyes. Mahayana sidestepped monasticism by producing varieties of popular Buddhism that offered "instant" nirvana and avoided awkward questions of the present location of ancestors.

Ancestor Worship

As each generation dies, it needs to be comforted and cared for by the correct ritual observances of the living. This double merit system ensures blessing for the departed dead and for their descendants. Ancestors without caring relatives can haunt and demonize the living. Such beliefs were widespread in China, Korea, and Japan. The living viewed their bodies as extensions of their ancestors, and they were responsible to live worthily of their ancestors. Male children were essential to the proper carrying out of ancestor worship.

Confucianism

K'ung-Fu-tzu, Master Kung (551–479 B.C.), Latinized as Confucius, China's first philosophic genius, was the first demythologizer. He reinterpreted the primal religion of China from superstitious magic into an ethical system. This greatly honored philosopher changed a superstitious people believing in good and bad luck into a moral people concerned with right and wrong behavior. *Jen* means to be "authentically human," ideal sainthood achieved through virtue.

Confucius died despairing of persuading the ruler of his city-state to put his teaching into practice. Not until the great Emperor Wu of the Han dynasty (140–87 B.C.) did Confucianism become state orthodoxy in China.

No other single person has so deeply influenced the cultures and society of eastern Asia. Korea and Japan both accepted Buddhism to provide the philosophy and Confucianism the ethics lacking in Korean shamanism and Japanese Shinto.

Confucius was agnostic about God, referring to an impersonal "heaven" and only once "the emperor above." He did have to come to terms with ancestor worship, but even there he transformed filial piety from respect for or fear of the spirits of the dead into obedience toward elders while they are still living. This principle extends to all relationships—the junior respects his senior, the mentor who reciprocates with affectionate responsibility toward his protégé. In Japan, this principle known as *oyabun-kobun* (father part, child part) governs many other areas of life—in business, in education, and even in the relationship between pastor and flock.

The Five Relationships provide a sequence of moral priorities for life as well as for the moral dilemmas of literature and drama. "Teacher-disciple" is not one of the five, possibly because Chinese bureaucracy had a paranoiac fear that a new teacher would gain a following that might result in a revolution.

Relationship		Chinese		Japanese	Korean
Lord and retainer	2	Mandarin temporary	1	Hereditary lord	2
Father and son	1	Filial piety	2		3
Older and younger brothers	3		3		4
Husband and wife	4		4		5
Friend and friend	5		5		1

Though all three countries are strongly influenced by Confucian relationships, their emphases are now different. The Japanese emphasize the hierarchical relationship with the feudal lord (or company president); the Chinese stress the familial relationships; the Koreans stress the friend-friend between the classmate peer group. Church growth in Korea may owe something to Confucius because classmates join the same churches.

Taoism

In China, Taoism represents original Chinese folk animism together with occult and magical elements. Because of competition with Buddhism, it later developed into something much more philosophical. The onerous requirements of Confucianism, with its relationships and duties, were balanced by the Taoist "watercourse way" of least resistance. The foolish man trying to escape from his own shadow and the sound of his own frenetic footsteps would escape all that pressure if he would lie down in the shade! There are clear affinities between Taoist quietism and Buddhist meditation. If the Brahman in Hinduism and the Busshin in Buddhism represented the underlying principle of the universe, then that concept already existed in China as the Tao (the Way).

Avalokitesvara, the Bodhisattva who lowers his eyes, patron saint of Tibet, possibly by assimilation with the Tibetan goddess Tara, undergoes a sex change to become the goddess of mercy, the kindly madonna Kwanyin in China, or Kannonsama in Japan. If Buddhism had to mutate to become acceptable in China, it also influenced Chinese religion. The Chinese people have always been most pragmatic, and what has survived as Chinese religion is essentially chop suey, leftovers from all the religions that the Chinese have tried over the course of a long history, thrown into an appetizing hash.

The most brilliant contextualized translation appears in the Chinese translation of the prologue to John's gospel: "In the beginning was the Tao, and the Tao was with God, and the Tao was God," so that Jesus later reveals Himself to His disciples: "I am the true and living Tao." Philo's concept of the Logos seems to find a clear dynamic equivalent in the Tao.

Shinto

Shinto means "the way of the gods." It represents the primal religious animism of Japan, a worldview that related the Japanese to the natural beauty of their islands and the sun goddess alleged to have created it. It exists in several forms: Shrine Shinto with its countless local shrines, and its priests who perform cleansing ceremonies and officiate at the dedication of building sites and at traditional weddings; State Shinto, which enabled the militarists to manipulate the Japanese nation into imperialistic wars of aggression; and Imperial Shinto, the religion of the royal family, the descendants of the sun goddess, who offer sacrifices for the sins of the people each year. Shinto lacks philosophy and ethics, which may explain why the Japanese accepted Buddhism to supply the first and Confucianism the second.

Having seen something of the indigenous religious beliefs, we return to the mutations of Mahayana Buddhism that developed in China and Japan.

Zen Sects

Indian meditation (*Dhyana*), the seventh stage of Yoga technique, became Ch'an meditation in China around A.D. 700 and ultimately Zen in Japan. Enlightenment is achieved by self-effort through solving conundrums set by the teacher that bring the aspirant to the point of intellectual impasse. Its atheistic disciplined minds appealed especially to the Japanese warrior class.

The Pure Land Sects

These sects emerged around A.D. 334 in China (though originating farther west). They offer salvation by grace, that is, by the power of another through calling on the name of the Bodhisattva Amitabha or Amida, the lord of light in faith. The Pure Land or Western Paradise is heaven presided over by Amida, like a loving heavenly father. The wicked have more hope of salvation than the righteous, who are tempted to trust in their own righteousness instead of in the mercy and merit of Amida. Those who call on his name in faith enter the "right established state," similar to a state of grace in Catholicism or assurance of salvation in Protestantism. Such people will enter the Western Paradise when they die.

Was this Bodhisattva, the Buddha of the West, so-called because he was modeled on Apollo, the Greek god of the sun in Gandhara, or Ahuramazda, the Zoroastrian god of light in Persia, or could there have been some osmosis from Nestorian Christianity and Jesus, the Light of the World? The teaching of salvation by faith in the grace of God suggests some measure of influence from or syncretism with Christian beliefs

Nichiren Buddhism

This nationalistic cult in Japan was founded by a remarkable thirteenth-century Japanese patriot called Nichiren. It uses the Lotus Sutra as a mantra, chanting endlessly "Namu myoohoo renge kyoo" (Hail to the Lotus Sutra of the perfect truth), and uses a worship object with the names of Buddhas and Bodhisattvas and demons written in Chinese characters upon it. Sookagakkai is a relatively recent modern sect based on Nichirenism, which has formed its own political party called the Clean Government party.

Sikhism

The ability of Hinduism to metamorphose when confronted with another religious belief system is well illustrated by a Hindu bhakti sect, which developed during the period when monotheistic Islam had been introduced into India. This resulted in the teaching of Guru Nanak (who was a contemporary of Martin Luther) and his nine successor gurus, which is set forth in the sacred scriptures of Sikh religion, the Granth Sahib. This collection of hymns with its exalted doctrine of one god is enshrined in every Sikh temple, and in many it is read from cover to cover by a team of readers every weekend (it's the same length as a Christian Bible!).

Sikhism was a protest reform movement reacting against nominal Hinduism and nominal Islam during the Mogul period when Islamic rulers controlled India. "There is neither Hindu nor Moslem, so whose path will I follow? I will follow God's path. God is neither Hindu nor Moslem and the path I follow is God's," said Guru Nanak.

Sikhism remains a monotheistic bhakti sect of Hinduism, which uses both Hindu (e.g., Ram and Hari) and Muslim (e.g., Allah, Alakh, and Agam) names for God, and which theoretically abandoned caste. Its underlying philosophy is still monistic, but it has an attractive doctrine of God, of which its stipulation that God is not incarnating is the biggest obstacle to

Sikhs understanding Christian belief. They do have a concept of self-interest or ego, close to the Christian idea of indwelling sinfulness. God's look of grace will deliver from sin.

Sikhs may be recognized traditionally by the five *k*s—the uncut hair (*kesa*), the comb (*kangha*; not the turban as such), special underpants (*kachs*), the dagger (*kirpan*), and the steel bracelet (*kara*). Persecuted by the Mogul emperors, who martyred two of the ten gurus, the Sikhs of the Punjab developed as a formidable fighting force characterized by great courage. They have a great love of music and are extremely hospitable: the basement of the temple serves as a restaurant where all eat together as brothers, regardless of caste. Outside the Punjab many modern Sikhs abandon most of the *k*s except for the bracelet when attending the temple, and teenagers brought up in the generation gap between cultures find themselves torn between tradition and modernity.

Conclusions

All this information shows that we cannot oversimplify what we say about Eastern religions, which are extraordinarily diverse and complicated systems. The following points seem worth making.

1. These belief systems are based on underlying monist philosophy, which is entirely different from Judaism, Christianity, and Islam. The effect is to make it very difficult for a less-well-informed monist and a badly informed Christian to understand what the other is trying to explain. The concepts of creation, individual responsibility for sin, forgiveness of sins, and the new birth seem virtually incomprehensible. Arguments about the historical Resurrection are meaningless. "I think; therefore, I am" becomes "I have the illusion of thinking and so I have the illusion of being!" The Christian evangelist may be excused if he is tempted to think that his hearers have been brainwashed to prevent their understanding.

2. Although neither Ramanuja's Advaita bhakti teaching on salvation by grace nor the Buddhist Pure Land sects' salvation by

faith in the power of another can be identified with Christian belief, both provide categories and language we can use to help explain what Christians believe.

3. Buddhists and Hindus alike are hungry for salvation—from a cycle of endlessly repeated rebirths and a succession of pointless lives, weighed down by karmic encrustation like barnacles on a ship's hull, or on the other hand, from the unsatisfactoriness and suffering caused by their own sinful human desires. There is great attractiveness in the world-transfiguring gospel of Jesus rather than the world-denying aspects of ascetic Hinduism and Buddhism. However, Christian jargon like *new birth* is liable to be misunderstood, owing to its confusion with reincarnation rebirths.

4. Forgiveness of sins, deliverance from karma offered in the gospel, and the indwelling power of the Holy Spirit to reproduce the beautiful holiness of Jesus in our lives are crucial aspects of the gospel that need to be carefully explained. They are most attractive to needy human beings.

5. Determination to touch the heart and establish empathy and to build real friendships is basic. No amount of talk about what Jesus *can* do will avail unless people can see evidence of what He has actually *done* in our lives. This requires great patience in establishing mutual confidence and providing opportunity and time for the seeker after truth to see the reality of Jesus Christ working in our lives through His Holy Spirit. With our Western passion for the necessity of intellectual grasp of the gospel, we may be mystified by their reversal of our priorities— entering into a genuine experience of Christ through His Spirit first, and only then working it all out intellectually afterward.

For Further Reading

General Studies
Fernando, A. *The Christian's Attitude to Other Religions.* Wheaton: Tyndale, 1987.

Neill, S. *Christian Faith and Other Faiths.* Leicester: InterVarsity Press, 1970.

Smart, N. *Background to the Long Search.* London: BBC, 1977.

Hinduism and Sikhism

Allen, J. *Yoga: A Christian Analysis.* Leicester: InterVarsity Press, 1983.

Basham, A. L. *The Origins and Development of Classical Hinduism.* Oxford: Oxford University Press, 1989.

Zaehner, R. C. *Hindu Scriptures.* London: Dent, 1966.

———. *Hinduism.* Oxford: Oxford University Press, 1962.

Buddhism

Chen, K. *Buddhism in China.* Princeton, NJ: Princeton University Press, 1974.

Conze, E. *Buddhist Scriptures.* Harmondsworth and New York: Penguin, 1959.

Covell, R. *Confucius, the Buddha and Christ.* Maryknoll, NY: Orbis Books, 1986.

Yamamoto, J. I. *Beyond Buddhism.* Downers Grove: InterVarsity Press, 1982

JUDAISM
by John Fieldsend

Many Christians have shared with me their perplexity that when they try to get into a discussion about their faith with their Jewish friends, there seems to be no meeting; the conversation seems to pass each other. We need to ask why that is. At first it may seem natural to us that because the Christian faith originated in Judaism, and because we have so many of our Scriptures in common, with Jewish people we should have the least communication problems. We begin by looking briefly into the reasons why that is not so.

We have to understand that although Jewish people have a continuity of history as the people of Abraham, Isaac, and Jacob, there has been a vast development of their faith over the centuries. That development is marked not only by continuity but also by periods of quite radical change. So marked was it, especially in the first century of the common era,[1] that one Jewish scholar has written, "In this relatively short period of time two great religions developed—Rabbinic Judaism and Christianity."[2]

There is a Jewish tradition that Moses seeks permission from God to attend in spirit a lecture given by Rabbi Akiva.[3] As the lecture and the ensuing discussion develop, he has no idea what they are talking about until Akiva discloses that he is expounding a legal teaching brought down by Moses from Mount Sinai. Geza Vermes questioned whether Jesus of Nazareth would have been equally dumbfounded had He eavesdropped incognito at the Council of Nicaea where His nature was the subject of much heated debate.

The reason for this radical change is of course the destruction of the temple in C.E. 70, the sacking of Jerusalem in C.E. 134, and the beginning of Jewish diaspora, which was to be the Jewish experience for the ensuing centuries. Up to that point Judaism, apart from the seventy years of the Babylonian captivity, was a sacrificial religion. The covenant was signed and sealed by the shedding of blood (see Gen. 15:17; Lev. 17:11). Because of the constant temptations of the pagan cults to share in their immoral practices, Jewish sacrifices could take place only at the Jerusalem temple. No temple—no sacrifices; it was as simple as that.

But it becomes plain that Judaism without temple and sacrifices is very different from its biblical origins. The new leaders became known as rabbis; hence, the name for the new Judaism is rabbinic Judaism. The Christian faith also developed out of Judaism at that time. Its basis is not that the sacrifices have been abolished because there is no longer a temple, but that they are no longer needed because they have been fulfilled in the one

complete sacrifice of Jesus (see Heb. 9:11–15). We need therefore to understand that when we are speaking of atonement in
sacrificial terms, we are speaking of something that is alien to rabbinic Judaism, and it needs careful explanation. We cannot take it
for granted that our Jewish friends will relate easily or naturally
to it.

Another area that can become a minefield for noncommunica-
tion is the understanding of the Messiah. Belief in the person of
the Messiah has been replaced in many areas of Judaism by the
concept of a messianic age. And in more orthodox branches of
Judaism, where a personal Messiah is still awaited, we need to
realize that in rabbinic Judaism He is a purely human figure, and
His ministry is very different from Christian expectations.

If these are some of the possible potential areas for miscommu-
nication between Christians and Jews, we also have to consider
other responses from our own Christian friends, which may be
the cause of perplexity for us when we express the desire to
share the gospel with Jewish people. And we need to be clear in
our own minds just how we understand the position of a Jewish
person who comes to faith in Jesus as his or her Messiah. We
know that when people from other faiths become Christians,
they cease to be members of their previous faith community. But
what about Jews who commit themselves to Jesus, their Jewish
Messiah? Is it not reasonable that they continue to call themselves Jews? Certainly Paul did. We shall now look at some of
these aspects in more detail.

Inevitably, within this brief space, I have to be very selective in
the areas to cover. The main purpose is to give you the confidence to understand that though for present-day Judaism the possibility that Jesus might be the Messiah does not seem remotely
plausible, the picture is very different if we look back into earlier
Jewish sources. As Jewish people are quick to say, Judaism is not
a faith that has become fossilized in the past. It is a living, developing faith for today. We are very happy to accept this analysis

but would wish our friends, both Jewish and Christian, to be open to the possibility that at least some of these developments might not have been in the right direction. Centuries of conflict with Christianity, for which the church must take the larger share of the blame, have driven Judaism to take a direction away from beliefs that might be construed as Christian. That is understandable, but these developments have also distanced Judaism from its biblical roots and from its Messiah.

Much of this discussion will concentrate on rabbinic material not easily available to the nonspecialist Christian reader. Much relevant New Testament and other Christian material has had to be omitted. However, this is generally easily obtainable, and to this end, the section "For Further Reading" is included.

Atonement? Who Needs It?

Christianity starts with one idea about man; Judaism with another. The idea that Judaism starts with is that man is created in the likeness of God. You do not have to go far, according to Judaism, to discover that it is possible to bring forth the divine within you and the divine in other men. . . . It is with that opportunity that I begin as a Jew. Christianity begins with the basic assumption that man is essentially depraved and sinful—that left to himself he can do nothing. He has to be saved. . . . I have never thought of salvation. It is not a Jewish problem.

So wrote Rabbi Abraham Heschel.[4] Christians may feel that the rabbi misunderstands the doctrine of original sin; but even allowing for that, there is obviously a fundamental divergence today on this subject between Christians and Jews.

From the point of view of the Jewish Scriptures alone, the human race, though originally created in the image of God, is a fallen race. It grieved God that He had made humankind; the human heart is deceitful above all things; there is none that does good, not even one. These are not isolated proof texts but part of a consistent theme that runs through the Scriptures regarding the fallen nature of humankind. Indeed, the magnitude of the problem was reflected in the radical nature of the remedy: vicarious life sacrifice. Consider this verse: "For the life of the flesh is in the blood, and I have given it to you upon the altar to make atonement for your souls; for it is the blood that makes atonement for the soul" (Lev. 17:11).

There is a watering down of the biblical teaching of the fallenness of humankind and the need for an objective, God-given atonement. For the rabbis, the problem is not so big that only God can solve it; people have within themselves all that is needful. But of course, Jewish theologians are not blind to human sinfulness. Rabbinic Judaism teaches that within a person reside two inclinations, a good and a bad (a *yetzer ha-tov* and a *yetzer ha-ra*). But these are only inclinations; they can be resisted and channeled in the power of the human spirit. And even the evil inclination is not absolutely evil. It can be described as the inner drive, the drive to get on, the drive to survive, the drive to procreate. Were it not for the *yetzer ha-ra*, remarks a rabbinic Midrash on Genesis 7:9, a man would not build a house, marry, have children, or engage in commerce.

In a similar vein is a legend in the Talmud (Yoma 69b) that the men of the Great Synagogue wanted to kill the *yetzer ha-ra*, who warned them that if they were successful, the world would go down (i.e., come to an end). They therefore imprisoned him (i.e., the *yetzer*) for three days and then searched the land for a new laid egg without finding one (i.e., all the hens had lost their reproductive capacity).

We might summarize that the evil inclination relates to the practicalities of living out humanity while the good inclination has to do with the spiritual dimension, the relationship with God, though in Judaism this dichotomy is much less evident than it is in much traditional Christianity. Evil is seen as using what is God-given in ways that are self-centered rather than God-centered. The important thing to understand is that the evil inclination need not be, in New Testament terms, put to death, put off, crucified; indeed, it must not be. Rather, it needs to be channeled and directed in the service of God.

The Jewish view of the physical world is that it, too, is intrinsically good. We have the privilege and, indeed, the obligation to derive pleasure from it and to avail ourselves of its goodness. These are points that Christians need to hear, but for the moment we shall concentrate on the nature of the Jewish view of the fallenness of the created order and its remedy, and see how far they have developed from their biblical beginnings. The thrust of much Jewish teaching is that the prophets were already guiding Israel away from sacrifices toward the sufficiency of repentance and right action. This teaching is based on such passages as the following:

> Samuel said:
> "Has the LORD as great delight in burnt offerings and sacrifices,
> As in obeying the voice of the LORD?
> Behold, to obey is better than sacrifice,
> And to heed than the fat of rams" (1 Sam. 15:22).

> For You do not desire sacrifice,
>   or else I would give it;
> You do not delight in burnt offering (Ps. 51:16).

> With what shall I come before the LORD,
> And bow myself before the High God?
> Shall I come before Him with burnt offerings,
> With calves a year old?
> Will the LORD be pleased with thousands of rams,
> Ten thousand rivers of oil?
> Shall I give my firstborn for my transgression,

The fruit of my body for the sin of my soul?
He has shown you, O man, what is good;
And what does the LORD require of you
But to do justly,
To love mercy,
And to walk humbly with your God? (Mic. 6:6–8).

It would surely be more accurate to say that the prophets were preaching against a false security in the automatic efficacy of the sacrifices without the need for repentance and right personal and social behavior; they were not against sacrifices per se. That is clear from the way David concludes the well-known Psalm 51.

Orthodox Judaism sees the temple sacrifices as no longer relevant and necessary, yet still looks forward to the rebuilding of the temple and the reinstitution of the sacrifices during the messianic era. The Amidah prayer of the Siddur concludes "that the Temple may be speedily rebuilt in our days. . . . And there we will serve Thee with awe. . . . Then shall the offering of Judah and Jerusalem be pleasant unto the Lord, as in days of old, and as in ancient years."[5]

This tension within Orthodox Judaism has not been satisfactorily resolved. The Reform and Liberal movements within Judaism have so reformed the liturgy that it no longer anticipates the restoration of temple or sacrifice, viewing any objective doctrine of atonement of this nature as part of a primitive religion discarded a long time ago by modern persons come of age.

We can now begin to understand why, in the inevitable absence of sacrificial atonement in Judaism since C.E. 70, the biblical doctrine of sin has had to be toned down. We do, however, have to ask whether this is consistent with the teaching of the Talmud.

Why are idolaters lustful? Because they did not stand at Mount Sinai. For when the serpent came upon Eve he injected lust into her: [as for] the Israelites who stood at Mount Sinai, their lustfulness departed; the idolaters, who did not stand at Mount Sinai, their lustfulness did not depart (Shabbat 145b–146a).

This is saying that following Eve's fall, depravity did enter into the human race, but Israel, by taking upon itself the yoke of the Torah, was delivered from it. ("Idolaters" in this context is to be understood as "Gentiles.")

However, the footnote of the Soncino edition of the Talmud explains that those who accept the moral teaching of the Torah (implying not only Jews) are freed. This "reinterpretation" of the Talmud releases gentile Christians from the traditional charge of idolatry. Rabbi Sylvia Rothschild, in the Easter Sunday 1991 "Heart of the Matter" television program, explained that for a Christian to believe in the divinity of Jesus was not idolatry, but for a messianic Jew so to believe clearly was!

Rabbi Dr. Dan Cohn-Sherbok, a visiting professor at the University of Essex, in an article entitled "Why Today's Society Needs to Reconsider the Forgotten Doctrine of Original Sin,"[6] writes,

The rabbis taught that death was the result of Adam's disobedience; they did not teach a doctrine of original sin. Nonetheless, they believed that the wickedness of man was great in the earth, and that every imagination of the thoughts of his heart was only evil continually (Genesis 6:5); they explained this condition by positing the existence of the evil inclination.

Dr. Cohn-Sherbok continues, "Drawing on this tradition Paul taught that sin came into the world through Adam and one man's trespass led to the condemnation of all men (Romans 5:18)." He then traces this line of thought through Augustine and the Protestant Reformers—they stressed the complete depravity of human beings—and concludes, "In the modern world this Judeo-Christian understanding of inherent human evil has largely been lost." In favorably quoting Paul in Romans 5:18, Dr. Cohn-Sherbok is not willing to accept the consequences of verse 19: "For as by one man's disobedience many were made sinners, so also by one Man's obedience many will be made righteous." Nevertheless, a new look at the doctrine of original sin is not entirely off the Jewish agenda.

The Messiah—Biblical Teaching and Jewish Understanding

At the center of the divide between Judaism and Christianity is the figure of Jesus. Is He the Messiah? What are Jewish messianic beliefs and expectations, and on what are they based?

The twelfth of the Thirteen Principles of Faith in the Siddur, the Jewish prayer book, reads, "I believe with perfect faith in the coming of the Messiah, and, though he tarry, I wait daily for his coming."

Rabbi Shmuel Arkush, on the previously mentioned television program, portrayed the person and work of the Messiah as seen in Orthodox Judaism in this way:

The Messiah will be somebody who will rebuild the third Temple, he is somebody who will ingather the exiled Jewish people, he is somebody who will bring peace to the Jewish people and through them to the whole world. These are the three major jobs of the Messiah; and this is what the Jewish people are awaiting as their Messiah. Christianity has taken our patented invention, the Messiah, our man, and elevated him to great heights of being the Son of God, which from a Jewish point of view is unnecessary, and not only unnecessary but in fact it excludes him from being the Messiah. These three jobs are still waiting to be done.

Rabbi Sylvia Rothschild clearly summarized the difference: "The Messiah for Christians as I understand it is that he has to be divine. He is, if you like, man's God whereas the Jewish Messiah would be God's man. And the split is in that sense theologically total."

On the other hand in Reform and Liberal Judaism, belief in a personal Messiah is replaced by belief in a messianic age. Its beliefs were stated in the Reform "Pittsburgh Platform" of 1885:

> We recognize in the modern era of universal culture of heart and intellect the approaching of the realization of Israel's great messianic hope for the establishment of the kingdom of truth, justice and peace among all men. We consider ourselves no longer a nation, but a religious community, and therefore expect neither a return to Palestine, nor a sacrificial worship under the sons of Aaron, nor the restoration of any of the laws concerning the Jewish state.

The rise of anti-Semitism, bringing a response in the rise of Zionism, and the beginnings of the Shoah (the Holocaust) already seen in the 1930s, led to a revision of the "Pittsburgh Platform" in 1937, in Columbus, Ohio. There a more positive statement about return to Palestine, the land hallowed by memories and hopes, was introduced: "We affirm the obligation of all Jewry to aid in its upbuilding as a Jewish homeland . . . a haven or refuge for the oppressed. . . . This is our messianic goal."

It is obvious that both descriptions, the Orthodox and the Reform, preclude any idea that Jesus might be the Messiah.

What Do the Ancient Rabbis Say?

Let us take as one key test passage Isaiah 53, which modern rabbis, Orthodox, Reform, and Liberal, say has no messianic connotations. Yet Rabbi Moshe El-Sheikh of Safed wrote, "Our rabbis with one voice accept that the prophet is speaking of the King Messiah, and we ourselves shall adhere to the same view."

In the Babylonian Talmud (San 98b), we read, "The Messiah—what is his name?—The rabbis said: His name is 'Leper Scholar' as it is written 'surely he hath borne our griefs and carried our sorrows. Yet we did esteem him a leper, smitten by God and afflicted.' "

Rabbi Moshe Kohen ibn Crispin, writing in the middle of the fourteenth century, commented,

> The expression "My Servant" they [certain contemporary commentators] compare rashly with Isaiah 41:8 "thou Israel art my servant"; where the prophet is speaking of the people of Israel: here, however, he does not mention Israel, but simply says "My Servant": we cannot therefore understand the word in the same sense. . . . I am pleased to interpret it [i.e., Isaiah 53] in accordance with the teaching of our rabbis of King Messiah, and will be careful, so far as I am able, to adhere to the literal sense: thus, possibly, I shall be free from the forced and far-fetched interpretations of which others have been guilty.[7]

These interpretations of Isaiah 53 could be multiplied many times, but there are also other prophetic passages, such as the Bethlehem prophecy of Micah, which is accepted as messianic by the ancient rabbis, and which we find fulfilled in the life of Jesus.

The Bethlehem 5:2 prophecy is especially interesting in that it is accepted as messianic in the Targum Jonathan, written early in the second century C.E. Targums have "long enjoyed a sanctity second only to the Hebrew Text." To quote Targum Jonathan:

> And you, O Bethlehem Ephrath, you who were too small to be numbered among the thousands of the house of Judah, from you shall come forth before Me the Messiah, to exercise dominion over Israel, he whose name was mentioned from before, from the days of creation.[8]

Abraham ibn Ezra, commenting on Isaiah 9:6, wrote, "There are some interpreters who say that 'Wonderful Counsellor, Mighty God, Everlasting Father' are names of God, and only 'Prince of Peace' is the name of the child. But according to my view . . . all are the names of the child."⁹

In the face of his own interpretation, Ibn Ezra went on to take the popular rabbinic view that Isaiah was taking the verse to refer to Hezekiah. The suggestion was that since Hezekiah would have been only thirty-nine years of age at the period of history he saw it as referring to, he could well be called a child. However, it is clear from its usage in the Hebrew Scriptures that *yeled* consistently means "child," and not "young man." We can conclude only that he was trying to avoid the inevitable conclusions of his own deductions as to the real identity of the Messiah.

In the time of Jesus, according to the records in the Talmud, the same debate had already begun, and it was to continue into the present time. Rabbi Hillel said,

> There shall be no Messiah for Israel, because they have already enjoyed him in the days of Hezekiah. Rabbi Joseph said: May God forgive him (for saying so). Now when did Hezekiah flourish? During the first Temple. Yet Zechariah, prophesying in the days of the second, pronounced: Rejoice greatly O daughter of Zion, shout for joy, O daughter of Jerusalem; behold, thy king cometh unto thee! He is just, and having salvation; and riding upon an ass, and upon a colt, the foal of an ass (Sanhedrin 99a).

On Jeremiah 23:6, Midrash Eicha (Lamentations) 1:51 comments, "What is the name of the King Messiah? To this answered Rabbi Abba bar Kahana: 'Jehovah is his name, for it is written, "This is the name whereby he shall be called—Jehovah Zidkenu."'"¹⁰

In fact, Dr. Alfred Edersheim (1825–89), an Austrian Jewish scholar who came to faith in Jesus and joined first the Presbyterian and later the Anglican ministry, has cataloged in his classic work *The Life and Times of Jesus the Messiah* over 450 Old Testament passages that were recognized by the ancient rabbis as prophecies of the Messiah. This whole outlook can be summarized in two Talmudic quotes: "All the prophets prophesied only for the days of the Messiah" (Sanhedrin 99a); and "The world was created only for the Messiah" (Sanhedrin 98b). The argument, therefore, between Jesus and the religious leaders of His day was not about whether certain passages in Scripture were messianic prophecies. The disagreement was on the nature of that messiahship.

What Kind of Messiah?

When we look deeper into the biblical prophecies regarding the Messiah, we find, in both the Old Testament and the New Testament, two threads of teaching that appear to give distinct and sometimes almost contrary pictures: one shows the Messiah's suffering and sacrifice (e.g., Isa. 53), and the other His sovereignty and eternity (e.g., Ps. 110). Christianity has brought these two streams together in the first and second comings of Jesus. He came first in humility to suffer and give His life as an atonement for sin. He will come again in power and glory to judge and to reign.

Judaism has sought to reconcile these by positing two Messiahs, who are described as Messiah Ben Joseph and Messiah Ben David. Messiah Ben Joseph is seen as the first commander of the army in the messianic wars. Having achieved many great victories, he is to die in a great battle in which Israel is defeated by Gog and Magog. His corpse lies in the streets of Jerusalem for forty days, but neither beast nor bird dares to touch it. Then Messiah Ben David comes and brings about the resurrection of his forerunner.

My son, the Messiah, shall be revealed with those who are with him, and those who remain shall rejoice four hundred years. And after these years my son, the Messiah, shall die, and all who draw breath. And the world shall be turned into primeval silence seven days, as it was at the first beginnings (4 Ezra 7:27–30).[11]

And the land shall mourn, every family apart (Zechariah. 12:12). Two have interpreted this verse. One said: "This is the mourning over the Messiah," and the other said: "This is the mourning over the Evil Inclination (which will be killed by God in the Messianic days)" (Sukkah 55b).

The rabbis have taught: The Holy One, blessed be He, will say to Messiah Ben David, may he be revealed soon in our days! "Ask of Me anything, and I will give it to you, for it is written, 'The Lord said unto me, Thou art My son, this day I have begotten thee, ask of Me and I will give thee the nations for thy inheritance (Psalm. 2:7–8).' And when he will see that Messiah Ben Joseph will be slain, he will say before Him 'Master of the world! I ask nothing of you except life!' God will say to him 'Even before you said "life" your father David prophesied about you, as it is written, "He asked life of Thee, Thou gavest it him" (Psalm. 21:5)' " (Sukkah 52a).

It has been said that the breach between Christian and current rabbinic views regarding the Messiah is, humanly speaking, unbridgeable. What I have sought to show is that there was, in the teaching of the ancient rabbis, an understanding of the messianic prophecies with which the New Testament fulfillment in Jesus is not in conflict.

Having now established that there is no biblical reason for Jewish people to reject the possibility that Jesus could be the Messiah, we shall now move on.

Is the Gospel for Jewish People?

Some Common Objections

Two Covenant Theology. Briefly stated, this position takes the viewpoint that Jewish people relate to God through the Mosaic covenant (i.e., Torah observance), whereas Gentiles receive God's covenant through faith in Jesus. It is agreed that salvation for the Gentiles came through the Jews, but it is not the way for the Jews. In Judaism and Christianity we have two equally valid faiths. We need dialogue to build up relationships. Evangelism destroys that trust.

Dispensational Theology. Not in its entirety, but some aspects of dispensational teaching emphasize that we are still in the dispensation or age of the Gentiles. God now wants to save the Gentiles. The time will come when the age of the Gentiles will be complete—then, and only then, will all Israel be saved. Therefore, to seek to evangelize Jews now is premature. It is, in fact, going against the time scale of God and working against His will.

Others, who would not subscribe to such a clearly defined dispensational or premillennial theology, are nevertheless so caught up in the whole area of prophetic fulfillment that evangelism becomes something of a secondary issue. Such people are not against evangelism of Jewish people, but it is not something on their list of priorities. It is not so much a thought-out theological position. Rather, it is a theological imbalance. Nevertheless, it is clearly a factor evident among some evangelicals, especially in Israel, today. Many dispensationalists deny that they are against evangelism, but they fear that evangelists muddy the waters.

Replacement Theology. This comes in two varieties. In its more extreme form, the Jewish people, by reason of their unfaithfulness to God, and especially in having been the cause of the crucifixion of Jesus, have been finally rejected by God as His special people, and they have been replaced as the people of

God by the church, which is seen as the "New" Israel. In its softer form, the Jewish people in the Old Testament period are seen purely in terms of a preparation for something greater to follow, that is, the church. The Jewish people, as a people, are seen as a kind of prototype to be dispensed with when they have served their purpose.

This viewpoint is not against the evangelism of Jews as individuals. Rather, it stresses that Jews are not now a special people group, and as far as evangelism is concerned, they are part of the people among whom they live and can be evangelized as part of that people. It isn't that Jewish people don't need the gospel, but this emphasis on Jewish evangelism is a red herring, especially when they are a small minority (as with other minorities).

We have been looking at some objections to the evangelization of Jewish people from mainly the Christian viewpoint. Now we shall look at them from the Jewish point of view (though the two covenant theory also is a Jewish view).

Christianity as Historically Mistaken. Jewish thinkers are increasingly coming to accept, even to value, Jesus as one of their illustrious sons. It is generally accepted that the Christian faith came into being as a sect within Judaism. But the Jewish assertion is that (1) Jesus did not make the great claims for Himself that Christianity now claims for Him, or (2) if He did, then He was mistaken. (Now Paul, rather than Jesus, is seen as responsible for founding this new religion.)

Guilt Paralysis. This is a point of view that by reason of the scale of anti-Semitism that has been in the church throughout its history, and especially the involvement of the church in the Holocaust, or the Shoah, either by the direct involvement of the few or by the abdicating silence of the many, and despite the positive protests of the very few, the church is so caught up in guilt that it has no right to proclaim the gospel to Jewish people.

As Rabbi Lionel Blue has pointed out in a recent British TV series, Christianity has as its badge and motif a symbol of extreme suffering. Christians have been at their truest and best when they have shared in the suffering of their Lord, and at their worst when, in those times that they have been in the dominant position, they have inflicted suffering on others. Evangelism is crass insensitivity.

There is confusion of two separate issues: (1) Is Jesus the Jewish Messiah? and (2) Has there been, and is there still, anti-Semitism in the church? In any case we don't evangelize out of right but under divine compulsion.

The Presentation of the Gospel for Jewish People

In one sense, as far as the content is concerned, it is the same as for everyone else. There is only *one* gospel—Christ died for our sins—according to the Scriptures.

However, as far as the presentation of the gospel is concerned, contextualization is the flavor of the month, so to speak. People involved in the study of mission currently speak of three types of cross-cultural evangelism. Dr. David Stern, a messianic Jewish leader and author in Jerusalem, speaks of a fourth kind for Jewish evangelism[12] in that the gospel doesn't need cultural adaptation for Jewish people. The gospel was given in a Jewish context in the first place. It was then contextualized for a gentile culture, first by the apostle Paul, and then by others.

In presenting the gospel to Jews now we need not, and should not, attempt another cultural transplant. We need rather to understand the gospel as it was originally given. We are not trying to turn the clock back by two thousand years, and as we have already seen, the Judaism of today has also changed. But we need constantly to remind ourselves that the gospel, though universal in relevance, was first given in a Jewish context, and that was not incidental: it was the fulfillment of the plan and purpose of God after two thousand years of preparation.

Some years ago, when I invited someone from outside our parish to judge a fancy dress competition at our Scout and Guide summer fair, he awarded first prize to a girl in a wonderfully realistic Chinese outfit. I had to tell him afterward, "She is a Chinese girl. She wasn't dressed for the competition!" (She didn't need to try to contextualize herself.)

To describe how some people see Jewish evangelism, I shall make three assertions, support them by Scripture, and then draw some conclusions.

First, the Old Testament (Jewish Scriptures) speaks of condemnation. The New Testament speaks of salvation:

> But if the ministry of death, written and engraved on stones, was glorious, so that the children of Israel could not look steadily at the face of Moses because of the glory of his countenance, which glory was passing away, how will the ministry of the Spirit not be more glorious? For if the ministry of condemnation had glory, the ministry of righteousness exceeds much more in glory. For even what was made glorious had no glory in this respect, because of the glory that excels (2 Cor. 3:7–10).

Second, the Old Testament speaks of preparation. The New Testament speaks of fulfillment:

> For the law, having a shadow of the good things to come, and not the very image of the things, can never with these same sacrifices, which they offer continually year by year, make those who approach perfect (Heb. 10:1).

Third, the purpose of evangelism is that people who are under condemnation might come into salvation:

> But before faith came, we were kept under guard by the law, kept for the faith which would afterward be revealed. Therefore the law was our tutor to bring us to Christ, that we

might be justified by faith. But after faith has come, we are no longer under a tutor (Gal. 3:23–25).

Now let me say at once, before we look at any conclusions, that I do not argue with any of these Scriptures, though I have to say that they don't tell the whole story. There are condemnation in the New Testament and grace in the Old Testament. These Scriptures portray the content of our evangelistic message, but in terms of Jewish evangelism, the conclusion we so often draw is this: (1) this is Jewish (condemnation, preparation, etc.) and (2) this is Christian (grace, salvation, etc.). When a Jewish person comes to faith in Jesus, he is brought from being a Jew into becoming a Christian—that, I believe, is a false conclusion based on three valid premises. So where does the reasoning break down?

A common hidden premise is that the Old Testament is Jewish and the New Testament is Christian. In fact, the New Testament is just as Jewish as the Old (Jesus and the apostles are Jewish). Preparation and fulfillment, yes, but *not* Jewish preparation for the sake of "Christian" fulfillment.

Behold, the days are coming, says the Lord, when I will make a new covenant with the house of Israel and with the house of Judah—not according to the covenant that I made with their fathers in the day that I took them by the hand to lead them out of the land of Egypt, My covenant which they broke, though I was a husband to them, says the Lord. But this is the covenant that I will make with the house of Israel after those days, says the Lord: I will put My law in their minds, and write it on their hearts; and I will be their God, and they shall be My people. No more shall every man teach his neighbor, and every man his brother, saying, "Know the Lord," for they all shall know Me, from the least of them to the greatest of them, says the Lord. For I will forgive their iniquity, and their sin I will remember no more (Jer. 31:31–34).

The heart of the problem lies in a false understanding of covenant in the Bible, the view that there is an old covenant and a new covenant: the old has to do with law, the new with grace. We then neatly apply Hebrews 8:13: "In that He says, 'A new covenant,' He has made the first obsolete. Now what is becoming obsolete and growing old is ready to vanish away."

The fact is that there are not just two but many covenants in the Bible, and succeeding ones do not replace but build upon their precursors. For example, there are the Abrahamic covenant, the Mosaic covenant, the Davidic (kingship) covenant, the marriage covenant of Isaiah 62, the new covenant of Jeremiah 31, and others. These all build upon one another and find their fulfillment in the New Testament. (For more detail about this outworking, I refer readers to my *Messianic Jews*, chapters 6, 8, 10, and 12.)

Conclusion

I hope that you will be both enthused and better equipped to share the good news of Jesus, the Jewish Messiah, with His own people, and also recognize the validity of their retaining their Jewish identity.

Now may the God of patience and comfort grant you to be like-minded toward one another, according to Christ Jesus, that you may with one mind and one mouth glorify the God and Father of our Lord Jesus Christ. Therefore receive one another, just as Christ also received us, to the glory of God. Now I say that Jesus Christ has become a servant [of the Jews] for the truth of God, to confirm the promises made to the fathers, and that the Gentiles might glorify God for His mercy, as it is written:
   "For this reason I will confess to You among the Gentiles,
   And sing to Your name."
And again he says:

"Rejoice, O Gentiles, with His people!"
And again:
"Praise the LORD, all you Gentiles!
Laud Him, all you peoples!"
And again, Isaiah says:
"There shall be a root of Jesse;
And He who shall rise to reign over the Gentiles,
In Him the Gentiles shall hope."
Now may the God of hope fill you with all joy and peace in believing, that you may abound in hope by the power of the Holy Spirit (Rom. 15:5–13).

For too long the Gentiles have been rejoicing without His people, even at the expense of His people. But how can His people rejoice without the knowledge of their Messiah? How shall they hear unless someone tells them?

How beautiful upon the mountains
Are the feet of him who brings good news,
Who proclaims peace,
Who brings glad tidings of good things,
Who proclaims salvation,
Who says to Zion,
"Your God reigns!" (Isa. 52:7).

For Further Reading

Dunn, J. D. G. *Commentary on Romans.* Waco: Word, 1991.
———. *The Partings of the Ways.* Valley Forge: Trinity, 1991.
Ellison, H. L. *The Mystery of Israel.* Exeter: Paternoster Press, 1966.
Fieldsend, J. H. *Messianic Jews.* Eastbourne: Monarch Pub. and Olive Press, 1993.
Fruchtenbaum, A. *Hebrew Christianity.* London: Ariel Press, 1983.

———. *Jesus Was a Jew.* London: Ariel Press, 1981.

Guinness, M. *Child of the Covenant.* London: Hodder and Stoughton, 1985.

———. *A Little Kosher Seasoning.* London: Hodder and Stoughton, 1994.

Jessup, G. *No Strange God.* London: Olive Press, 1976.

Riggans, W. *Covenant with the Jews.* Eastbourne: Monarch Pub.

———. *Jesus Ben Joseph.* Eastbourne: Monarch Pub., 1992.

Rosen, M. *Yeshua: The Jewish Way to Say Jesus.* London: CWI Pub., 1987.

Shanks, H., ed. *Christianity and Rabbinic Judaism.* London: SPCK, 1993.

Stern, D. H. *Restoring the Jewishness of the Gospel.* Jerusalem: Jewish New Testament Publications, 1988.

———. Trans. *Jewish New Testament.* Jerusalem: Jewish New Testament Publications, 1989.

Telchin, S. *Betrayed.* Basingstoke: Marshall Pickering, 1982.

Wright, C. *Knowing Jesus Through the Old Testament.* Basingstoke: Marshall Pickering, 1992.

ISLAM
by Patrick Sookdheo

If you were to ask a Muslim when Islam began, you would probably get an answer such as, "It is as old as time. It is as old as Allah's creation, as old as Adam and Abraham and Moses. Was not Abraham himself a Muslim, and his son Ishmael the father of the Arab race? Did not Allah establish his covenant with Ishmael for all generations? Did not Hagar find water for Ishmael at the Zamzam well in Mecca, which was one day to be the very heart of the Muslim world? Does not the Qur'an contain the unchangeable and eternal word of Allah, which was revealed in the Arabic tongue?" All this is part of orthodox Muslim theology.

If we are to find what is distinctive about Muslim belief, we must first look at the person, character, and career of the Prophet himself.

The Prophet Muhammad

1. *His Background and Early Life.* Muhammad was born about A.D. 570 into the Quraish tribe. His birthplace was the wealthy merchant town of Mecca, which was an important trading center for western Arabia, linking the land-borne trade routes to the maritime trade routes. Mecca was also famous for its shrine, the Kaaba. It was the focus of a cult of sacred stones, including the black stone, and was the center of pilgrimage for tribes throughout Arabia. Before Muhammad preached among them, the Arabs believed in one supreme being called Allah, but more attention was given to other gods and goddesses. Besides the gods and goddesses they had a cult of sacred stones. Some remained on hillsides; others, such as the Kaaba, were moved and placed in the house of Allah. The cult manifested itself in three principal ways—pilgrimages, processions, and sacrifices.

Muhammad's father died before he was born, and his mother died when he was six years old. His grandfather took care of him for a short while but soon died. He was then brought up by his uncle, Abu Talib.

Little else is known about his childhood and youth, but as an adult, he became an esteemed member of the merchants' guild at Mecca. He was called Al-Amin, "the trustworthy one." He traveled a good deal with trading caravans and came into contact with Jews, Christians, and others. The Jews, being traders, had settled in the trading cities on the caravan routes, taking with them their rabbis, Scriptures, and synagogues. Hence the Arabs had a superficial knowledge of Old Testament stories and Jewish folklore, some of which turn up in the pages of the Qur'an. The Christianity that Muhammad first encountered had been brought to Arabia chiefly by Christians fleeing from the Byzantine Empire because they had fallen victim to the intricate christological controversies of those days and had been condemned as heretics. Contact with such informants—badly instructed, divided over doctrine, and probably speaking imperfect Arabic—no doubt contributed to the fact that Muhammad developed a very inaccurate picture of the Christian faith. A number of Meccan merchants, including Muhammad, had traveled to Gaza and Damascus in the Byzantine Empire, and some to Christian Abyssinia (Ethiopia), which exposed them only to external features of Christianity.

A wealthy widow, Khadija, put him in charge of her caravans, and when he was twenty-five, she rewarded his fidelity by marrying him. The marriage seems to have been surprisingly successful, for Muhammad took no second wife until after Khadija's death, some twenty-five years later. Seven children (three boys and four girls) were born to them, but only the girls survived. One of his daughters, Fatima, achieved fame in Muslim history as Ali's wife and the mother of Hassan and Hussein. Khadija's wealth enabled Muhammad to have leisure time, and thus opportunity for seclusion and prayer.

2. *His Later Life and Call.* At the age of forty, Muhammad began to experience visions, which convinced him that Allah had a special task for him. One day when he was meditating in a cave on Mount Hira, outside the city of Mecca, he was visited by the angel Gabriel, who commanded him to preach Allah's warning to the world.

3. *The First Converts.* The response to his early and private preaching was limited. His first converts included his wife, Khadija, his nephew Ali ibn Abu Talib (who was only nine years old at the time of Muhammad's first revelation), and his adopted son, Zaid, who had formerly been his slave. The first free male adult to make profession of Islam was Abu Bakr, a wealthy merchant, who was a significant early convert. Fifty converts were made during the period 610 to 613.

4. *Opposition.* Muhammad then began to preach publicly. By 616, he had aroused such strong opposition that many of his followers had to flee from Mecca to take refuge in the Christian kingdom of Abyssinia. It was a long, hard struggle for another six years. Then in 622, Muhammad took the decisive step of withdrawing with his followers, some two hundred in all, from Mecca to Medina. He had been invited there by a party of Medinan inhabitants who had met him, accepted his claims, and prepared their fellow townsmen for his advent. This withdrawal (*hijra*) was the turning point in Muhammad's career. It is considered to mark the beginning of the Muslim era, and it is the point from which the Muslim calendar is dated. In Mecca, Muhammad had been a rejected prophet pointing his countrymen to Allah and warning them of judgment to come. In Medina, he eventually became a statesman, legislator, and judge.

5. *Jewish Opposition to Islam.* At first Muhammad recognized the validity of the Jewish and Christian faiths, being content to preach as the prophet to his own people. He chose Jerusalem as the direction in which a Muslim should face when praying, and he adopted several other Jewish practices. However, friction developed when the Jewish tribes failed to recognize him as a true prophet or to practice the customs of Islam.

Muhammad began to assert the absolute character of the revelation that had been given to him, and he claimed that it was a renewal of the religion that Abraham had professed. He gave up any attempt to reconcile Islam with Judaism. It was toward the Kaaba at Mecca that Muslims were to face during prayer and not toward Jerusalem as previously commanded.

6. *The Spread of Islam.* As Muhammad's power and influence increased, so did armed encounter. He rapidly conquered the whole of Arabia, stamping on it the religion of Islam. After he died in 632, Islam continued to spread until it became one of the dominant world religions. Muhammad was the first man to unify the Arabs into one people. By the end of the seventh century, the

Arabs had burst out of Arabia and conquered the southern provinces of the Byzantine Empire including Syria; Egypt; Persia, which was under the rule of the Sassanids; and much of North Africa. By 712, they had crossed the Mediterranean and conquered Spain. Muslims continued to dominate the whole of the Middle East during the Middle Ages. Islam currently has approximately one billion adherents.

The Qur'an: The Book of Islam

Muslims believe the Qur'an to be the direct word of Allah revealed to Muhammad during the last twenty-three years of his lifetime. The Qur'an holds a place of exalted reverence in a Muslim's heart. It is said to have existed eternally, engraved in Arabic on tablets of stone located in the seventh heaven. The Arabic language is therefore considered to have an inherent status above that of any other language. Arabic speakers have special prestige in the eyes of Muslims.

Muslims insist that the Qur'an is the earthly edition of a portion of the heavenly book that is preserved near Allah's throne. But the Qur'an is sprinkled with words borrowed from Persian, Hebrew, Greek, Latin, Syriac, and Coptic that date it to a particular epoch and culture. A renowned classical exegete of the Qur'an, Jalad-ud-Din Sayutti, provides a list of 122 loan words from foreign languages.

The Content of the Qur'an. The Qur'an is about the same length as the New Testament. It was said to have been revealed to Muhammad by the angel Gabriel. The prophecies were not delivered in any systematic order and were thus subject to a great deal of rearrangement both during Muhammad's lifetime and after his death, when the complete book was edited from scraps written on parchment, stone tablets, camels' shoulder blades, and so on. Many of the suras (chapters) consist of a collection of prophecies or parts of prophecies that were originally preached at different times and refer to different circumstances. Where there is contradiction between parts of the Qur'an, the later revealed suras are considered to annul the earlier ones.

The Qur'an is divided into 114 suras, arranged not chronologically but roughly according to length. The first sura is a prayer to Allah used daily by Muslims. It has a similar place in the life of a Muslim to the Lord's Prayer in the life of a Christian. It runs,

> Praise be to Allah,
> The Lord of the worlds,
> The merciful,
> The compassionate,
> The Lord of the Day of Judgment.
> It is thee we serve,
> And to thee we call for help.
> Guide us in the straight path,
> The path of those on whom thou has bestowed good,
> Not of those on whom anger falls,
> Or those who go astray.

In all the other suras, Allah, not the Prophet, is the speaker. The earliest suras bear some comparison to the Psalms in length, subject matter, and rhythmic form. They differ in approach, however, because they are not the striving of the human heart after God, but Allah speaking to humankind, using the Prophet as a mouthpiece.

The Significance of the Qur'an. Muhammad is seen as the last, but not the only, prophet of Allah. Muslims do not worship any of the prophets; they consider them examples and models for humankind. Consequently, some Muslim sects (e.g., Wahabis) dislike being called Muhammadans because they claim that they are worshipers not of Muhammad but of Allah. The prophets were considered human servants of Allah. Muhammad was the final prophet or messenger, and the Qur'an the final message of Allah to humankind. The messenger's task was to spread the divine message, in its uncorrupted form, to his people. Earlier revelations (i.e., the Jewish and Christian Scriptures) are believed to have been distorted, if not totally falsified. The Qur'an plays a special part in the lives of most Muslims, who have to recite verses from it five times a day in their prayers and should try to learn by heart as much of it as possible. No pious Muslim would ever make a noise while the Qur'an is being read aloud.

Historical Errors and Myths in the Qur'an. The Qur'an contains material that appears to contradict historical statements in the Bible. For example, the Qur'an says that Haman was Pharaoh's minister (Sura 28:6). It also says that Mary, the mother of Jesus, was the sister of Aaron (19:28) and the daughter of Imran, or Amram (3:35–36), and hence was identical with Miriam, the sister of Moses and Aaron. It is also stated that Noah's wife and one of his sons perished in the Flood and that Pharaoh's wife was a true believer.

Some myths and apocryphal details in the Qur'an include the following:

- A raven sent by Allah demonstrated to Cain how to bury his brother Abel (5:30–34).
- Two angels, Harut and Marut, taught magic to the Babylonians (2:102).
- Solomon talked with birds and ants (27:15ff.).
- Three men slept in a cave with a dog for at least three hundred years (18:10–25), which is an apocryphal Christian fable.
- Jesus spoke from the cradle (19:29–30). He made birds out of clay and imparted life into them (3:49). This material is found in the apocryphal Infancy Gospel of Thomas.

The Beliefs of Islam: The Six Articles of Faith

1. *Allah.* The central point of Islam is the unity of Allah. Associating anything with Allah, either as equal or as partner, is

condemned. Thus, Allah is said to have no partner, wife, or children. He is one, a self-existent unity. Muslims deny the Trinity and the lordship of Jesus Christ. They interpret the Sonship of Jesus literally, saying that Christians believe He was the result of physical union between God and Mary. The Holy Spirit is identified with the archangel Gabriel. Jesus is depicted in the Qur'an as a great miracle worker and one of the greatest prophets. The Qur'an implies that He never died on a cross; the classical commentators wrote a new version of the passion story in which God called Jesus up to heaven when the Jews sought to crucify Him and threw His likeness on to someone else, who was crucified by mistake in His place. Traditions add that Christ is to come again, when He will acknowledge Islam, have children, break the symbol of the cross, demolish churches, and kill Christians, except those who believe in Him.

Judgment and justice are basic to Allah's nature. He demands that human conduct be given its due reward or punishment.

Muslims believe that Allah created heaven and earth in six days. His work did not end with creating heaven and earth, but his creative activities are still going on. The creation of Adam and Eve in Paradise, in one of the heavens, was the start of the human race. Adam and Eve were simultaneously seduced by Satan, who tempted them to eat the forbidden fruit. Allah accepted their repentance, the sin was forgiven, and both were sent to earth. Muslims believe all children are born free from sin, though touched by Satan at their birth. If they die during childhood, they are sinless and go to live in Paradise. Jesus was the only child not touched by Satan at His birth.

2. *Angels.* Great prominence is given to angels in the Qur'an, and anyone who denies them is an infidel. They are created from light. They are regarded as servants of Allah through whom he reveals his will. The greatest is Gabriel, the revealer of Allah to Muhammad, who is also called the Holy Spirit. He strengthened

Jesus. The other archangels include Michael, the provider, Israfil, the trumpeter of doom, and 'Izra'il, the custodian and the one with the care of the faithful at death.

There are also an indefinite number of ordinary angels. Two recording angels attend on every Muslim; one on the right records good deeds, and one on the left records sins. There are also two angels called Munkar and Nakir, who visit every newly buried corpse in its grave. Making the corpse sit up, these angels examine it in the faith. If the replies are satisfactory, it is allowed to sleep in peace, but if it does not confess the apostle Muhammad, they beat it severely—some say until the day of resurrection. Animals are said to hear its cries, although humans cannot. The angels are fighting for believers against demons. Demons are created out of fire; like human beings, they are male and female, and among them are both believers and infidels.

3. *The Scriptures*. Jews, Christians, and Muslims are regarded as "people of the book." Muslims hold that the Law was revealed to Moses, the Psalms to David, the gospel to Jesus, and the Qur'an to Muhammad. They claim that Jews and Christians changed and distorted their own Scriptures, so Allah sent the Qur'an as the final revelation to humankind.

4. *The Prophets*. Muslims accept all the prophets of the Old Testament, John the Baptist and Jesus in the New Testament, and some extrabiblical prophets. A believer who denies any of the prophets ceases to be a Muslim: "Each one [believer] believeth in Allah, His angels, His books, and His apostles" (2:285). They believe that Jesus was the greatest of the prophets prior to Muhammad. He was sinless, but not the Son of God, merely the servant of God.

Through the prophets, Allah has mercifully deigned to interfere in human history in order to remind people of the Last Day and the life hereafter, to guide them in all the activities of life on to the right path leading toward final election. There was no progressive enlargement of the message except amendment or annulment of some previously given laws; the same basic truths were revealed by the prophets until the arrival of Muhammad, the "seal of the prophets," who linked up with the faith of Abraham.

Now the final stage of revelation has been reached, a stage that will last till the Day of Judgment. No new prophet will come in the future. Therefore, Muhammad has communicated not only religious doctrines but also many rules and regulations for the community of the faithful (Muslims), who have an obligation to bear witness to this fact and to conduct the affairs of Allah and of humankind among all people.

5. *The Day of Judgment.* The Day of Judgment is a principal theme of Qur'anic teaching, and it is closely connected with the Resurrection. The day will be preceded by clear signs and natural catastrophes, the appearance of the Antichrist, tumults and seditions, and commotion in heaven and earth (101:5; 70:8–9). The sun and moon will be darkened (75:8; 81:1), and Christ will return.

On the Last Day, the angel Israfil will sound the trumpet and

> All who are in the heavens
> And on earth will swoon,
> Except such as it will
> Please Allah [to exempt].
> Then will a second one be sounded, when, behold,
> They will be standing
> And looking on! (39:68).

After the Resurrection, people will wander about for forty years, during which time, the books containing the records kept by the recording angels will be given up. Then follows the weighing of the deeds on the eschatological scales:

> Then those whose balance [of good deeds] is heavy,
> They will attain salvation:

> But those whose balance
> Is light, will be those
> Who have lost their souls;
> In Hell will they abide (23:102–3).

Then everybody, believer or unbeliever, has to cross a very narrow bridge. Some Muslims will be saved immediately; some will fall headlong into hell and afterward be released. The infidels will all fall into hell and remain there forever.

The common belief of Muslims is that believers who have committed sins must undergo temporary punishment in hell; this can be mitigated, shortened, or remitted at the Prophet's intercession. The name most frequently given in the Qur'an and tradition to paradise, the abode of the blessed, is *janna* (garden). The Qur'anic description of paradise is expressed in very concrete terms (e.g., 47:15; 55:46–78; 56:11–38). These suras show us that the Muslims' paradise is essentially a garden of sensual delights in which there are beautiful women, couches covered with rich brocades, flowing cups, and luscious fruits.

6. *The Decrees of Allah.* Tradition includes as one of the six articles of faith "the Divine Decree for better or worse, for sweet or bitter." This article is a post-Qur'anic addition. Muslims must believe that Allah's omnipotence is at work in the whole of creation and, therefore, also influences human actions: "Allah hath created you and what ye make" (37:96). On the other hand, everyone is considered responsible for personal deeds: "That Day [judgment] will every soul/Be requited for what it earned" (40:17). This contradiction between the determining power of Allah's omnipotence and a person's responsibility for actions is one of the principal problems to which the different Muslim schools of thought have devoted their attention during the course of the centuries. Under the influence of orthodox schools, the doctrine of absolute predestination—fatalism, which is much closer to hyper-Calvinism in Christianity—is quite widespread

among Muslims. *Maktub* (it is written), *maqdur* (it is decided), and *kismat* (it is my lot) are expressions commonly used by Muslims. A fatalistic attitude of passivity and lassitude has at times been the cause of stagnation in Islam and has hindered cultural and technological developments.

The Five Pillars of Islam: The Practical Duties

Like other religions, Islam demands of its followers articles of faith and works. Together they complete the surrender to Allah, which is Islam. The practices prescribed are often called the Pillars of the Faith.

1. *Recital of the Creed.* The creed is a simple one: "There is no god but Allah, and Muhammad is Allah's messenger." A recital of the creed is enough to enroll a new convert into the ranks of Islam.

2. *Prayer.* Ritual prayer plays an important role in the life of the devout Muslim. The prescribed worship with ritual movements must be performed five times a day at fixed times. These prayers are compulsory for men and women over the age of ten, and they may be performed by oneself or by a congregation. Prayers earn more merit if they are offered in a mosque.

Before prayer Muslims must clean themselves. The ritual consists of repeating the name of Allah, the Beneficent, the Merciful, while washing the face, arms, hands, ankles, and feet with clean water. When there is no water, ablutions can be performed by wiping sand on the face and arms.

Before the beginning of each set of daily prayers in the mosque, the faithful are called to prayer by the muezzin who cries from the minaret of the mosque, "Allah is the greatest. I bear witness that Muhammad is the messenger of Allah. Come to prayer. Come to prosperity. Allah is the greatest."

Once inside the mosque the people take up their positions facing Mecca. There are eight separate acts of devotion, each with a particular posture to be adopted. For the first three acts, the Muslim stands, for the fourth he bows, for the fifth he stands, and for the sixth he kneels, his forehead touching the ground. He then kneels up, bows down to the ground again, and then kneels again. Once the required number of bows has been performed, the ceremony is completed by saying, "Peace be upon you and the mercy of Allah."

The mosque is the focal point of the Muslim's devotions. It must have a courtyard with a supply of running water to provide pure water for ablutions. Other features include a pulpit, a lectern carrying a copy of the Qur'an, and a *mihrab*, which is a small semicircular recess facing in the direction of Mecca. All Muslims face the *mihrab* during prayers. Women are not prohibited from attending the services in the mosque, but they are not encouraged to do so because of the responsibilities of the home. However, women often attend services, and many mosques have special quarters for women to worship in.

3. *Fasting*. Fasting means abstaining from eating, drinking, smoking, and having sexual intercourse from dawn to sunset in the month of Ramadan. It is compulsory for all men, women, and children above the age of ten, who are not mentally or physically sick. Also, women who are menstruating or have a puerperal discharge will not fast. It is primarily a spiritual and moral discipline, designed to enable physical desires to be conquered. Because the Muslim calendar is lunar, Ramadan falls at a different time each year.

4. *Almsgiving*. There is no satisfactory Arabic etymology for the word *zakat* in Arabic. It is derived from the Aramaic *zakut* from the Jewish usage. *Zakat* means "purification." It is the amount a Muslim *must* give annually. It consists of one-fortieth of money and merchandise, one-tenth or one-twentieth of agricultural produce, and different rates for cattle. *Zakat* is described as the wealth taken away from the rich and given to the poor and needy, to those who are serving the cause of Islam, and also to those who perform acts of benevolence. There is a second type of almsgiving called

sadaqah, an optional freewill offering. This offering is regarded as a solemn duty, for generosity is highly regarded in Islam.

5. *Hajj (Pilgrimage to Mecca)*. This pilgrimage is obligatory once in a lifetime for those who can afford it. It is performed during the sacred month of Dhu'l-Hijja (the month of pilgrimage). There is great merit in going to Mecca to ask for forgiveness and to perform the ritual around the Kaaba. Muslims believe that Abraham cast out Ishmael so that Ishmael could establish a shrine at Mecca. The sacrifice of a ram instead of Ishmael (not Isaac) underlies the pilgrimage.

Death

Muslims believe that what is experienced after death is a complete representation of the state of life in its present form. The afterlife will not be a different kind of life but only an image of this life. At death the soul receives a temporary body to experience in the grave the reward or punishment for the deeds done in this life before receiving a permanent body for heaven or hell.

On his deathbed the Muslim (if capable) repeats the creedal formula, "There is no god if not Allah himself." The body is bathed before the saying of funeral prayers and then taken to be buried. The grave is dug in the direction of Mecca, and the face is turned toward it. That is why Muslim communities in the West require their own separate graveyards. Some Muslims in the West send the bodies back to their home countries to be buried in large graveyards, which are visited by pious men who pray for the dead in the life hereafter.

Prohibitions

The following things are prohibited for Muslims: drinking alcohol, eating pork or the meat of animals not ritually killed or of strangled animals, lending money on interest, gambling of all types, having sex outside marriage, lying, stealing, cheating, murdering, and committing suicide. Animals to be eaten must be slaughtered in the name of Allah; otherwise the meat is forbidden.

Islamic Sects

Sunni and Shia. The great schism in the Islamic world is between the Sunni and Shia groups. Sunnis are orthodox Muslims who believe that what is contained in the Qur'an and the Sunna defines the limits of the beliefs and actions of Muslims. They regard the caliph (successor of Muhammad) as an ordinary man, chosen for his post as head of the community either by his predecessor or by popular vote.

The Shiite sect began as a protest against the caliphate system of the Sunnis. Shiites believe that Muhammad left the guidance of the faithful in the hands of Ali, his cousin and son-in-law. Consequently, they believe that the leadership of Islam should center in Muhammad's family. Shiites believed in the doctrine of an infallible, divinely appointed Imam in every age to whom Allah entrusted the guidance of his servants. This continued until the disappearance of the twelfth (some say seventh) Imam in 874, who they say is now in hiding until the Day of Judgment. This belief in all Imams is exalted into an additional pillar of Islam. About 20 percent of Muslims are Shiites, and the sect has several subdivisions. Sunnis are also divided into a number of sects.

Ismailis. The Ismaili sect has approximately twenty million adherents. It is a branch of Shia Islam, and it is the only group that accords to a living figure the status of Imam, in the sense of the inheritor of the spiritual and temporal mantle of the Prophet. A branch of Ismailis considers Karim al-Huseyn, the present-day Aga Khan, the forty-ninth Imam. The Ismailis believe that they are indebted to the Imam and so tithe 10 percent of all they have for him, this money being collected at the monthly festival of Chandrat. Birthday gifts are also given to the Imam, the size of which is a competitive element within the community. Ismailis are well known for their charitable works.

Ahmadiyya Movement. This sect was founded by Mirza Ghulam Ahmad of India at the end of the last century. He claimed to be the promised Messiah whom Allah had appointed for reforming humankind and reestablishing the superiority of Islam over all other religions. The sect, however, has now formed two major groups, their main division occurring over the status of Ahmad. The members of the first group, the Qadiyanis, say that Ahmad was a prophet, but the seceders (Lahoris) say he was merely a reformer.

The distinctive doctrines of this movement include the following:

1. No verse of the Qur'an can be abrogated.
2. The need for *jihad* (holy war) has lapsed, and coercion in religion is condemned.
3. Muhammad was not the last prophet.
4. Jesus is dead and did not ascend bodily into heaven.
5. Hell is not everlasting.
6. Apostasy is not punishable by death.
7. Any innovation in religious practice is culpable.
8. Revelation is the privilege of the true believer only.
9. Belief in Ahmad as Messiah is essential.
10. Spirituality in religion is more important than legalism.
11. The medieval scholars need not be followed in their interpretation of the Qur'an, but only the Prophet's companions.

Numbers 3, 4, and 9 are anathema to orthodox Muslims, and on more than one occasion, other Muslims have massacred Ahmadis.

The Ahmadis claim that they seek to uplift humanity and establish peace throughout the world. They claim they are Muslims "real and true." Orthodox Muslims, however, disagree with their doctrines and feel this sect is not really Muslim. They have been declared a non-Muslim community in Pakistan, Saudi Arabia, and certain other countries.

The Christian Approach to Muslims

One striking feature of Islam is that it does not separate the sacred side of life from the secular. Someone living in a Muslim community cannot fail to be affected by Islam, even though he or she may have strong personal convictions. Opting out of Islam would lead to total isolation from the community. Consequently, it is easier to be outwardly compliant (e.g., attending the mosque) than to defy or ignore religious obligations. We need to bear this in mind as we present the gospel to Muslims.

When proclaiming Christ in an Islamic context, we must remember that many traditional Christian terms such as *Son of God, incarnation, atonement, vicarious death,* and *resurrection* are all, according to the Qur'an, delusions or mere conjecture (e.g., 9:30; 4:157).

Points of similarity between Islam and Christianity provide a good basis for starting a discussion. Consider some ways of approach:

1. Commend the high moral standards of Muslims.

2. Islam is weak on teaching about sin. For the Muslim, there is no true mediator between God and people. By discussing the righteousness of God, for example, by quoting from Romans, and thus showing the seriousness of sin in God's sight, you can lead on to the salvation offered in Christ and communion with God through the work He has done.

3. A Muslim is a human being with personal needs that Christ alone can meet. Understanding and sympathetic words can lead to an opportunity for you to give a personal testimony. You should tell the Muslim how you came to know God, to be forgiven, to have peace with God, and to have assurance of

heaven. It is useful to give actual personal examples of how God has answered prayer.

4. Encourage the reading of the Scriptures. This is one of the most powerful and effective methods. Luke's gospel includes a genealogy that is acceptable to Muslims. Matthew also has a ready appeal for Muslim readers because of its strong Semitic apologetic concerns. Encourage Muslims to read about Christianity from Christian books with the aim of showing the Scriptures are not corrupted.

5. If the authenticity of Scripture is questioned, ask for the parts that have been changed to be pointed out. Explain that the early biblical texts were available before Muhammad's time. This subject can lead to profitable discussion and Bible study because many Muslims will be prepared to read Scripture and answer questions.

6. Start with the prophets that the Muslim accepts, and lead up to the coming of Christ. Dwell on the person and claims of our Lord, praying that the Holy Spirit will open the Muslim's eyes to perceive the truth.

Among the prophets mentioned in the Qur'an, only Jesus receives the title of the Messiah. This occurs eleven times, all in suras dating from Muhammad's time in Medina (3:45; 4:157, 171, 172; 5:19 twice; 5:75 twice; 5:78; 9:30, 31).

Muslim commentators have, in general, recognized the origin of the word *Messiah* as meaning "anointed one," but they have interpreted this anointing in various ways. Tabiri believes that Jesus received from Gabriel an anointing that preserved Him from the evil the devil inflicts on human beings from the time they are born. Thus, the angel told Mary that a holy Son would be born to her (19:19). But this anointing is also understood in the sense of a special blessing that Jesus received from God. This blessing would account for the fact that Jesus, a righteous man (3:46), was blessed wherever He might be (19:31). In the active sense, Jesus is the Messiah because He anointed the eyes of the blind with holy oil, because He laid His hands on the sick to heal them, and because He cleansed them from their sin. There is, too, a somewhat mystical interpretation that traces the word *Messiah* to the root word *saha*, meaning "to wander." According to this view, Jesus was called the Messiah because of His life of constant pilgrimage or wandering.

The divinity of the Messiah is vehemently denounced in the Qur'an as a perversion by gentile Christians of pagan origin. Therefore, place emphasis on justifying the divinity of Jesus from the messianic prophecies recognized by Jewish commentators of the Hebrew Scriptures.

Thus, Micah declared that the Messiah existed before His birth in Bethlehem, "whose goings forth are from of old, from everlasting" (Mic. 5:2). The same arguments can be applied to Daniel 7:13–14, a prophecy that Jesus referred to as being fulfilled in His person (Matt. 26:64). Isaiah announced that the Messiah would be called *Immanuel* (Isa. 7:14), which means "God with us" (Matt. 1:23). The titles "Mighty God" and "Everlasting Father" are found among the titles of the Messiah listed in Isaiah 9:6–7. In Zechariah 9:9, the Messiah is mentioned as King of Zion, who is "just and having salvation." It can be shown from Isaiah 45:21 that "a just God and a Savior; there is none besides Me."

Although in Islam the true knowledge of the person of the Messiah and His mission is obscured and lost to sight, the declaration that Jesus is the Messiah may still prove to be the Athenian altar "to an unknown God" to lead Muslims to the genuine Messiah of God.

Ubaydullah, a relative of Muhammad, was the first convert from Islam to Christianity. He was converted during the early Meccan period. Ibn Ishaq reports, "He used to tell the Prophet's companions, 'we see clearly, but your eyes are only half open.'" The eyes of those who believe in the Messiah will be fully opened only by the shining forth of "the light of the knowledge of the glory of God in the face of Jesus Christ" (2 Cor. 4:6).

Comparison Between Islam and Christianity

ISLAM

God

Muslims believe in the unity of Allah. He has no equal partner or son.

CHRISTIANITY

Christians believe in the Trinity of God the Father, God the Son, and God the Holy Spirit; not three gods but a unity of the Godhead. "[Baptize] them in the name of the Father and of the Son and of the Holy Spirit" (Matt. 28:19).

Creation

Allah created heaven and earth in six days. His work did not end with that act, but his creative act is still going on.

"And on the seventh day God ended His work which He had done, and He rested on the seventh day from all His work which He had done. Then God blessed the seventh day and sanctified it, because in it He rested from all His work which God had created and made" (Gen. 2:2–3). God is the sovereign ruler over His creation, therefore, its sustainer (see Ps. 33).

Jesus Christ

He is not the Son of God.

He is the Son of God. "And suddenly a voice came from heaven, saying, 'This is My beloved Son, in whom I am well pleased'" (Matt. 3:17).

The virgin birth is accepted as true.

The virgin birth is accepted as true.

Jesus was a great miracle worker, one of the greatest of the prophets.

Jesus was the fulfillment of the Law and the Prophets. "Do not think that I came to destroy the Law or the Prophets. I did not come to destroy but to fulfill" (Matt. 5:17).

He was not crucified or resurrected; He directly ascended to heaven.

"[Jesus] was delivered up because of our offenses, and was raised because of our justification" (Rom. 4:25). "When He had by Himself purged our sins, [He] sat down at the right hand of the Majesty on high" (Heb. 1:3).

The Second Coming

Christ is to come again and have children, to break the symbol of the cross and acknowledge Islam. There is a Day of Judgment appointed by Allah.

Christ is to come again to judge. "Then they will see the Son of Man coming in the clouds with great power and glory. And then He will send His angels, and gather together His elect from the four winds, from the farthest part of earth to the farthest part of heaven" (Mark 13:26–27).

Sin

Adam and Eve sinned simultaneously in heaven, both being deceived by Satan who tempted them to eat the forbidden fruit. Allah accepted their repentance, the sin was forgiven, and both were sent down to earth.

Satan tempted Eve to sin on earth. Eve then tempted Adam to sin. "So when the woman saw that the tree was good for food, that it was pleasant to the eyes, and a tree desirable to make one wise, she took of its fruit and ate. She also gave to her husband with her, and he ate" (Gen. 3:6). "Therefore the LORD God sent him out of the garden of Eden to till the ground from which he was taken" (Gen. 3:23).

Children are born sinless.

Original sin is a basic doctrine. "Therefore, just as through one man sin entered the world, and death through sin, and thus death spread to all men, because all sinned" (Rom. 5:12).

Jesus was sinless, like other prophets.

Only Jesus was without sin. "For He made Him who knew no sin to be sin for us, that we might become the righteousness of God in Him" (2 Cor. 5:21).

Salvation

Only works are taken into account.

"For by grace you have been saved through faith, and that not of yourselves; it is the gift of God, not of works, lest anyone should boast" (Eph. 2:8–9).

Heaven

It is a place of sensuous pleasure where all material gifts will be lavished on the righteous, and they will engage in physical pleasures.

It is a place of worship and holiness. "The twenty-four elders fall down before Him who sits on the throne and worship Him who lives forever and ever, and cast their crowns before the throne, saying: 'You are worthy, O Lord, to receive glory and honor and power; for You created all things, and by Your will they exist and were created' " (Rev. 4:10–11).

Prophets

Muslims accept all the prophets of the Old Testament, and John the Baptist and Jesus in the New Testament. Muhammad was the final prophet.

Christians accept all the prophets, but Jesus is greater than all of them. "God, who at various times and in various ways spoke in time past to the fathers by the prophets, has in these last days spoken to us by His Son" (Heb. 1:1–2).

Angels

They are servants of God.	They are messengers of God.
The greatest is Gabriel. He is regarded as the Holy Spirit, and he brought the message of Allah to Muhammad.	Gabriel is the angel who appeared to Daniel, Mary, and Zechariah.

For Further Reading

Ali, A. Y. *The Holy Qur'an: Text Translation and Commentary.* Leicester: Islamic Foundation, 1975.

Anderson, N. *Islam in the Modern World: A Christian Perspective.* Leicester: Apollos, 1990.

Encyclopaedia of Islam. Leiden: Brill, 1960.

Guillaume, A. *The Life of Muhammad.* Karachi: Oxford University Press, 1967.

Hitti, P. K. *History of the Arabs.* 10th ed. Basingstoke: Macmillan, 1970.

Hughes, T. P. *Dictionary of Islam.* Lahore: Premier Book House, 1964.

Watt, W. M. *Muhammad: Prophet and Statesman.* London: Oxford University Press, 1964.

―――. *Muhammad at Mecca.* Karachi: Oxford University Press, 1953.

―――. *Muhammad at Medina.* Karachi: Oxford University Press, 1956.

All the above books are available (by mail order if desired) from the International Institute for the Study of Islam and Christianity, St. Andrew's Centre, St. Andrew's Road, Plaistow, London E13 8QD. A full catalog of specialized books on Islam is available from the same address.

News Bulletin

For those wanting to keep abreast of events in the Muslim world, in particular in relation to persecuted Christian minorities, a bimonthly bulletin is available from the International Institute for the Study of Islam and Christianity, St. Andrew's Centre, St. Andrew's Road, Plaistow, London E13 8QD.

Chapter 6

Christian Confidence in an Age of Pluralism

Michael Green

All Western countries are "plural" societies these days. Many races, faiths, and cultures make up the texture of the land. Immigrants from Europe, Africa, and Asia form a growing proportion of our population, and together they help to shape our culture and share in our common life.

But this neutral and very evident fact of *plurality* must be distinguished from *pluralism* in the sense in which it will be used in this chapter. *Pluralism* is a prevalent and pervasive ideology that has swept through much of our society and has greatly influenced Christian thought. It distinguishes between facts and values. Facts are public: we are all expected to agree with them. There are scientific facts like the boiling point of water and historical facts like the Battle of Gettysburg. Facts are public, and we agree on them.

But it is very different with values and beliefs. They are extremely diverse. There is no publicly accepted norm. In the area of beliefs and values, pluralism rules. You have your views; I have mine. It does not matter, so long as we do not inhibit each other's freedom to express our private values and follow our private beliefs. None of them is absolute. None of them should be taught as "truth" like facts. They are all relative. And in matters of religion, certainty is impossible and would in any case be undesirable because it would be censured as imperialist and would prove socially divisive. All religions lead to God. Sincerity, not truth, is the supremely important thing. Tolerance is what matters.

That, then, is our modern situation. On facts we must all agree. On beliefs we agree to differ. In a climate like that, it is very difficult to take a stand for the uniqueness of Jesus Christ as the Way, the Truth, and the Life. To make such a claim is one of the fastest ways to win the reputation for being narrow, intolerant, and fanatical. It will attract disfavor not only from atheists, agnostics, and adherents of other faiths but often from fellow church representatives as well—who all, in their creeds and liturgies, profess to believe in one God and one Savior of the world, Jesus Christ!

What has happened to account for this yawning chasm between what the churches profess to believe and what many of them actually believe?

We shall examine the root causes of the change, but it is evident that the current political correctness makes two assumptions. First, that we all know what we mean by God and religion, though in fact both are slippery concepts. And second, that all religions lead to God, just as all spokes of a wheel lead to the hub: it makes no difference which one you go up. All arrive at the center.

That is thought to be the only enlightened view that tolerant people can hold in what has become a global village. And if it conflicts with some of the more dogmatic claims of Christianity, that is too bad: they must be dropped or reinterpreted. It is happening all the time. Jesus is now seen as a great charismatic religious leader, among others, or as the embodiment of some abstract ideal—guru, freedom fighter, or "man for others." In neither case can we—nor should we—swallow the time-honored but untenable dogma of Jesus being God incarnate.

Views like that are very common. What are we to make of them? This chapter will take us into rather more detail than some of the others because pluralism is both complex and widespread.

Pluralism Is Not New

People often suggest that twentieth-century thought has made historic Christianity untenable. We form part of a generation that has now become too sophisticated to believe orthodox Christianity anymore. But this view is mistaken. It is not the discoveries of the twentieth century that have led to pluralism, but the collapse of Enlightenment views that have held the intellectual stage for two centuries and more. In the heady days of Descartes, Locke, and Hume, there was a cheerful ditching of the notion of divine revelation and a deep confidence in the power of reason to provide foundations for our truth-claims. But it has not happened. The goal of finding universal truths in a universal morality based on reason alone has proved illusory. There are no absolutes in ethics or philosophy to which reason can point with certainty. And the crisis in modern thought is due not to some suddenly discovered flaw in Christianity but to the breakdown of that rationalistic worldview. Pluralism expresses secular human despair at finding any universals. So all viewpoints are up for grabs: you simply take your pick.

But it would be quite wrong to suppose that pluralism is new. It did not originate in the late twentieth century, though the current climate in our secular society is particularly suited to it. No, pluralism has always been an option. It was there in Abraham's day. The Old Testament is the story of the people of Israel attempting to stand up for the one true holy God who saves, in the face of immense religious pluralism all around them—from the Canaanites, the Moabites, the Egyptians, the Assyrians, the Babylonians, the Zoroastrians, and the Romans. The people of Israel needed no lessons from us in the phenomenon of pluralism. They knew all about it at first hand—and they weren't going for it. As the Romans found out to their amazement, the people of Israel were passionately monotheist, and they would die rather than allow the merest shadow of polytheism to infect their holy land. And die they did in the hundreds of thousands throughout the various uprisings when the country was under direct Roman rule. Opposition to pluralism was an essential article of their faith. There was one true God—and no runners-up.

It was precisely the same with the first Christians. Their message of one God who had revealed Himself decisively in Jesus the Messiah, one way of cleansing for human sins and frailties, one kingdom of love and loyalty to God into which all nations were invited, one way of acceptance depending not on religious pedigree or moral achievement but on the sheer generosity of God—all this they maintained with fearless courage in the face of a religious pluralism that makes our version look mild.

Naturally, they were unpopular. Yet had they adopted one of the "correct" religious attitudes, the early Christians would have been left undisturbed by the Roman authorities. For the Romans were very broad-minded in matters of religion. When they conquered your territory, they tended either, like the Hindus, to add your special deity to the existing pantheon or to identify him, as modern pluralists would, with a deity of their own who fulfilled roughly the same function. It was only when the first Christians stood out and refused the twin expedients of addition and identification that they were vilified and often persecuted.

So let us not buy into the idea that pluralism is a new problem, and that the proper Christian response is to go along with it. It is not new. And we are not to succumb to it.

Visser t'Hooft, the first secretary of the World Council of Churches, rightly observed, "It is high time Christians should rediscover that Jesus Christ did not come to make a contribution to the religious storehouse of mankind, but that in him God reconciled the world to himself."

Pluralism Has a Growing Appeal

Though far from new, as we have seen, pluralism undoubtedly has a large and growing appeal in the modern cultural climate. There are historical roots for this.

One lies, obviously enough, in the widespread influence of the Enlightenment. If, for all practical purposes, you eliminate God, as many Enlightenment thinkers did, how are you to evaluate rival religious claims? Without revelation, how can you choose between them? A pluralist attitude is called for.

The other lies in the Romantic movement, which had a large following in the early nineteenth century. An important thinker who was influenced by this movement was Friedrich Schleiermacher. Acutely sensitive to the possibility of historical or scientific assaults on the faith, Schleiermacher maintained that the essence of Christianity was not the self-revelation of the transcendent God who had acted and spoken in Jesus Christ. No, the essence of Christianity and all other religions lies within: God-consciousness. The inner world of feelings and intuition, the sense of awareness of God—that was something that neither history nor science could disprove. I find his writings obscure, but this seems to be a central thrust of them. He thought he was defending Christianity, as did Rudolf Bultmann a century and a half later, but both were undermining its foundations. Schleiermacher believed in Christianity not because it was final or authoritative—its doctrines were all negotiable—but because Jesus had experienced that God-consciousness in a completely pure form and had offered some approximation of it to His followers.

But the rot had set in. "Let no one offer the seekers a system making exclusive claims to truth," he said, "but let each man offer his characteristic, individual presentation." Such a view leads directly to late-twentieth-century talk about experiencing the divine in a variety of ways, the world spirit, the life force, reality, and the like. In this view Christianity has no special claim to truth.

Jesus is different in degree, not in essence, from any other great teacher. Calvary provides one way to salvation, to be sure; but there are plenty of others. The Scriptures, like other holy books, are purely human documents with many good and true thoughts about divinity and morality in them. And all religions lead to God.

Clearly, then, pluralism owes much to the Enlightenment, with its rejection of revelation, and to Romanticism, which offers us a diffuse and vague God-consciousness, a trip within to the realm of feeling.

And the twin roots of the Enlightenment and Romanticism are clear to see in modern writers on the subject. Hans Küng sees salvation being available to men and women through whatever religion and culture they happen to have been born in. John Hick talks about "global religious vision" and a spirituality that is totally relativist.

Ralph Waldo Emerson cried, "Man is weak if he looks outside himself for help. It is only when he throws himself unhesitatingly on the God within him that he learns his own power." That might have been written not by a Christian theologian but by Shirley MacLaine. It is pure New Age thinking. And it fits in not only with the New Age but with traditional atheism. There is no God out there, up there, beyond our world, to whom we can turn and from whom we can expect an answer to our prayers. The path is not up there or out there but *in there*: the trip within leads to the only divinity there is, and you find it in the recesses of your own being.

It is instructive to note the development of this essential unbelief, even though it is often clothed in religious terminology. A vague wholistic vision has taken the place of the distinction between God and people, as taught by orthodox Christianity, and between the duality of humankind and nature, as taught by the Enlightenment. Now we are encouraged to see humankind and nature as different dimensions of a single cosmic unity. But as C. S. Lewis perceived long ago, once you lose sight of a transcendent, personal, holy God, you are on a stopping train to pantheism. And that is where pluralists like John Hick, Jack Spong, Don Cupitt, Paul Knitter, and their colleagues are inescapably headed.

I do not for a moment want to deny that sort of outlook is very attractive. We have a new global consciousness these days. The confrontation of the superpowers is, hopefully, a thing of the past. The survival of the race depends on racial harmony and cooperation. But we do not need to deny our Christianity in order to engage in the pursuit of peace and cooperation among nations.

We also have a new understanding of other faiths these days. People from all over the world jostle in our streets. There are more Muslims than Baptists in Britain, for example, and many of them are very highly motivated to win recruits. But what truth is there in Islam or Hinduism or Sikhism that is worthy of universal application, but cannot be found in the life and teaching and enabling of Jesus of Nazareth?

There is a further problem. It is evident these days that the missionary movement of the last century was far from pure. It was often attached to colonialism or neocolonialism by the Western powers. It has been seen as the acceptable faith for people in developing countries who want to advance themselves. The gospel and Western culture have become dangerously intertwined. We can only repent of those things, but we have no cause to repent of fulfilling the Master's call to go and make disciples of all nations. Many of the Christians in the developing countries thank God for the missionary movement that brought the gospel to them and delivered them from bondage to animistic powers. There is an important distinction between the gospel of Christ and the cultural package in which it is received and passed on. It is not easy to disentangle the two, but every country and every generation must seek to test culture in the light of the gospel—whether that culture be national or Western. It is highly significant that the gospel is growing fastest in those parts of the world that might have justly complained about Christianity being a Western export.

These, then, are some of the reasons for the growing appeal of pluralism, matched as they are by the decline of zeal, Bible reading, and churchgoing in Western Europe, as well as the diminished influence of Christian standards on culture and legislation. A post-Christian West is in no condition to resist pluralism.

Pluralism Will Not Do

Christians ought not to fear pluralism, though unfortunately many do. We feel we dare not advance our convictions for fear of embarrassing or hurting others. So we stay silent. Or perhaps we feel that we will get shot down in flames by the adherent of some other religion of which we know little or nothing.

But such fears should not haunt us. Pluralism is very much in the air, and that gives us, along with others, every right to be heard. There is no reason why we should not humbly but confidently speak of Christ, as our forebears did, and let the truth prevail. Of course, we do so in a world where many views are being offered: there is nothing new in that. Of course, we do so in a world where many cultures coexist: there is nothing new in that, either. The Christian gospel has always been proclaimed against such a background.

What is new is the claim that all viewpoints are equally valid, so long as they are sincerely held, the claim that the real danger is the person who believes in truth. Such a person is thought to be a sort of intellectual fascist. But that does not follow in the least. We are called to bear witness to the gospel and let the truth prevail. After all, if Christianity is not true, we shall not want to have anything to do with it. If it is an illusion, we shall not want to credit it. But if it is the truth of God, we need have no embarrassment in putting it before one and all for consideration, saying, as it were, "I am interested only in the truth, as I hope you are. Try this for size."

We should not fear pluralism, then, but we should have nothing to do with it, either, for a number of reasons.

1. *Pluralism makes some very strange assumptions.* One is that affirming the truth of Christianity belittles other faiths. It seems arrogant and triumphalist to claim to have found the truth. It puts others down. Not at all! If you are truly Christian, you respect all human beings, created as they are in the image of the God who created you. You revel in all things that are true in their convictions. You listen to discern whether their insights may correct your understanding of the good news. But you do not need to abdicate your convictions to do so. Respect for others, even flat earthists, does not mean that you have to agree with them.

Another assumption is that because there are so many religious views in the world, they all ought to be regarded as equally valid. That is a deep-seated fallacy, which philosophers have noticed through the ages: the attempt to deduce what ought to be from what is. There is a diversity in religious faiths: that says nothing about whether that ought to be the basis on which we evaluate them all. And it certainly does nothing to suggest that none of them may be right.

Another assumption is that all religions lead to God. That sounds wonderfully liberal, but it is nonsense all the same. How can all religions lead to God when some of them do not believe in a personal God at all, like Buddhism, while others believe in many gods, as in animism? Still others believe in an inscrutable deity who cares nothing about the world he set in progress, while another maintains that God is personal, loving, intensely concerned with us, and has come to rescue us from our predicament of alienation from Him and from each other? The whole idea of God is different in these contrasting viewpoints. The notion that all religions lead to God is ludicrous.

That point may be granted, but your liberal pluralist may respond, "These admittedly different faiths have a common core to them. We need to restate 'God' as 'ultimate reality.' Naturally, people's perception of that reality will be determined by the country and the culture in which they were born." That sounds so reasonable until you ask whether the ultimate reality of satanism is the same as the ultimate reality of the Father of Jesus. In any case, it is an untenable view. It would make truth dependent on the country of your birth!

If I had been born in Russia and brought up as a communist, would that make communism true? If I had been born in ancient Rome, I would probably have been a polytheist. Would that make it true? Moreover, this liberal dogma makes no allowance for the remarkable phenomenon of people from all over the world coming to see that their culture pointed them to the fuller light revealed in Christ. It stumbles on the rock of conversion— and about seventy thousand of those take place every day, mostly in countries where Christianity is emphatically not the religion in which people were born and raised.

Another assumption underlying pluralism is that in the last analysis, sincerity is all you need. Believe it sincerely, and you will be fine. But this is so self-evidently crazy that nobody would attempt to apply it to any other area of life. I may sincerely believe that a bottle of whiskey a day is good for me and act on it, but that will not prevent cirrhosis of the liver. Sincerity is no guarantee of truth. We can be sincere and wrong.

These are very insecure foundations for the modern Western liberals to advance a doctrine of pluralism, and I see no good reason to follow them.

2. *Pluralism is based on an outdated liberalism.* One of the great attractions of liberalism is its rejection of dogmatism and its appeal to human experience. So it is very attractive to suppose that in our global village, all religions are basically much the same, and their adherents experience more or less the same things. But that is an entirely unjustified assumption, and it is not borne out by the religious experience to which liberals appeal.

A Muslim fundamentalist zealously killing Christians in northern Nigeria may not be having at all the same religious experience as the animist seeking to buy off the evil spirits or the Hindu guru meditating on reality. If you ask converts from other faiths, they will tell you, as they tell me, that their experience is totally different from what it was in their pre-Christian days.

I think of one Indian, nurtured in Hinduism, who is now an Anglican priest. He told me that he profoundly valued his cultural heritage, but that nowhere in Hinduism did he have any concept of God as Father, personally and intimately concerned for him. And nowhere did he hear of any way of dealing with the wickedness within him, for which he has now found a medicine in the atoning cross and risen power of Jesus. Try telling him his religious experience is just the same in Christianity as it was in Hinduism. It is profoundly unconvincing.

Indeed, this liberal view that all religions bring you into touch with the same reality and share a common core is neither convincing nor, as is claimed, objective. "Why should we accept a liberal interpretive standpoint, which owes little if anything to Christian beliefs, and is only 'objective' in the minds of those who espouse it?" asks Alister McGrath. "*All* vantage points are committed, in some way or other. There is no neutral Archimedean point."

He goes on to draw attention to an even more serious consideration. The liberal worldview is on the way out. Though so dominant in the sixties and seventies (and still among theological professors reared during that era), liberalism is as dated as the Enlightenment of which it is the offspring. A new school of interpretation is on the way up, called postliberalism. It rejects both the Enlightenment appeal to "universal reality" and the liberal assumption of a "common core of religious experience" underlying all religions. Instead, it emphasizes the importance of history in shaping the values and faith of a community.

Postliberalism will not be the last word in theology. But at least it is a move in the right direction and a warning against being taken in too much by a politically correct liberalism, which has been on the wane since the 1980s. If Christian churches attach their approach to other faiths to the dated worldview that all religions are basically the same, they will discover the truth of Dean Inge's famous dictum: "He who marries the spirit of the age today will be a widower tomorrow."

3. *Pluralism displays a disturbing arrogance.* Despite all its emphasis on openness to other viewpoints, liberalism is profoundly dogmatic and arrogant: it is right, and others are wrong. Professor John Macquarrie makes the point with characteristic clarity:

What is meant by liberal theology? If it only means that the theologian to whom the adjective is applied has an openness to other points of view, then liberal theologians are found in all schools of thought. But if "liberal" becomes itself a party label, then it usually turns out to be extremely illiberal.

It does in this instance. Pluralists tend to pour scorn and even hatred on traditional Christian beliefs. John Hick denounces "exclusive" approaches to religions as "wrong" (whereas on his presuppositions he should only declare them as having a different perspective). He calls the traditional "salvation through Christ alone" statements of the 1960 Congress on World Mission "ridiculous." Rosemary Radford Ruether thunders, "The idea that Christianity, or even the biblical faiths, have a monopoly on religious truth is an outrageous and absurd religious chauvinism."

There is a lot more intemperate language of that sort in the pluralist collection *The Myth of Christian Uniqueness.* The pluralists show themselves to be open to anything except biblical Christianity. It may sound very liberated to maintain that there is a "God behind God" to which all religions point and in which all religious experience shares. But this very soon becomes a liberal form of fundamentalism. They will join hands with all from whatever faith who hold this pluralist view but will ridicule Christians who hold to Scripture and to Christian orthodoxy.

And that seems to me to betray a double arrogance.

It seems arrogant of Christian theologians to imagine that they know better than the Jesus they profess to serve. He took His stand unwaveringly on the divine revelation of the Old Testament. How do they airily wave away the authority to which their Master held so firmly? That smacks of arrogance to me.

It seems arrogant, also, to pay no attention to what the real adherents of other faiths say. Ask a Muslim in the Persian Gulf if he thinks all religions are different roads to the same goal, and your life may be in danger. I do not exaggerate. I simply wish to point out that it is not the different religions but the Western pluralists who cling so rigidly to this dogma that all religions have a common core and are fundamentally the same. They have succumbed to the very absolutism that their theory was invented to avoid.

Lesslie Newbigin makes this point with his usual perceptiveness. He refers to the story, beloved by pluralists, of the blind men and the elephant.

> The real point of the story is constantly overlooked. The story is told from the point of view of the king and his courtiers, who are not blind, but can see that the blind men are unable to grasp the full reality of the elephant and are only able to get hold of part of it. The story is told constantly in order to neutralise the affirmations of the great religions, to suggest that they learn humility and recognize that none of them has more than one aspect of the truth. But, of course, the real point of the story is exactly the opposite. If the king were also blind, there would be no story. The story is told by the king, and it is the immensely arrogant claim of one who sees the whole full truth, which all the world's religions are only groping after. It embodies the claim to know the full reality which relativizes all the claims of the religions.

You see, only the king is able to bring together the apparently unrelated experiences of the blind men who are each feeling some bit of the elephant. And the king who sees all this turns out to be none other than the Western pluralist! A touch of arrogance perhaps? Are we not all blind beggars, pluralists included, to whom God in His kindness has made Himself known?

4. *Pluralism is morally defective.* It does not have anything to offer us in our moral dilemmas. It is both ethically irresponsible and morally impotent. Why?

The God we worship will determine, to a large degree, the way we act. Worship a cruel God or an evil God, and your lifestyle will show it. To claim that it does not much matter which religion we adhere to is in effect to say that it does not much matter what behavior we adopt. The two are integrally connected. And that is overwhelmingly evident today when decline in religion in Western countries is accompanied by massive moral collapse.

Relativism in belief and relativism in morals go together. The result is disastrous. Think of the unwanted girl children left exposed to die on the hillsides of ancient Greece. Think of the human sacrifices to the fish deity in ancient Polynesian religion. Think of the murder and gang rape carried out by practitioners of satanism. Are we to believe that these all spring from differing insights into the same ultimate reality, as the pluralists claim?

Not only is pluralism ethically irresponsible; it is also morally impotent. It gives you no ethical standard and offers you no moral power. It is implacably opposed to the life-transforming experience that Christians call conversion and the new birth. Such opposition is tragic, for the gospel of Christ makes tremendous moral transformations all over the world. Charles Darwin was so impressed by the changes brought about through the missionary work in Tierra del Fuego that he became an associate member of the South American Missionary Society!

History is studded with the lives of men and women from every religious background, and from none, who have found in Jesus Christ a moral power that brought them an undreamed of liberty. This happens to societies as well as to individuals. Think, for example, of the Sawi tribespeople in Indonesia, savage cannibals and ruthless killers, for whom treachery was the highest virtue. Through the courageous and imaginative evangelism of the Canadian missionary Don Richardson, whole villages of these people were won to Christ and their way of life utterly transformed for the better. There is no such life-changing power in the "least common denominator" approach of pluralism.

Well did C. S. Lewis observe:

The God of whom no dogmas are believed is a mere shadow. He will not produce the fear of the Lord, in which wisdom begins, and will therefore not produce the love in which it is consummated. There is in this minimal religion nothing that can convince, convert, or console. There is nothing therefore which can restore vitality to our civilisation. It is not costly enough. It can never control or even rival our natural sloth and greed.

5. *Pluralism is allergic to the question of truth.* The danger, as the pluralists see it, is not error but intolerance. Openness, tolerance, is the only virtue in fashion today. It is the great insight of our times, and as Allan Bloom has put it so sharply in *The Closing of the American Mind*,

> The true believer is the real danger. The study of history and of culture teaches that all the world was made in the past; men always thought they were right, and that led to wars, persecutions, slavery, xenophobia, racism and chauvinism. The point is not to correct the mistakes and be really right; rather it is not to think you are right at all.

It is the claim to be right that is such an affront to modern tolerance. It is the claim to be right that so distresses writers like John Hick. But is he not guilty of precisely the same intolerance? He accepts all faiths, *except* the biblical revelation, and he clearly thinks he is right in so doing.

But is he? What if there is a living God who made this world and all that is in it? What if He does love us with an everlasting love despite all the rebuffs we give Him? What if He did come to show us what He is like? What if He did stoop to burden Himself with all our moral filth? What if He does offer the power of resurrection life to all of whatever faith and none, who will accept it? There is a massive truth question here, and it will not go away.

Beneath all the talk about openness and toleration, there is a disturbing possibility: that people may base their lives on a lie, or that present patterns of oppression may continue and be justified upon the basis of false beliefs. To quote Alister McGrath again,

> Even the most tolerant pluralist has difficulties with that aspect of Hinduism which justifies the inequalities of Indian society by its insistence upon a fixed social order. Even the most tolerant of individuals finds difficulty in justifying the Hindu practice of forcibly burning alive a widow on her late husband's funeral pyre.

Were the British wrong to put an end to this practice in the nineteenth century? According to pluralist principles, they were. Can you believe *that*?

The pluralist position is so weak and unconvincing in this area of truth. In the end, the only reason for accepting the Christian gospel (or any other conviction for that matter) is not because it is culturally inherited or politically correct or socially convenient *but because it is true.*

6. *Pluralism is destructive of the Christian gospel.* This liberal pluralism, put forward with the best of motives by some well-intentioned Christian writers, ends up by destroying Christianity itself. It does so in two ways.

First, it shows itself willing to abandon all the Christian distinctives that cannot be assimilated into other worldviews. In so doing, it abandons the core of the gospel. In what other faith do you hear of the divine coming to seek you out, burdening Himself with your wickedness in order to release you from it, breaking the death barrier, and offering to come and take up residence within you? These are essential Christian distinctives. You have to abandon them all if you are going to move wholeheartedly into the pluralist camp. It is often done covertly, and with endless equivocations, but nevertheless Christianity is abandoned.

The fact is that Jesus is not in the least like any other religious leader who has ever lived. Christianity is Christ. So the pluralists have to cast doubt on the deity of Jesus, His achievement on the cross, and the fact of His resurrection if they are even to put forward their case. That does not interpret or modify Christianity. It abolishes it.

Second, pluralists destroy Christianity by substituting religious experience for biblical witness as the criterion of belief and behavior. They locate truth in altered consciousness rather than in a historical event. So we are saved not by God's grace but by knowledge. Arthur Schopenhauer said as much in the nineteenth century. So did the Gnostics in the third. So did Plato in the fourth century before Christ. The God of grace, of transcendence, of intervention, is jettisoned.

There is an evident loss of transcendence in the theological fashions of our day, process, liberationist, feminist, and neomystical. It is a dangerous tendency. They all offer us a religion where human experience and imagination replace divine revelation.

The battle is on. It lies between historic Christianity with its belief in the reality of a supernatural God and the uniqueness of His Son Jesus, and the new spirituality embodied in many of the recent theological fashions and religious movements, along with the New Age. It is the battle between monotheism and pantheism, between a catholic evangelicalism and a neo-Gnosticism. One side defends both the particularity of divine revelation and the universality of its offer and its claims. The other champions a homogenizing global religious vision. This battle is deeply rooted in all the denominations. We have to choose.

Christian Confidence in an Age of Pluralism

How can we Christians hold our heads high in a climate like this? I close this chapter with three grounds for the confidence I have in full-blooded New Testament Christianity.

The first is *historical.* So much religious talk is like soap in the bathtub. You cannot get hold of it. But with authentic Christianity you can. It is totally dependent on what happened 1,950 years ago. It is totally dependent on the person and achievement of Jesus of Nazareth. Destroy Him, and you destroy Christianity. Take Jesus away from the center of Christianity, and the whole thing collapses like a pack of cards. Many, many people have tried to do just that, and they have failed.

Jesus' bold claim to be the way to God, the truth about God, and the very life of God has not been dislodged. The evidence about Jesus on which Christian belief rests has been more carefully sifted than any other evidence in all history. Yet the person, the teaching, the claims, the death, and the resurrection of Jesus remain like a great offshore rock that all the fury of the waves down the centuries has been unable to smash. In that rock lies the nub of the whole Christian faith. It is impregnable.

My second ground for confidence is *rational.* There is a tremendous rationality about historic Christianity. It makes sense of humankind and nature, God being the author of both. It makes sense of our moral and religious instincts, anchoring them in ethical monotheism. It makes sense of reason—a God-given faculty that is nevertheless subordinate to God. It makes sense of beauty, truth, goodness, creativity, communication, activity, leisure, play, love—anchoring them all as aspects of the God and Father of Jesus Christ, who exemplified them all perfectly during His life on earth. It makes sense of our awesome dilemma: How can a holy God tolerate unholy people like us? How can He have us back without compromising His holiness? It makes more sense of sin and suffering than any other faith. It has proved the spur for exploring God's world, for concerning ourselves with ecology as stewards of God, for education, peace, justice, medicine, and care for the needy and the helpless. All these concerns spring from the very heart of the Christian God. It makes sense of the origin of the world, shrouded though that is in mystery. It makes sense of the laws of physics.

It makes sense of other faiths—not ways of salvation, but often pointers to salvation: what Karl Barth called "little lights" and "other true words." It makes sense of particularity and universality—God's grace available to all yet brought by One. It is coherent. It makes sense at a profound level, in a way that the New Age with its contradictions and pluralism with its intellectual shallowness do not. It makes sense. That is what gives me confidence.

My third ground for confidence is *empirical.* Christianity works. All over the world, in all manner of cultures, you find the transformation that Jesus brings. To be sure, it is only partial in this life, but its lineaments are always the same. The direction moves from crime to caring, from lies to truth, from drunkenness to sobriety, from materialism to generosity, from self-centeredness to service. The movement may be slow, for human nature is rugged, intractable stuff. But the direction is always the same. That gives me confidence.

When I have the joy of leading people to the feet of Jesus, I do not think or hope; I *know* that so long as they keep in touch with Christ, they will grow in His likeness—and He, remember, is the ideal for human life. They will move toward that goal. They will become more deeply and fully human, the beings they were intended to become.

Other faiths produce saints from time to time, and that is wonderful. It generally happens after profound searching and meditation and self-discipline on the part of the disciple. But the supreme glory of Jesus is that He takes all sorts, often from the very cesspools of society, and shows in them the fragrance of His new indwelling life. He, not the disciple, is the main agent at work. He gradually restores to that man or woman the divine image implanted originally by God but marred by the Fall. There will be many a failure, many a fall, but the changes become more and more evident through the years. Jesus is in the life-changing business! I know whom I have believed, and I am not ashamed of the gospel that always has been and still remains the agency of that transformation.

Chapter 7

Apologetics in the Life of the Church

Michael Green

The modern church is weak in the whole area of apologetics. In Britain this is in striking contrast to the situation a few decades ago when towering figures such as C. S. Lewis, Cecil Day Lewis, Dorothy L. Sayers, J. R. R. Tolkien, and T. S. Eliot made their presence felt within a church that realized the importance of apologetics. In the United States we have been a little better off, with men like Norman Geisler, J. P. Moreland, Josh McDowell, and Ravi Zacharias giving serious attention to a reasoned defense of the Christian faith—as did Francis Schaeffer, in a more popular mode, before them. Nevertheless, it is hard to deny that the situation is bleak in most churches, where a short sermonette is the only piece of instruction normally given, high on the "feel good" factor and low on content.

Two prevailing attitudes have developed within the church during the last twenty years, each with little time for apologetics. The liberal strand is committed to dialogue—more specifically, to a type of dialogue that explores other people's views but makes no attempt to get them to change their minds. The more conservative strand is committed to preaching and other forms of direct evangelism, and it tends to regard apologetics as a waste of time. This approach regards the human mind as fallen and fatally infected by the Fall. Preaching is the God-given way of allowing divine light to reach such people. Neither group, in consequence, has much time for apologetics. And over the course of a few decades, this creates serious problems.

It affects the pastors, who do not learn how to argue for the faith as well as proclaim it. As a result, the increasingly large secular population, who have never been reached by anything specifically Christian, see no good reason why they should change their minds about this matter. They remain unpersuaded.

It affects the laypeople in congregations, who become less and less sure of what they believe. There is a growing chasm between the worlds of faith and reason. Christian observance often applies only to Sunday mornings, and it has little effect on thinking and lifestyle for the rest of the week.

It affects the theological seminaries. There are hardly any theological colleges or seminaries in which apologetics features as a proper, well-taught subject on the program. Yet what could be more important than being able to give a good reason for our beliefs in a world that sees no a priori grounds to accept them? It is to me an astonishing mark of the backwardness of theological education that we continue as if the West were still Christian. We pay scant attention to evangelism and apologetics, two vital elements of the ever-growing missionary requirements of the church.

So how can things be changed for the better? What is the agenda for churches that want to make sure that apologetics finds its place in everyday life and witness?

Apologetics Integrated

Apologetics must be integrated into the teaching and ministry of the churches—something that the mainstream churches have generally failed to do. How can this best be done?

Here are some suggestions that could be carried out in any church. First of all, you cannot have any solid apologetics unless you have a clear starting point. That starting point is not human speculation but divine revelation. We can, by definition, know practically nothing about God unless He is pleased to disclose it to us. He has done that in the Scriptures and particularly in the person who forms their centerpiece, Jesus Christ. He is the touchstone by which Christian teaching must be measured. Therefore, it stands to reason that the stance of any church purporting to offer a credible apologetic must be unambiguously biblical. Those who teach need to do so on the ground of Scripture, properly understood against its background and its connection with other parts of the Bible. If this foundation is in place, the prerequisites for apologetics will have been laid.

Next comes the training course. Any church worth its salt needs to have a variety of courses training its members in the content of their faith. This needs to be done in as user-friendly and attractive a manner as possible. Often it is best to take some of the areas where Christian faith contradicts the culture of the day and show why Christians take the stance they do. Sometimes it could be done by taking some of the common heresies and showing good reason for rejecting them. Sometimes it could be done by taking central Christian beliefs and showing why they are important. Christian education must not stop at puberty, as so often it does in many churches. It must be intentional. It must be clear and appealing. And it must be seen to be relevant.

Reading is another way of approaching the situation. If once a year the church chose a significant book dealing with issues at

the heart of Christian faith in its interface with contemporary unbelief, it could prove a marvelous training tool. Members of the
congregation would read the book and would meet a few times
in the course of the winter to discuss a couple of chapters at a
time. This would go a long way toward building up a critical faculty within the fellowship of faith. It would also give people confidence in expressing themselves when they have made due
allowance for alternative viewpoints.

But the age of print is slowly disappearing. It is being replaced
by the visual style of communication. No doubt this will soon
give way to the information highway, but at present the TV
screen and celluloid are primary modes of communication and
church instructors neglect them at their peril. Taking a group of
people out to see a film and then discussing its basic assumptions,
their strengths and weaknesses in the light of the Christian faith,
could be an invaluable exercise. Not only would it sharpen critical faculties, but it would bring doctrine to life. Moreover, it
would make it easy for members of the congregation to discuss
their faith in the context of a well-known film or television program that is on everybody's lips.

Another way to teach apologetics is to go visiting with a
younger colleague. This would expose him or her to the common
objections to the Christian faith and excuses for keeping clear of
it, which are prevalent in our society. That, in turn, would provoke a strong motivation to discover a convincing Christian answer to these issues. It would also show the younger person how
the senior visitor operates in conversation with people from a different viewpoint.

Another way of doing it would be to hold a series of joint
meetings with Hindus, Muslims, Jewish people, and New Agers.
Christians would discover what members of other faiths actually
believe as opposed to what the textbooks say they believe. It
would show areas that are held in common and those that are
not. It would challenge Christians to give a good reason for the

hope that is within them, and to do so with courtesy and humanity. This is such an obvious thing to do, and yet when did it ever happen in your church?

For certain people, it may be right to immerse themselves in a different philosophy or religion for a while in order to understand it from the inside. Kenneth Cragg did that with Islam. Lesslie Newbigin did that with Hinduism. And recently, Dr. John Drane has done that with the New Age movement. All of them have written with a sensitivity, a profundity, and a sharpness far beyond the capability of those who have never lived within the culture they are debating.

Perhaps the most important means of training a church in apologetics is the simple but time-consuming one of mentoring. Jesus did that with His twelve disciples. First, He took them with Him wherever He went, and they watched Him operate. Then He gave them a small share in what He was doing, such as distributing food during the feeding of the five thousand. Then He gave them short, carefully regulated periods of practical mission, such as the mission of the Twelve and the mission of the Seventy. He equipped them and sent them out, and they reported back to Him. Finally, they were able to go out in lifetime mission and to train their successors. This mentoring of apprentices is the best of all methods of training. It is sad that in the modern church we have very largely abandoned it in favor of the printed page, the academic seminary, or the television screen.

The expedients I have suggested above could be carried out by almost any church, given the motivation. But I thought it would be helpful to see what some of the really fast-growing churches today are doing in this area of apologetics. I refer, of course, to the Community Churches in North America or the New Churches in Britain. How do they go about this whole area of teaching apologetics?

One major approach centers on an intensive course, of up to six weeks, usually associated with the attempt to plant a new church in the area. The first week is given to careful training in the development of one's personal walk with God, informal worship, interdependence in a small group, and mutual ministry. Problems get sorted out, and hang-ups are dealt with. There is a lot of interactive teaching on the nature of the gospel, on how to initiate a conversation in various situations and how to face the most common objections to the good news of Jesus Christ. There is some teaching in management skills, in telling one's spiritual story attractively and simply, with great stress placed on the use of nonreligious language.

People are given the opportunity to learn through role play. One method that can be effective is to carry on from this beginning with an individual: "You should be a Christian because. . . ." Another is to assume that someone comes up to you, saying something like this: "I have noticed that there is something a bit unusual about you, and it seems to be linked up with this Christianity thing. Please tell me more." You can scarcely have a clearer example than that of someone who is ready to respond to Christ!

But could you introduce such a person to the Lord? The young people involved in these intensive training courses learn to do just that—something that many people who have been faithful church attenders for many years would probably not be able to do. The secret lies in *learning through doing*—in other words, apprenticeship. That is how the great artists and craftsmen of the Middle Ages trained people. In fact, even the ministers learned their skills in this way at that time. That is how the Hebrews trained people: a rabbi would take a group around with him, talk with them, and teach them all that he knew.

But we in the modern West have opted for a more Greek model of intellectual appreciation rather than learning from discussing things with real people. As a result, we are ill at ease in an outreach situation. We have not been properly prepared for it. But these teams of young people give a few weeks of their summer to this apprenticeship in evangelism and apologetics. They live alongside their mentors in a church hall where they sleep on the floor and cook their own food. They spend a good deal of time doing open-air ministry on the streets—amusing, outraging, challenging. And that immediately gets them into a situation in which apologetics comes into play. They at once begin to put into practice what they have been learning and come back to their tutors for more at the end of the day.

Here we find the constant interchange of learning and doing, individually and collectively, accompanied by living and working closely together in pursuit of a common goal. What a marvelous way in which to learn the trade! It is something to which working people can give a week or two in the summer. Students with longer vacations can offer more. This approach certainly needs to be developed by the mainline churches.

Why? Because people see our church buildings but would no more go into them than I would go into a Masonic Hall. I would not know what to do. It is not my scene. I would feel uncomfortable. Thoughts very much like these go through the minds of nonchurchgoers when you pester them to come to church with you. They think that the church is for insiders, people who like that kind of thing. And if you are going to change their minds, they need to see Christians coming out from their ecclesiastical castles and doing their thing in the open air and where they are not six feet above contradiction.

This coming out of our building does two valuable things, even in a very short campaign. It shows people in the vicinity that Christians are alive and well—and fun! It shows that they are not afraid to stand up for Jesus Christ, and that they are keen to share what they have with all and sundry. That is quite an image breaker. And it gives a lovely taste of active ministry, deep companionship, and reasoned faith for those who share in it. Many of them want more.

And more is provided. For example, Steve Clifford, a very experienced team director, heads up TIE (Training in Evangelism) for the Pioneer group of New Churches. In addition to these short-term teams, he and his colleagues have a carefully thought-out year-long training program, mostly in apologetics and evangelism, through which they train young leaders. And I have to say that very often these young leaders are more effective after a year of such training than a lot of seminarians after three years in a college. They may not know much over such a range of subjects, but they know the heart of the matter better and how to apply it to the needy people all around them who are without God and without hope in the world.

This second approach centers on a year-long period of training, which is both intensive and varied. It concentrates on four areas in particular: (1) lectures and seminars, (2) personal study, (3) practical experience, and (4) personal development. All of these are undertaken within a fellowship of worship and ministry. Because most Christian bodies do not train their leaders in this way, it may be worth glancing a little more closely at what they offer.

Currently, they have some sixty people in training, with five full-time leaders, grouped in three regions, each of which has a regional director. They are placed in church-planting situations for the most part so that learning and doing can be readily combined, and a new church can, hopefully, emerge from their efforts. A core of experienced leaders works with them. Fifty days in the year are devoted to study; there are three residential periods and other training days, on some of which all sixty meet together.

The classroom work is divided into five main sections:

1. A foundational course in theology
2. An overview of the whole Bible, with one gospel studied in depth
3. Careful teaching on all kinds of evangelism
4. Various aspects of the Christian life, including discipleship, spiritual gifts, sex, money, time management, teamwork, and prayer

5. The world, with at least some attention to green issues, cults, matters of race, color, and gender, youth culture, missions, and church history

In addition to this classroom work, time is assigned to personal study, reading, and assessment. Each student keeps a personal journal and talks over its contents with his or her tutor from time to time.

All trainees are sent to a local church in the region, where they are exposed to a variety of work and learn as much through carefully monitored experience as through classroom work. Each is given a taste of ministry in another country and gets to experience large-scale Christian conferences and celebrations. All work for a period with ACET (AIDS Care Education and Training), one of the leading Christian ministries to AIDS victims. Finally, considerable care is taken with the personal development of students through regular meetings with their tutors, the deepening of discipleship, and the monitored acquisition of apologetic and pastoral skills.

I believe that the New Churches have much to teach the old established churches in the areas of apologetics and evangelism. The approach is integrated with life, with practical experience, and with real people (rather than stereotypes). It is both demanding and fulfilling, and it does not seem to lead to a sense of disenchantment, which is so common in most residential theological seminaries. At any rate, it is a good beginning at equipping suitable people in the churches with an all-around Christian development, which includes apologetics but does not concentrate on it at the cost of excluding worship, evangelism, fellowship, and personal holiness. The New Churches, as they are the first to admit, are far from perfect, but they have regained a principle that most churches have lost. That may be one reason for their advances not only in numbers and effectiveness but also in the quality of their Christian lives.

Apologetics and Preaching

As we have seen, apologetics is generally missing from present-day preaching. Neither liberal nor conservative preachers have much time for it. Yet apologetics is a vital tool for strengthening the Christian faith of congregations and enabling them to reach out confidently to their friends and neighbors with a gospel that can withstand the more common objections they encounter.

So why is there this weakness in contemporary preaching?

One reason, as we have seen, is the lack of conviction among pastors that this is an important area of ministry. But there are other reasons. One is the prevalence of family services and Communion services in many churches. In the case of the former, the talk is generally directed toward the young or to the parents through the young. It is therefore fairly basic in content. At Communion services, the emphasis tends to fall on devotion rather than edification. In addition, in Episcopal and Roman Catholic churches, there is often strong pressure to preach on the epistle or gospel of the day, thus making any regular teaching about the truths of the faith problematic.

Another reason is the decline of the sermon as a means of communication. Nobody listens to anyone else for fifteen undiluted minutes in any other sphere of life. As a result, people don't develop the power of concentration needed to cope with it. In addition, preaching is often not assigned a position of prominence by many ministers, who throw their energy into committees, social or pastoral work, chaplaincies, or even further degrees. Though there are some obvious exceptions to this rule, especially outside the mainline churches, the trend is undeniable. This is not an age of great preachers.

Preachers rarely seem to wrestle with great themes. If they do, they generally fail to communicate in memorable ways. I long to be like the pastor in an inner-city church who gave his working-class congregation a brilliant summary of Bishop Butler's *Analogy of Religion* in a style so simple and so memorable that none of them would be likely to forget it—without, of course, ever referring to Bishop Butler or his celebrated book! That is an art possessed to perfection by Jesus Christ, the greatest intellect this world has ever seen, who nevertheless spoke in parables, the force of which nobody could evade.

If these are some of the causes of our weakness in effective apologetic preaching, how can the situation be remedied? In a number of ways.

1. The most obvious is in the church itself. Preaching needs to have well-digested and well-argued biblical teaching at its core. We are not in business to provide placebos; we are to build strong Christians. And Scripture, thoroughly understood and attractively presented, provides nourishment for the souls of the congregation in a manner that nothing else can ever hope to match. Preachers must take pains to work hard on their sermons. They will be assiduous in visiting both inside church circles and outside them to see the concerns to which the good news needs to be related. The good preacher will be a bridge between profundity and relevance. Alas, so many abuse the pulpit that they achieve neither.

Preachers need to be familiar with the same events, books, newspapers, plays, or television programs as their congregations, and to wrestle with them as channels through which the truth of God can find its entrance into hearts and minds. There will be times when the people need to go away with a very clear understanding of how God has acted to meet us in our suffering, how He can accept us when we are so unacceptable, how we can be confident that He exists, and why we are quietly sure of the reality of life after death. These are vital things. They affect everyone.

The preacher may not have much influence outside his or her flock—but the congregation will. Every Monday sees them scattered all over the neighborhood in their places of work. How marvelous it would be if they went confident of where they stood as Christians and why. That should not be beyond the power of most preachers if they take real trouble with applying the gospel to the questions that real people really are asking. An excellent idea here is to plan courses of sermons from time to time, well advertised and custom-made to the needs of the locality. That is a great place for apologetics.

2. Another whole dimension to apologetic preaching needs to be considered. However, it would be wise to forget the word *preaching* in this context because it is a turnoff for many people. It conjures up memories of dreary addresses, formal churches, antiquated clothes, and bubble gum in the choir seats. As a result of these folk memories, preaching is, for many people, one of the most unpopular of all activities. What I have in mind is the presenting of the Christian faith in an attractive way on neutral ground. It may be a debate in a town hall or university lecture room. It may be an impromptu gathering after a funeral or in a home discussion group. It may be at an event organized by Christians who are in contact with people on the fringe. A speaker may have been invited to speak on a highly relevant aspect of the Christian faith. I recall subjects like "Choose Freedom!"; "Is Life Worth More Than the Funeral Expenses?"; "Why Bother with Jesus?"; "Can Values Stand When Faith Has Crumbled?"; all drew large crowds of interested inquirers.

A church doing that sort of outreach will not lack inquirers coming within its doors to find out more about what makes it tick. And if there are a healthy visitation program led by laypeople and a willingness to discuss the faith in coffee shops and restaurants, the news will soon get around. And increasingly, that church will develop an interested fringe of occasional visitors who can, with love, prayer, and diligence, be won into wholehearted discipleship.

3. This leads into a third area of preaching, one that has a noble history reaching back to Jesus and His apostles, but that seems to have fallen into disrepute today. I refer, of course, to

open-air preaching. You will tell me that this has had its day. But that is not the case. Perhaps the old-fashioned type of open-air meeting is a thing of the past, with dreary-looking men urging all and sundry to repent and meet their God. But that is not the only way of proclaiming the good news in the open air. It can be done by using questionnaires or by stopping and chatting to people in shopping malls. It can have a tremendous effect if a baptism or Eucharist is carried out in the open air; the opportunities for discussion afterward with interested passersby are considerable.

But the most obvious sort of open-air ministry is for a group from the church to go to a well-populated place and draw a crowd through music, drama, dance, clowning, or the like. In between the various items someone can explain, in the most down-to-earth language, the wonder of God's love and our need to make a response. If you try this, you will understand why apologetics is so important. You will be assailed from all sides with objections, ridicule, anger, and interest. You will learn the questions that are on people's hearts. You will learn to distinguish the real issues from the smoke screens. You will find the agenda for a truly relevant apologetics. And gradually, you will get better and better at dealing with the issues and have more and more impact.

Apologetics and Teaching

One of the gifts of the ascended Christ, according to Ephesians 4:11, is leadership in the church: leaders exist not to do all the work themselves but to equip fellow Christians for their own ministries. A particular function of the ordained ministry is the *role to equip*. Unfortunately, this role is all too often missing. Many Christians restrict their church activity to Sundays, apart from choir meetings on weekday evenings and perhaps a women's meeting sometime. That is to miss the tide.

I have found that committed members of congregations are eager to learn and willing to sacrifice time and effort in order to be of more use to their Lord. In a previous parish, I recall starting with a twelve-week training course for leadership in general. Thirty people were in it, a mixture of volunteers and people I had approached personally. As a result, the key people in the congregation were present. We looked at the universal imperative to be ministers of Christ, at mutual ministry in the body of Christ, at helping others to faith, and at growing in prayer and expectancy. Each evening had a time of worship led by one of the congregation, followed by supper.

The group was divided into smaller sections, each of which was allocated a group tutor. In that way, a large number of issues were tackled over the course of three months. Every group with its tutor found a weekend of outreach in which to serve in another church. This proved to be valuable basic training in leadership. On top of it, we were able to offer supplementary courses in subjects such as counseling, New Testament Greek, drama, and preaching. It had a profound effect in building up the congregation—so much so that it was adopted by the diocese.

Apologetics is a necessary part of such equipping. You could set up an eight-week course on the basic elements of the Apostles' Creed. You would look at different objections to belief in God. You could examine current attacks on Jesus Christ, especially His resurrection. You could wrestle with issues of relativism, humanism, pluralism, and many of the other current "isms" that are idolatrous seducers from the one true God. You could offer a course on the different streams that have made up the river of modern skepticism—and how to face them. You could look at eight of the most common cults that trouble the locality. You could look at a series of ethical issues or the New Age. To have, for example, three eight-week courses on topics such as those just mentioned during the year could do untold good in training the congregation.

Of course, it can be done in other ways. How about using a video? You might play the *Jesus* film. You might use the *Tom*

Landry Halftime Report, which has an enormous appeal to sportsmen and -women. You might use the David Watson video-tapes on Christian essentials, entitled *Jesus Then and Now—* older but still very useful. You might use one of the modern apologetic tapes like *If Christ Is the Answer, What Are the Questions?* (published in South Africa), *It's No Good Shouting!* (published in Britain), or *Good Question* also put out in Britain by the Evangelical Alliance and attractively presented by television personality Steve Chalke. These all raise the most central apologetic issues. It is easy to instigate a lively discussion after any of them.

How about choosing a significant book—such as Lesslie Newbigin's *Gospel in a Pluralist Society,* Allan Bloom's *Closing of the American Mind,* or Alister McGrath's *Intellectuals Don't Need God and Other Modern Myths*—and reading a chapter a week, then meeting to tease out its implications?

There are many ways of going about it, but I doubt if we shall change the face of modern Western societies until teaching is taken seriously in our churches, and people learn to be able to give a credible account of the faith within them.

Apologetics and Theological Seminaries

How do the approaches and ideas developed in this book relate to the world of theological training for ministry? I write as one who has worked in theological seminaries for much of his ministry, so I can claim to know something of their strengths and weaknesses. It is my conviction that very radical changes need to take place in the patterns of training that we have come to take for granted.

First, it would be helpful if theological seminaries stopped playing at being universities. Their teaching often takes the same form as university teaching. It is often carried out by teachers with an academic bent of mind, who would prefer to be teaching in university contexts, had they been able to find jobs there. The academic year is patterned on the university year, with long vacations. And the practical experience to which students are exposed is pathetically small.

Moreover, the standpoint from which the academic teaching is done often shares in the secular presuppositions of the university, where the biblical material is often seen as merely fallible human documents, recording human convictions about God in different ages. That is emphatically not what the teaching of the Christian community is about. The result is that students often emerge with a serious schizoid tendency in their attitude to the Bible. They know in their hearts and from their devotional lives that it is in some sense the Word of God. Yet they think that they know from their studies in the (generally skeptical) literature of the subject that it is full of errors. So what are they to teach their congregations?

There are other problems. There is little team teaching in many colleges, and as a result, students tend to be trained to keep doctrine, prayer, worship, and so on in different mental compartments. They can emerge without any integrated overview of theology, just as they emerge with little or no experience of sharing it with others. Who would train engineers, teachers, or doctors in such a manner? There is a great need for radical reform.

Second, it would be very helpful if the training lasted for eleven months of the year. We have seen in a previous part of the chapter how well the New Churches make use of the time in training their upcoming leadership and how much they can pack into a single year's preparation. Think how much we could do with two years. And think how it could relieve the funding problem, which is now threatening to bring the whole traditional seminary system to a grinding halt.

Third, it would be advantageous if much of the training were on the job rather than in the classroom, and if it took place under competent practitioners rather than under theoretical academics.

Both have their places, and both are needed if we are to prepare people properly for the increasing challenge of ministry in a largely non-Christian society.

Fourth, there needs to be a major concentration on apologetics and evangelism in the classroom. Teachers need to be recruited who are able to teach and to take students out with them and practice these two disciplines. I made it a rule for my students at Regent College, Vancouver, that nobody should graduate without engaging in practical evangelism, standing up to the objections of those who did not believe the Christian faith.

This rule immediately had three effects: (1) it raised the profile of the subject; (2) it equipped people on the job; and (3) it brought about a climate of intercessory prayer, spiritual battle, and carefully honed preparation in the college as people prepared to go out on mission. The sad thing is that few colleges today teach apologetics or evangelism, and in even fewer, instructors go out with their students into the chill winds of the agnostic world to learn by doing. When you do that, it transforms a college!

Finally, my longing would not be to see apologetics and evangelism tacked on as two further subjects at which the long-suffering college staff are urged to have a go. Anyone engaged in theological education will know of the relentless pressure to ad*ᵈ* this and that subject to an already overcrowded curriculum. My goal would be to *see all subjects taught with evangelism and apologetics in mind.* In other words, how can what is taught be made relevant to those who are outside the faith? That is the question the teachers should ask themselves in teaching their subjects.

The study of Augustine would be revolutionized if students appreciated that the barbarians are at our gates today, just as much as they were at the gates of Rome in the fifth century. His priorities for Christian ministry make sense today. The study of Gnosticism could spring to life if it were seen as a major precursor of the New Age. Arianism would mean a lot more if it were related

to the tenets of the Jehovah's Witnesses. And a doctrine like justification by grace through faith could be enormously sharpened if
it were contrasted with the legalism of so many contemporary
cults—not to mention the assumptions of many church members. The church has a right to expect this sort of training from its
theological colleges—deeply grounded in God's revelation, yet
carefully and imaginatively applied to the church and the unbe-
lieving world into which the students will go and minister.

In a word, there needs to be a radical transformation of theological formation in the seminaries. We are producing people
whose spirituality may be shallow while their knowledge of academic theology may be great. We are producing people whose passion for evangelism may be nil while their knowledge of minute
details of church history may be massive. We are producing a generation of ministers oriented toward books while they are being
called to work in a world of people, many of whom rarely read.

If we take seriously the communication of the Christian faith
in our generation, these things must change. But there will be
massive opposition from within the seminaries. Their very existence would be threatened by the radical transformation suggested in this book. It is impossible to exaggerate the importance
of equipping young men and women to be pastors, evangelists,
and teachers at the end of the twentieth century.

Apologetics Down the Street

If apologetics is to be any good, it must be earthed—that is, it
must touch ordinary unchurched people where they are. One of
the most effective ways of doing this was discovered by accident
by a pastor named Michael Wooderson. It all began with a man
at a funeral saying, "I wouldn't mind finding out more about the
Christian faith." That man was totally unchurched. He was not
into reading books. He was not into going to church, either. So
what was Michael Wooderson to do?

Michael hit on an idea, which has now become one of the most effective ways of combining apologetics and evangelism at street level in Britain. It would have a lot to offer in the United States. Michael would be the first to tell you that he was very influenced in his thinking and approach by the Jehovah's Witnesses (who were very active in his area) and by James Kennedy's *Evangelism Explosion*. Both, though coming from different assumptions, embodied three important principles. One was *systematic visiting*, aimed at uncovering interest and taking it further. A second was *setting up study groups*, preferably in the homes of interested inquirers. The third was *sending the new converts out visiting* at an early stage before they realized that churchpeople generally did not do that kind of thing.

He developed these three principles into an approach described in *The Church Down Our Street*. Michael is gifted at making personal relationships. He discovers people in his area who would like to learn a little more about the Christian faith in the course of home visiting. However, he does not go himself; he sends in a small lay team, whom he has trained for the task. The idea is to aim for six visits, if all works out well, by a team of three persons from the church. (This number is significant: it allows inexperienced people to be trained on the job and deepens fellowship within the church.) In the course of these visits, the church team gives enough information to the people in the home to allow them to make an informed decision for or against Christ.

Of course, it is not all one-way teaching. It is full of discussion. The teaching itself is basic, but the relationships are vital. Much depends on the quality of the first visit. If that goes well, those on the receiving end are generally intrigued and keen to welcome the team back the following week. They are fascinated to see laypeople like themselves feeling so enthusiastic about the gospel that they are willing and able to take the time and make the effort to share it.

This method—a combined evangelistic strategy and means of training in apologetics—is making a lot of headway in Britain, and it has considerable potential for use elsewhere. Until recently, I taught evangelism in Canada. I found that this method is well received and widely practiced among the most outward-looking Canadian congregations, and it yields a high proportion of positive responses to Christ, leading on to active incorporation into the life of the church. It would be invaluable in the United States to complement mass and lifestyle evangelism approaches.

If you stop to consider the matter, you will notice that it combines six strands, each of which has a long history of use within the church, but each of which, in isolation, has become tired and jaded—(1) visiting, (2) evangelism, (3) home groups, (4) lay training, (5) apologetics, and (6) nurture. These strands, taken together and put into a highly flexible and people-centered package become a strong rope.

Another type of outreach also combines making relationships, commending the good news, answering difficulties, and discovering spiritual realities such as Scripture, prayer, fellowship, and pastoral care. This is the Discovery Group or Nurture Group, a short course of eight or so evenings, skillfully led in a relaxed manner for those who are feeling their way toward Christ or have just become His followers. The ones in which I have been engaged for many years have been primarily directed toward those who have made some profession of faith or want to do so. Given a group of eight such people, about half of them would have taken the initial step of commitment to Christ in repentance and faith. The other half would not yet have done so.

On the first night, we all introduce ourselves and say where we are on our journey of faith or unbelief. It is fascinating to hear the variety of positions. The one thing that you can be sure about is that they will be in a different place in two months. Subjects such as Christian initiation, assurance, Bible reading, prayer, the church, the sacraments, and Christian service are dealt with, at the rate of one an evening. The group will study an appropriate passage of Scripture. There will be a short talk and wide-ranging discussion. There will be short, heartfelt prayers by the members as the evening draws to a close. There will be personal interviews at least twice during the course with one of the leaders. And suitable literature will be available, week after week.

In this caring environment of openness, clear presentation, and experience of answers to prayer, new converts grow rapidly. This growth immediately challenges those who have not yet come to faith because they can see the difference that faith makes to the others. They then need the quiet personal assistance and care of one of the leaders, who will explain that they cannot grow until they have been born, and that the new birth is God's gift to those who come to faith in Christ.

It will be clear that apologetics features prominently in this kind of evening. Those who come in from the cold, so to speak, will bring all manner of strange beliefs and preconceptions with them. The leaders will need all of their apologetic skills. But more than that, they will need pastoral skills to appreciate when they should speak and when they should allow serious misconceptions to pass by unchallenged. I try to make a distinction between misconceptions that are really troubling a person and ones that are part of his or her non-Christian baggage. The former need tackling and addressing; the latter will fade away when the person comes to faith. Yet the former need not necessarily be dealt with there and then. This could easily distract the group from its agenda. They can be discussed privately later. I also occasionally take time within the group to discuss an objection or difficulty raised by one of them if it seems to be the sort of thing that would be helpful to the group as a whole.

In these Discovery or Nurture Groups, a number of people on the edge of the faith come to join it as the group life intensifies and the weeks pass by. An excellent example of how effective these groups can be is provided by the Alpha Groups, which are

sprouting all over Britain. These originated at Holy Trinity Bromp-
ton, one of London's leading churches. They were originally designed as Nurture Groups for new Christians, with a sprinkling of
not-yet-Christians around as well. They rapidly became popular,
with attendance soaring into the hundreds. As a result, the
groups soon changed in their nature. Instead of providing nurture
for new Christians, they became transformed into the most effective apologetic and evangelistic agencies in the church. People
who had not yet come to faith were attracted in large numbers.
What was happening to their friends? Where was this new joy
coming from? How had a totally new direction and discipline entered their lives?

Those were the sorts of questions raised by Alpha Group
members among their friends and acquaintances. So by the time
one Alpha Group had ended, there was a waiting list of new people seeking access to the next one. That is how these groups
grow. And naturally, they now spend a lot of time in the first part
of the course on basic apologetics and explaining (and encouraging!) the way to faith in Christ before going on to build up the
new converts. Needless to say, Alpha Groups are catching on in
other parts of Britain. They have considerable potential for other
urban areas in the Western world.

Churches can arrange many other types of groups for agnostics. I have had the privilege of leading a good many such groups.
They are demanding and very rewarding. To offer such a group
has many advantages. It shows that you are not in the least afraid
to have your Christian faith subjected to honest inquiry and sharp
criticism. It attracts people who would not normally be seen dead
in church. It is normal for members of the group to have been
encouraged to attend by family or friends who have been praying
for them for some time. It is great to have prayer support from an
interested party in the background. Another advantage is that
when those who have opposed Christianity are converted, they
usually become courageous and articulate advocates of the faith

they once derided. So it is well worth doing! Why not call such a group Agnostics Anonymous and inject that extra nuance of challenge? My friends Roger and Mushy Simpson have been running these groups in Scotland as a regular part of their program for some years, and their church has grown enormously as a result.

These groups can be run in a number of ways. You might invite people for supper on the first evening and ask them what topics they would like to include, making sure that you have one session dealing with the resurrection of Jesus and another on the whole area of personal commitment. It is a great mistake to allow these evenings to touch the mind alone. They must also reach the will.

Another approach is to offer people a short course on basic Christian beliefs, giving reasons for your faith in God, in the divinity of Jesus Christ, and your conviction that the Spirit of God is still available to enter the lives of those who welcome Him. You will need to have sessions on suffering, other religions, and the church. You will also need to allow ample time for discussion of the subjects to be covered and all sorts of things that are likely to emerge during the course.

Another way is to use appropriate video material, such as David Watson's *Jesus Then and Now*, Francis Schaeffer's *How Should We Then Live?*, or *Gossiping the Gospel*, produced by the Uniting Church of Australia. Use the video as an introduction to the evening, and move on from there to the discussion that will inevitably arise. Some video packages provide helpful guidelines on how to respond to some of the issues that will arise, as well as indicate useful discussion starters for nervous leaders.

Yet another approach is to use inductive Bible study, such as the material developed by the Navigators in Jim Petersen's *Evangelism for Our Generation*, which has an excellent appendix giving a step-by-step investigative Bible study of John's gospel. Harold Shaw Publishers also produces extremely helpful material for inductive Bible studies, as does InterVarsity Press.

In the end, it is not critical what course you use or whether you make up your own. What *is* critical is the way in which you approach it. As stressed throughout this book, relationships are themselves effective apologetics. You need to build good, honest, and caring relationships with all the people in the group. Without them, you will get nowhere. Given them, you can probably make endless mistakes and be forgiven! I have found it important to make the aim of such a course abundantly plain. It is not yet another vague discussion about religion. Rather, it is an investigation into who Jesus is and the challenge that He offers us. This enables you to keep the discussion coming back to Jesus and the Resurrection, however wide-ranging the discussion may be.

Needless to say, the ambience of the meeting is of major importance. The atmosphere should be warm and hospitable, combining tough wrestling with truth with great consideration and love toward all the people present. Scripture has a power all of its own; those present may well be largely ignorant of it. It is very important to get people's noses into the appropriate parts of the Bible and come alongside them as a fellow seeker after truth, not as someone who professes to know it all.

Finally, all present need to be really honest in facing up to the evidence, even if it leads straight into the arms of the Jesus whom they have been so eagerly seeking to avoid. And I make it a practice to end the evening with prayer. This need not be a threat to anyone. I say, "Here is a prayer that any agnostic can pray, but it is also a prayer that could open you up to the living God if He exists: 'O God, please show Yourself to each of us in this room who does not know You, and give us the courage to entrust our lives to You.'"

I can offer three other pieces of advice. First, I need to pray and get others to pray. That is probably the most important thing of all.

Second, I need to get my "clients" to do some homework. I give them an attractively produced copy of a Gospel to read through and a book such as *You Must Be Joking* or *Who Is This Jesus?*, which I have written, or *Mere Christianity* by C. S. Lewis, or *The Case Against Christ* by John Young. That will get to them between meetings!

Third, I need to give careful thought and planning to each meeting. I leave members the maximum time to express their doubts and disbeliefs, and try to discern which ones to concentrate on and which to let fly by. And I make sure that when I do not know an answer, I admit it at once and offer to come back with some research on the subject next week.

One thing I can guarantee. If you run groups like this, your apologetics will be constantly sharpened and upgraded in the best of all training schools—that of frontline experience!

Chapter 8

Apologetics Among People Who Rarely Read

Michael Green

Culturally, we are in a remarkable situation. Despite all the educational advances in the Western world, a growing proportion of the population rarely reads. To give an example from just one Western country, statistics indicate that 9 percent of the British population are still functionally illiterate at the age of eighteen. That amounts to nearly five million people! I suspect that in the United States the proportion is considerably higher. A great many more people than that do not have any books in their possession and do not read a book from one year's end to another. Their reading is confined to work manuals, bills, cookbooks, and the tabloid press.

I have been reading the tabloid press recently, and I am profoundly impressed by the skills it displays. The size is accessible, the cost is right, the headlines are bold, and the tone is warm.

And though the stories are often scurrilous, they are almost all personal stories, keyed to the interests of the readers. (There are strong parallels with Scripture here! Perhaps as much as 70 percent of the biblical material is cast in the form of arresting and thought-provoking personal stories.) There is little abstract thought but usually a lot of sharp intelligence and frequently bold editorial comment.

People who try to reach this section of the British population with the good news have an enormous amount to learn from the tabloids. When I was principal of a British theological college, I used to get the editor of the *Mirror* (a tabloid with a circulation then exceeding six million a day) to the college every now and then to provoke the students and sharpen them up. It was always an outstanding occasion. He would then take one or two of the most promising communicators and put them alongside the *Mirror* trainees in journalism for a week or so. It was a real shock to them to see how the lead article of around 250 words went through six or eight revisions before it hit the press. If we took that amount of trouble with our preparation, we might find the problem of communication less formidable.

I am not aware that anyone has really mastered the art of effective and life-changing communication of the gospel with people who rarely read. But it is absolutely vital that we try. After all, the first Christians were for the most part illiterate. In many parts of the world today in which the gospel is spreading fast, people cannot read. Indeed, in some circles there is a deliberate rejection of the written word, on the grounds that it is a form of fascism! We ought to be able at least to examine some principles relevant to this, the biggest difficulty that confronts the progress of the gospel in the developed countries of the West.

At this point, we need to recognize some of the general differences in ways of learning between those for whom the written word is a comfortable medium and those for whom it is not.

People with developed literacy tend to think in straight lines of connected reasoning. They keep diaries and plan things in advance. They are at home with theoretical and abstract ideas. They have a planned and structured training, and they study on their own without the need for constant supervision. Their outlook and emphasis are individualistic. Their friends tend to be of similar class and occupation—often widely separated, in different parts of the country. They are men and women with degrees, career prospects, and high mobility.

In contrast, people who can read but rarely do, tend to think in a nonlinear manner, with the mind jumping from one thing to another. They are spontaneous and impulsive. They think concretely and in pictures. They learn empirically and in groups rather than by solitary study. Their emphasis is collective rather than individualistic, so as to ensure improvement in wages and conditions. Their friendships tend to be local—in the same street or club. Their skills are manual rather than academic. They often remain in more or less the same part of the country all their lives, in contrast to the much higher mobility of people with degrees.

These are some of the general differences between these two groups of people. They are radical. And so is the understanding of the gospel associated with each group. The minister—who is almost invariably a literate person—may well be concerned with doctrinal orthodoxy, church tradition, and the content of the gospel. The less literate person is much more concerned with what's in it for him and his friends. He wants to see the gospel in action, expressed in ways that connect with his experience of life. Indeed, even the implications of the gospel are seen very differently. The literate tend to express these in terms of individual conversion and individual growth in grace thereafter. Is it any wonder that those who depend on collective action and group solidarity assume that the gospel is not for them?

I have a great deal to learn in this area. In Britain, people like Eric Delve and Dan Cozens have pioneered the area of evangelism and apologetics among less literate persons. In what follows, I also owe a lot to people like John Oliver, Roy Dorey, Neville Black, Don Smith, Ray Lewis, Ian Rathbone, Chris Key, and others in the Evangelical Urban Training Project. The general principles that emerge from their experience can be summarized as follows.

Apologetics Through Relationships

People who communicate by letter and phone need to learn to communicate by being together with those whom they hope to help—and in settings where the latter feel at home and can call the shots. That is perhaps one of the greatest weaknesses of our middle-class churches. They become ghettos in which folks find their friendships and social life, and do not have to break out to those who live and think differently. Yet however different your background, you may help less literate people to come to Christ if you love them and spend time with them. That, after all, is the basic principle of the Incarnation. God loves the world so much that He did not send a telegram but sent His Son to be among us! We must make sure that we meet people where they are. They cannot know what you are really like until they meet you. And so relationship is the single most crucial principle for reaching those who rarely read. They will certainly not read our books!

Friendship is the way in. Everyone values friends. If we can both display friendship and lead on to the Friend who sticks closer than a brother, we shall cut ice. But it will take time. That is why it is so essential for those seeking to be effective in this sort of culture to stay put, get known, form relationships, and prove dependable over many years if the fruit is to come.

I have friends in Vancouver who made a particular point of spending extended time with a New Age community and offering insights from Scripture into their common discussions. This led in due course to a number of New Agers, who were genuinely seeking an authentic spirituality, entrusting their lives to Christ. Friendship was the key.

Friendship also serves two additional roles. It offers *encouragement*, especially vital in a world in which hope and joy are noticeably absent. Befriending people can open doors to the future. It can lead to their regaining confidence and self-respect. And perhaps most important of all, it models the way in which Christ befriended, accepted, and loved people who had been written off by the world. And it *offers the gospel through friendship*. For some of these people, their Christian friends will be the only way they have of gaining access to the gospel. They can't read; but they can watch and listen. Sometimes this friendship will remind them of their Christian heritage, somewhere in the distant past. It may encourage them to pick things up and start again. Or the friendship may be the first contact they have with Christianity embodied in a real life. By telling their stories, Christians can make a deep impact on this group of people. Which brings us to our next point for discussion . . .

Apologetics Through Stories

What sells local newspapers? Stories. What will you hear in any coffee shop? Stories. And what literary form is predominant in the Bible? Once again, it is the story. The Bible is by far the best and most exciting storybook in the world. It is also the most varied. And yet we so often manage to turn its pages into a quarry for doctrine. The Hebrew language, in which so much of the Bible is written, is a language of action, with lots of verbs. We have turned its contents into a language of theory, with lots of abstract nouns. We have departed from the Hebrew roots of our Christian heritage and adopted Greek approaches instead. And we need to repent of this!

We also need to become expert once again in the art of storytelling. Currently, we use the story as an illustration of some abstract or doctrinal point we are making. And then we try to apply it—and at once make the story boring and lose the attention of our audience. We need to give a much higher priority to stories as such in our communication.

Think of Dr. Paul White, a missionary in Tanzania, telling his Jungle Doctor stories to an excitedly attentive crowd in the mystery of an African night. Think of Billy Graham, on any showing the supreme Christian communicator of our day. How does he communicate so effectively? With stories. Think of Jesus Himself, the most spellbinding of all storytellers, on the hillsides and shorelines of Palestine. We need to learn from them.

Storytelling is not all speech on our part. We need to develop a genuine interest and enjoyment in listening to other people's stories. We need to help members of our churches to articulate their stories if they are to become effective agents of evangelism in our society. And we need to pay attention to the local and cultural factors that influence the lives—and stories—of ordinary people.

Above all, we need to immerse ourselves in the stories of the Bible, which are so often unknown today. For the story is so often sufficient in itself. It does not always need a postscript from us. Jesus constantly used stories in this way—*and refused to explain them!* He left people to wrestle with the enigmas they embodied, confident that this would bring them to a much better considered and wholehearted response in due course. We need to feel our way into the biblical stories, make them our own, and communicate them with verve and relevance when the moment is right. Telling our stories and telling His story are two things we can all do—if we work at it.

Apologetics Through the Visual

Even highly literate people absorb only about 20 percent of what they hear in a connected discourse. But if it is illustrated by some visual material, that proportion may well be tripled. We need to make use of the visual. This, alongside the relationship factor, may help to explain the effectiveness of Anglo-Catholic clergy in downtown London, England. People may not understand—or care much about—their theology. But their presentation of the faith is highly visual—and it communicates. We need never be afraid of the appeal of mystery in this highly pragmatic age. It is in such short supply that it often has an irresistible impact on people whose souls are made for it but are starved of it.

The greatest medium of communication today is entirely visual—television. So central has it become to the vast bulk of humanity that for many societies in the world, literacy may soon become irrelevant. You can move from a jungle culture to a television culture without ever having to learn to read. The book is not a necessity. If we want to communicate the faith to a non-book culture, we need to make effective use of television whenever we get the opportunity.

But the mass media alone will never suffice to spread the faith. Spreading the faith is incarnational; it needs a personal touch. Most of us communicate effectively to relatively few people at once. We would be wise to think how we can give a visual presentation to them—not just to children but to the adults as well. We need to investigate the whole world of comics for adults, which is a major industry in the United States and elsewhere. Think of *The Gospel According to Peanuts* by Charles Schulz and its impact if you need to be convinced of the importance of encouraging and developing top-grade graphic artists within the Christian community. We need more Delia Smiths and Galloping Gourmets with their cookbooks and blazing Christian faith. We need people to set out the Christian story diagrammatically, with short, clear script—like a maintenance manual on a car. Just think of the millions of copies that the evangelistic booklet *Journey into Life* has sold, largely because it is short, clear and, above all, *visual.* Or think of the way in which Lion Publishing has carved out an entirely new secular market with its themes and its visual impact. There is room for development in this area.

But to leave it there would be to miss some crucial aspects of the use of the visual to persuade the audience. Music is, on any showing, one of the most potent means of communication in a culture. The message we bring can be further enhanced if it is commended through music as well as words, and preferably music with a visual aspect (such as a soloist or an orchestra). A singer such as Cliff Richard, moving through his secular into his Christian repertoire, and pausing from time to time to speak of his encounter with Christ, is wonderfully persuasive.

Drama is another obvious way of making a direct point with one of those powerful three-minute sketches that were pioneered in the streets by the Riding Lights Theatre Company in the 1960s and are widely used throughout the world today. An effective approach is to weave a couple of such sketches into a speaking presentation, and increasingly, evangelists are coming to value it as a most helpful tool. But it can also serve an apologetic purpose if the sketch deals with some difficulty or tackles some problem head-on. Whether in the streets or parks, in churches or evangelistic outreach, drama is a marvelous way to complement the spoken word, and it always draws a crowd.

Another resource, the potential of which we have been slow to appreciate, is mime. It is more effective because it does not depend on words. It is therefore truly cosmopolitan and can communicate in any culture. We need to encourage such artists and work with them. If not, we shall never reach the nonliterary folk of whom there are so many in our modern Western society.

Apologetics Through Life Experience

All those working among the nonreading population agree that the best way of communicating is through life experiences. Roy

Dorey tells of some of the ways he has found helpful in this respect. He might get a group to talk about the dilemma of making choices—a universal experience. From that, it is actually not difficult to get to the Incarnation—God, too, has to make choices. You can get abstract ideas to come alive in a group of people who rarely read.

Roy is very experienced. He knows everyone has some experiences connected with death, suffering, hope, justice, love, and forgiveness. So he begins a discussion. First, he asks people what they believe about one of these issues. He follows that with a discussion about how they came to hold these beliefs. At this point, Roy shows people how Jesus and one of the stories He told relates to this issue. Finally, they go on to explore the difference it makes to the way they live.

Apologetics Through the Group

Our literate post-Enlightenment individualism is not going to get through to the collectivism of nonliterate people. Even if it were successful, it would cut them off from their friends. You need to deal with the group. To be sure, find and go for the leader—but deal with the group.

This will demand qualities that are not always found in evangelists and apologists. It will mean the readiness to affirm and tolerate diversity of opinion within the group. It will mean the readiness to affirm and encourage people so that they feel confident enough to formulate their questions and doubts about Christianity. It also means a genuine respect for them and where they are coming from. It will mean having a sense of what is going on in people and between people in a group. It will mean being able to work with a group in such a way that it comes to its own conclusions and decides on its own actions.

"Everyone," says Roy Dorey, "is a treasure chest of information and experience. Our task is to give people the keys to undo their treasures." And if the Christian worker has to change in order to reach such people, just think how much most churches are going to need to change before they can serve the local community in deprived areas, and ones in which literacy is not a highly valued skill. It is going to require a revolution. It is going to require an *incarnation!*

Apologetics Through Personal Discovery

In literate circles, we are accustomed to making decisions based on what we have read, reflected on, or been told by a reputable authority. In less literate circles, the discovery is the key—finding out by experience how a thing works. Thereafter, it is embedded in the memory, repeated in a variety of circumstances, and built into life. We want their Christian faith to be like that. It would be a lot richer than much of our experience. But we have to give them the tools to make the discovery themselves, not just as individuals, but as a group.

I wish I knew better how to bring that about. But I can think of occasions on missions when I have seen it happen. I recall one group of hooligans (all of whom had crossed swords with the police, and most of whom had spent time in jail), who came to make fun of us and rough us up as we proclaimed the gospel in the streets. They tried to destroy our visual aids and break up our meetings. We met them with firmness and love.

At the end of two weeks, we had an amazing meeting at which the leader and many of his friends entrusted their lives to Christ. The mayor of that city had also been converted. So I got him to meet them and listen to their problems, which he had legislated against but not understood. During that mission we had discovered a Christian youth worker. The sequel was the city authorities providing property in the city center for this group of youths to have a club. It was staffed by this Christian youth worker, who left his old job to join this new venture. It showed me the power of the gospel and the importance of relationships and loving persistence. But it also brought home the need for a group to cohere and to make their own discovery of Christ in their own way at their own time.

I am still a learner in this matter of trying to communicate the gospel effectively and argue its truth with those who do not use the medium with which I am most at home—the written word. I have a long way to go. But I know that it is one of the most important challenges facing apologetics and evangelism in our generation. I am determined to pursue it.

Chapter 9

Moving On

Alister McGrath

As the second millennium of Christian existence comes to a close, our eyes turn toward the next thousand years of history. What lies ahead? Whatever the answer may be, apologetics is going to be of vital importance in the next ten or so years—a period that many churches worldwide have designated "a Decade of Evangelism." Here is a vision to inspire and challenge us.

Apologetics serves two purposes, as we have seen.

First, it allows people to recognize and appreciate the attractiveness of the Christian faith. For some, it is like blowing the dust away from an ancient mosaic so that its beauty and glory can be seen. For others, it is like being given a pair of spectacles, which suddenly bring sharply into focus things that had been blurred and unclear. We have seen how care and consideration need to be given to individuals so that the full wonder of the Christian faith may be focused on special needs and hopes.

Second, it helps to remove barriers to faith. All kinds of obstacles come between people and faith—reasons of the heart, of the mind, and of culture. We can be far more effective in our witness to Christ in the world at large if we take time to understand these general factors. However, we can be even more effective in our witness to our friends and loved ones if we take the trouble to work out how these general principles relate to them as individuals. Everyone is different.

Earlier, we used the image of a road to faith. That road is littered with different obstacles for different people; we need to be sensitive to where people are. This book will help you identify some likely problem areas. It will allow you to work out how to respond to them. But the rest is up to *you*. You know your friends. How can you help them?

If you are able to help your friends and colleagues realize that Christianity is a profoundly attractive and viable option in the modern world, you will have achieved an enormous amount. And yet, something is missing. Agreement needs to lead on to personal commitment. How?

The Leap of Faith: From Agreement to Personal Commitment

Apologetics assures the world (and *reassures* Christians!) that Christianity is deeply attractive, and that it possesses coherence and credibility. Having done that, it can do no more. Yet more needs to be done. To appreciate this point, let us look at the example of one person who faced this point and wrote of his experiences with special clarity. In the end, a step of faith has to be made. But why? And how?

Sheldon Vanauken is an American writer, who studied English literature at Yale and Oxford universities. Vanauken came to faith at Oxford in the spring of 1951, with some friendly guidance from C. S. Lewis. Yet coming to faith was a difficult decision. Vanauken's dilemma was this: Christianity made a lot of sense. But how was he to enter into it? How could he move from knowing that Christianity was right to being a Christian? As the Danish philosopher Søren Kierkegaard had pointed out, it was perfectly possible to know what Christianity was all about without actually being a Christian. So how could this gap be bridged? How could someone move on from *knowing about Christianity* to *becoming a Christian*?

In his autobiography *A Severe Mercy*, Vanauken describes with stunning clarity the thoughts that go through many people's minds about the "leap of faith":

> How was I to cross it? If I were to stake my whole life on the risen Christ, I wanted proof. I wanted certainty. I wanted to see him eat a bit of fish. I wanted letters of fire across the sky. I got none of these. And I continued to hang about on the edge of the gap. . . . It was a question of whether I was to accept him—*or reject.* My God! There was a gap *behind* me as well! Perhaps the leap to acceptance was a horrifying gamble —but what of the leap to rejection? There might be no certainty that Christ was God—but, by God, there was no certainty that he was not. This was not to be borne. I could not reject Jesus. There was only one thing to do once I had seen the gap behind me. I turned away from it, and flung myself over the gap towards Jesus.

Vanauken here provides a brilliant statement of the dilemma confronting Christian apologetics while at the same time solving it in a highly personal and memorable manner.

Note the decision to believe. There is no contradiction. Faith is a *decision* to believe in God, trusting that the gospel promises are for real, and that one day they will be *seen* to be for real. The decision to believe breaks the paralysis of indecision that otherwise hovers around the gap of faith. Vanauken puts it like this:

> I *choose* to believe in the Father, Son and Holy Ghost—in Christ, my Lord and my God. Christianity has the ring, the *feel*, of unique truth. Of *essential* truth. . . . [But] a choice was necessary; and there is no certainty. One can only choose

a side. So I—I now choose my side: I choose beauty; I choose what I love. But choosing to believe *is* believing. It's all I can do: choose. I confess my doubts and ask my Lord Christ to enter my life. I do not *know* God is, I do but say: Be it unto me according to Thy will. I do not affirm that I am without doubt. I do but ask for help, having chosen, to overcome it. I do but say: Lord, I believe—help Thou my unbelief.

Vanauken here appears to have stumbled on one of the most powerful insights of the Christian faith. Coming to faith is about our decision to believe—at least, what seems to us, from our human standpoint, to be our decision.

So we can say to our friends: Choose to believe! Make that choice! Decide for Christ! And with that decision, the gap of faith is bridged. It is like someone reaching out and taking the bread that he knows is there. Or like Moses crossing the Jordan and finally entering into that long-promised and long-hoped-for land. Apologetics makes the case for faith; evangelism makes the decision for faith.

From Apologetics to Evangelism

In the end, apologetics feeds into evangelism. It provides a basis on which evangelism can build. Apologetics makes people receptive to faith; evangelism invites them to take that step of faith, noted above. Evangelism allows the consummation of all that apologetics promises.

This analysis allows us to understand some important points. First, the apologist need not be an evangelist. As we have said, there is a natural connection between them. However, the ordinary Christian believer may feel slightly apprehensive about putting his or her friends in a difficult position by asking them if they would like to become Christians. Yet those same ordinary Christians are doing a vital job—allowing those same people to see the Christian faith in a new light. One day, they may well decide to take that step of faith. It may well be that someone else will help them take that step of faith. One sows; another reaps. But that does not matter. What does matter is that sowing and reaping go on!

Second, it shows how important apologetics is in the ordinary life of the church. It enables people outside the churches to view Christianity more positively; it also creates a climate of confidence within the church by reassuring believers of the coherence, credibility, and relevance of their faith. And that needs to be done. A lot of Christians are hesitant about their faith, precisely because they lack confidence in it. Confidence and complacency are not to be confused. To have confidence in the gospel is to have confidence in God, not confidence in ourselves. One of the great insights of the gospel is that God is able to take ordinary people and do the most extraordinary things through them—if they will let Him.

Third, it allows us to see the importance of a regular evangelistic ministry in the local church. Many people still think of evangelism as something that happens at great rallies, organized by huge committees, and makes use of the talent of superstar performers. But evangelism is something that can and ought to go on in every small town Christian fellowship. Many Christians are apprehensive about this, feeling uncertain about how their friends would respond to an evangelistic sermon or talk. But one of the reasons why people feel apprehensive is that, at the moment, this is something unusual. Apprehension here reflects the simple fact that evangelism has yet to find its way into the normal pastoral life and preaching of the local church.

Churches will start to grow when people feel confident enough to talk to their friends about their faith, to bring them to church to hear regular competent presentations of the Christian gospel, and to respond to a sensitive and caring call for a personal decision to faith. Once this pattern becomes established in the life of a church, the potential for growth is enormous. It has yet to happen; but given time and commitment, it will happen.

From Evangelism to Spirituality

Apologetics creates a favorable climate for faith. Evangelism brings people to faith. And finally, spirituality keeps people in faith. One of the most important developments in the life of the church in the last twenty years has been the blossoming of interest in spirituality—that is, in ways of deepening one's faith through reading Scripture, praying, meditating, and all other proper means for Christians. In the past, the churches in the West tended to assume that the vast bulk of people were Christians. They didn't need to be evangelized; after all, they were all Christians anyway, weren't they? And they didn't need anyone to help them keep going in that faith, let alone to grow in faith. After all, whoever heard of someone stopping being a Christian? Complacency set in.

But not anymore. The modern churches have finally realized that they need to identify and deploy every resource at their disposal if they are to keep going and keep growing in the harsh godless world of today. Apologetics, evangelism, and spirituality are like the three legs of a stool, which bring stability to the life of the churches. Christian Nurture Groups have sprung up with the object of giving young Christians all the assistance and support they need. A new emphasis has been placed on discipling—the process by which converts become disciples. As the parables of Christ remind us, faith is like a plant—a plant that needs tending in its early stages if it is to grow. Yet grow it will, leading to a new generation of mature Christians, who will be the future treasure and hope of the Christian church.

For this reason, the local churches must give care and consideration to ways of deepening the faith of young Christians. And experience suggests that it is not simply people young in the faith who need help! Very often, older Christians find new depth coming to their Christian lives as a result of attending courses intended for those who have recently come to faith. "We never had these in our day," one woman said appreciatively to me as she reveled in discovering aspects of the Christian faith that were new to her. She was making up for lost time.

But our main concern must be people who come to faith for the first time. The powerful thrust of the Decade of Evangelism throughout the world runs the risk of being dissipated unless those who come to faith are kept in faith by every proper means of spiritual nourishment, encouragement, and guidance. Some come to faith because of the power of an evangelistic sermon, delivered by a preacher skilled in the art of delivery and a master of the oratorical arts. Yet the content of that sermon may live on only in the presence and personality of the preacher. The sense of immediacy, of personal dynamism and excitement, is lost once the preacher moves on. A new believer is left behind to discover the full implications of that important decision to begin the Christian life and adjust accordingly. Here, Christian spirituality has a vital role to play.

One of the most remarkable periods of renewal in the American church took place in eighteenth-century Massachusetts. It initially centered on Jonathan Edwards, whose preaching was instrumental to the revival. At the height of the Great Awakening, a young woman convert wrote a letter to Edwards. She had come to faith; she needed guidance, as she put it, as to "the best manner of *maintaining* a religious life." In that letter may be seen an anticipation of the modern realization of the need for sustained follow-up in relation to evangelism.

One of the most significant aspects of the Springboard initiative within the Church of England, headed up by Michael Green and Michael Marshall, has been the realization of the vital role of spirituality in a considered and realistic approach to evangelism. Spirituality is a means of keeping converts and enabling them to grow in faith. The emphasis on evangelistic techniques typical of the early 1980s is now being supplemented with a recognition of the need for the long-term spiritual care of those who come to faith. Evangelism makes Christians; spirituality keeps them.

At the practical level, this has many implications. It means stimulating others to *read the Bible*—and making sure we read it, too. One of the most helpful ways of doing this for new believers is for an older Christian to spend time with them and talk about the passage chosen for study. Bible studies can be ideal places to help young Christians develop the habit of reading the Bible and being nourished by what they find. All kinds of aids— for example, commentaries and study notes—may be of use in this respect.

It means encouraging new believers to *go to church*. The Christian life is not meant to be lived in splendid isolation. The church is a body, whose members are there to encourage one another and to build one another up. The sermon provides a potentially vital resource for spiritual growth for new believers. The sacrament of baptism can be a powerful public declaration of one's newfound faith to friends and neighbors as well as an encouragement to other church members. The sacrament of holy Communion can be a deeply moving reminder of the love of Christ for sinners and an affirmation of His continuing presence in the church. The fellowship of small groups within the church can provide a close and caring environment in which new believers can grow. Often churches arrange groups, such as Alpha Groups, with the needs of these people in mind.

Finally, we need to *mentor new believers*—set an example to them. Today's new believers are tomorrow's evangelists and church leaders. People learn by doing. Rembrandt and other great painters taught by personal example, allowing their apprentices to paint in areas needing large blocks of color. The Gospels show Jesus Himself encouraging His disciples to learn by doing.

The sequence of events in Luke 8—10 is especially interesting. In Luke 8, the disciples learn by watching Jesus preach, teach, and heal. In Luke 9, He sends twelve of them out to begin to share in His ministry. They are given some personal responsibility. And in Luke 10, Jesus sends out seventy-two such disciples! That same pattern can be repeated today as we try to encourage and teach by example. There is a vital role for both old and new believers in this task of looking ahead to the future.

And in the Long Term . . .

This book has tried to set out a vision of the importance of apologetics for ordinary Christians and ordinary local Christian churches. As we have emphasized, an enormous amount can be done. The future well-being of the Christian churches depends on Christians realizing that they can do far more than they realize, without risking losing vital friendships or relationships. A recent English survey examined the way in which men came to faith. One of the most important routes was the personal witness of the women they loved. Sharing their faith was, for them, an act of love—and as the results show, in many cases the act of sharing was deeply appreciated.

So we stand poised on the brink of the third millennium of Christian faith. The future lies unknown. However, we do know that the same God who called His church into being will remain with us as we seek to serve Him in the next millennium. We also know that the Christian future depends on our willingness to tell others about the attraction and power of the gospel. We owe it to our future to begin this in earnest right now!

Notes

Chapter 3

1. Kenneth S. Kantzer, "Afterword," in *Evangelical Affirmations*, by K. S. Kantzer and C. F. H. Henry (Grand Rapids: Zondervan, 1990), pp. 513–23; quote at p. 522.

2. David F. Wells, "The Nature and Function of Theology," in *The Use of the Bible in Theology: Evangelical Options*, ed. R. K. Johnston (Atlanta: John Knox Press, 1985), p. 177.

Chapter 5
The New Age Movement

1. However, more specific visions do arise revolving around the revelations of some charismatic New Age leaders, but such are held within certain sectors of the movement and are not universally held by the whole movement.

2. I conducted field research on this movement in the Vancouver area, Canada's "California" on the West Coast, which involved attending various New Age events/gatherings and interviewing people. To the question of what the New Age is about, most responses suggested a rather strong disillusionment with the conventional way of life, seen as meaningless and dehumanizing, and with the secular worldview as represented by modernism. However, in their recognizing that there has to be a spiritual dimension to life, these people are not looking to the church for direction. Most respondents' reply to the question of what they see as lacking in Christianity is that it is too rigid, dogmatic, and intolerant, and it fails to teach and practice unconditional love.

3. Charles Y. Glock, "Consciousness Among Contemporary Youth: An Interpretation," in *The New Religious Consciousness*, ed. Charles Y. Glock and Robert N. Bellah (Berkeley: University of California Press, 1976), p. 355.

4. See Robert S. Ellwood, *Religious and Spiritual Groups in Modern America* (Englewood Cliffs, N.J.: Prentice-Hall, 1973), chapter 2.

5. Two New Thought groups that have profited from the burgeoning NAM are Charles and Myrtle Filmore's Unity School of Christianity, established 1914, and Ernest S. Holmes's Church of Religious Science, established 1927, often referred to as the "Science of Mind," along with some Spiritualist churches, and numerous groups that are offshoots of such esotericism. If local leaders of these groups attempt to capitalize on the current spiritual quest, they tend to tap into the New Age market by offering New Age–related workshops, therapies, and teachings, making themselves a part of the New Age network.

6. Davis wrote thirty volumes from 1847 to 1885 where he outlines his visions of the afterlife, the various spirit worlds and planes of existence, and the progression of the soul toward God. Being one of the first channelers in America, he developed such "skills" through his involvement in mesmerism.

7. J. Gordon Melton, "The New Age Movement," in *The Encyclopedic Handbook of Cults in America* (New York: Garland Pub., 1986), p. 110.

8. In *Turning East: Why Americans Look to the Orient for Spirituality—and What That Search Can Mean for the West* (New York: Simon and Schuster, 1977), p. 32.

9. In *Getting Saved from the Sixties: Moral Meaning in Conversion and Cultural Change* (Berkeley: University of California Press, 1982), p. 312; also see chapter 1 for a good discussion of the counterculture.

10. Glock, "Consciousness Among Contemporary Youth," p. 354.

11. Ibid.

12. I do need to note that these areas of research/theories are not new in terms of originating in the 1960s. Rather, what began happening in a significant way was the coherent attempt by many to integrate and validate these various fringe or frontier areas of research and novel theories to articulate a new paradigm or model of reality and of human nature.

13. An important book that preceded hers in outlining aspects of the New Age is Mark Satin's *New Age Politics, Healing Self and Society: The Emerging New Alternative to Marxism and Liberalism* (Vancouver, Canada: Whitecap Books, 1978). However, it did not attain the popular appeal that Ferguson's work did.

14. Russell Chandler, *Understanding the New Age* (Dallas: Word, 1988), p. 56.

15. As quoted by Chandler, ibid.
16. (New York: Bantam, 1982), pp. 15–16.
17. Ibid., p. 16.
18. Ibid.
19. Ibid.
20. Melton, "The New Age Movement," p. 111.
21. I initially began my field research of the NAM with the assumption that it would be characterized by a universal belief in a new age dawning for humanity, marking an evolutionary leap for the human race and the birthing of a new utopian world of global peace and harmony. I have found this not to be the case. The idea of a new age dawning is rarely discussed and not universally believed in. Rather, the focus in New Age circles is on discovering oneself as a body-mind-spirit unity and experiencing and living out of a connection with the sacred seen to be present not just in oneself but in others, nature, and life at large.
22. This is why I find most Christian critiques of the New Age to be somewhat fallacious. The New Age view of "God" is quite fluid, diverse, eclectic, and ambiguous. Although there is much worthwhile discussion in *Apologetics in the New Age: A Christian Critique of Pantheism* by David K. Clark and Norman L. Geisler (Grand Rapids: Baker, 1990), the New Age's view of divinity and the cosmos is not really understood or addressed.
23. In *The Perennial Philosophy* (London: Harper & Row, 1944).
24. Ronald S. Miller and the editors of *New Age Journal, As Above, So Below: Paths to Spiritual Renewal in Daily Life* (Los Angeles: J. P. Tarcher, 1992), p. 3.
25. Leading New Age spokesperson David Spangler identifies four levels in the movement, although he uses different terminology and his fourth level is rather vague. See chapter 9 of his *Emergence: The Rebirth of the Sacred* (New York: Dell, 1984). Douglas Groothius has distinguished between mainstream New Age and New Age occultism in chapter 8 of his *Unmasking the New Age* (Downers Grove, Ill.: IVP, 1986). Thomas A. Haig in his master's thesis, "Meta-Modern Culture: The New Age and the Critique of Modernity" (Concordia University, Aug. 1991), discusses the differences and relationship between New Age consumerism and the New Age movement. Based on

such discussions and my research, the distinctions that I outline here seem to be helpful.

26. I should note that the New Age received a lot of press coverage in 1987, which in turn greatly increased the public's awareness of it. That largely resulted from two key events that captured the public's attention—Shirley MacLaine's television series based on her book *Out on a Limb*, and the Harmonic Convergence gatherings initiated by Dr. Jose Arguelles.

27. Some interpret this shift as constituting a quantum leap in human evolution where humanity will become a new species, more "godlike" in nature.

28. Do not conclude from this that most New Agers adhere to such teachings as some Christian authors have. This view reflects the thought within one faction in the movement and is mostly associated with channeling.

29. In the nineties, the trend is to move away from the New Age label and become more acceptable to mainstream society. Mainstream New Agers are fed up with being associated with the popular conception that the NAM is essentially about channeling, crystals, and UFO abductions. An example of this is in the March/April 1991 edition of the *Body Mind Spirit* journal where the editor discusses the question, "Is 'New Age' dead?" He says it is time to drop the label due to the negative connotations it has acquired, recognizing that the movement will continue despite a label. Therefore, the journal replaced its subtitle of "Your New Age Information Resource" with "Tools for Creating a Richer, More Fulfilling Life."

30. Ronald S. Miller et al., *As Above, So Below*, p. xii.

31. Ibid. This view of nature as sacred leads to a related tenet that is quite prevalent in New Age occultism as well and is akin to animism. It is held that consciousness is not confined to what we would commonly regard as sentient beings but is present in all things and is a part of the fabric of the universe. Hence, the planet has a consciousness of her own, commonly referred to as Gaia. Plants can exhibit a consciousness known as devas, and collectivities can as well, so that one can address the consciousness/deva of one's garden to see if it needs watering. One's own consciousness is linked with others enabling psychic communication, for everything is interrelated.

240 Notes

32. This role of experience in the movement is important to appreciate. As someone who has traveled through the NAM, Ted Schultz notes the importance and centrality of experience over belief. He makes the following insightful observation:

> Most adherents are attracted to the New Age belief systems less for the vague philosophies than for the tangible effects on their lives generated by practices like trance induction, meditation, physical therapies (like yoga and massage), psychologized counseling within frameworks like astrology and psychic reading, and the pleasure of love and friendship within a shared social context. For most New Age adherents, it seems a small step from experiencing the noticeable psychological and physical benefits of a prescribed practice to accepting wholesale the accompanying philosophy and cosmology.

In "A Personal Odyssey Through the New Age," in *Not Necessarily the New Age: Critical Essays*, ed. Robert Basil (Buffalo: Prometheus, 1988), p. 339.

33. I would exercise caution in too hastily concluding that all such energy work in terms of healing is a result of spiritistic/demonic influence or empowerment. (Although there is much worthwhile material in *New Age Medicine: A Christian Perspective on Holistic Health* [Downers Grove, Ill.: IVP, 1987] by Paul C. and Teri K. Reisser and John Weldon, I would like to add that much needs more understanding and research before some of their conclusions are to be drawn.) Without wanting to downplay the reality of demonic influences, there does seem to be rather convincing scientific evidence supporting the idea of conduits of energy running through and around the body, which can be manipulated by consciousness. See, for example, the compilation of such research along with New Age theorizing of such phenomena in Dr. Richard Gerber's *Vibrational Medicine: New Choices for Healing Ourselves* (Santa Fe, N.M.: Bear & Co., 1988).

34. See, for example, Mark Satin's *New Age Politics*, especially pp. 126ff.

Judaism

1. In Christian-Jewish dialogue situations B.C.E and C.E. (before the common era and common era) are used instead of B.C. and A.D.

2. Louis H. Feldman, *Christianity and Rabbinic Judaism*, ed. Hershel Shanks (London: SPCK, 1993), p. 1.

3. G. Vermes, introduction, ibid., p. xxii.

4. Abraham Heschel, quoted by Yechiel Eckstein, in *What Christians Should Know About Jews and Judaism* (Waco, Tex.: Word, 1984), p. 66.

5. *The Siddur* (The [Jewish] Authorized Daily Prayer Book), trans. S. Singer (London: Eyre and Spottiswood, 1962), p. 56.

6. Dan Cohn-Sherbok, "Why Today's Society Needs to Reconsider the Forgotten Doctrine of Original Sin," *Church of England Newspaper*, March 26, 1993.

7. S. R. Driver and A. Neubauer, *The Suffering Servant of Isaiah According to Jewish Interpreters*, vol. 2 (1877; reprint, New York: Hermon Press, 1969), pp. 99–100.

8. Targum Jonathan on Micah 5:2, Jerusalem (Hebrew) ed. (London: Deyfus, 1961), p. 195.

9. *The Commentary of Ibn Ezra on Isaiah 9:6*, trans. M. Friedlander (New York: Philipp Feldheim, 1873), pp. 51–52.

10. Midrash on Jeremiah 23:6, *Midrash Rabbah*, trans. H. Freudman (London: Soncino Press, 1977), 4:134.

11. 4 Ezra 7:27–30, *The Old Testament Pseudepigrapha*, ed. J. H. Charlesworth (London: Darton, Longman, and Todd, 1983), 1:537.

12. D. H. Stern, *Restoring the Jewishness of the Gospel* (Jerusalem: Jewish New Testament Publications, 1988), pp. 12ff.

Bibliography

Basic works by the authors of this volume:

Green, Michael. *Evangelism Through the Local Church.* Nashville: Nelson, 1990.

McGrath, Alister. *Intellectuals Don't Need God and Other Modern Myths: Building Bridges to Faith Through Apologetics.* Grand Rapids: Zondervan, 1993.

More technical works on apologetics include the following:

Allison, Brian. *Analytical Studies in Apologetics.* Unionville, Ontario: Brice & Bensa, 1990.

Blamires, Harry. *A Defence of Dogmatism.* London: SPCK, 1965.

Brown, Colin. *Philosophy and the Christian Faith.* Leicester: InterVarsity Press, 1969.

Bruce, F. F. *The Apologetic Defense of the Gospel.* Wheaton, Ill.: InterVarsity Press, 1959.

Casserley, J. V. L. *Apologetics and Evangelism.* Philadelphia: Westminster, 1962.

Christiani, Leon. *Why We Believe.* New York: Hawthorne, 1959.

Clark, David K., and Norman L. Geisler. *Apologetics in the New Age: A Christian Critique of Pantheism.* Grand Rapids: Baker, 1990.

Clark, Gordon H. "Apologetics." In *Contemporary Evangelical Thought,* edited by C. F. H. Henry. Great Neck, N.Y.: Channel, 1957.

Clark, Kelley James. *Return to Reason.* Grand Rapids: Eerdmans, 1990.

Corduan, Winfried. *Reasonable Faith: Basic Christian Apologetics.* Nashville: Broadman and Holman, 1994.

DeWolf, L. Harold. *The Religious Revolt Against Reason.* New York: Harper & Row, 1949.

Dyrness, William. *Christian Apologetics in a World Community.* Wheaton, Ill.: InterVarsity Press, 1983.

Evans, C. Stephen. *The Quest for Faith.* Wheaton, Ill.: InterVarsity Press, 1986.

Lewis, Gordon R. *Testing Christianity's Truth Claims: Approaches to Christian Apologetics.* Chicago: Moody Press, 1976.

Mitchell, Basil. *The Justification of Religious Belief.* Oxford: Oxford University Press, 1981.

Morey, Robert A. *A Christian Handbook for Defending the Faith.* Nutley, N.J.: Presbyterian and Reformed, 1979.

Morrison, Frank. *Who Moved the Stone?* London: Faber & Faber, 1930.

Mouw, Richard. *Distorted Truth: What Every Christian Needs to Know About the Battle for the Mind.* San Francisco: Harper & Row, 1989.

Neil, Stephen C. *Christian Faith and Other Faiths.* Oxford: Oxford University Press, 1970.

Newport, John. *Life's Ultimate Questions.* Waco, Tex.: Word, 1989.

Oden, Thomas C. *After Modernity . . . What? Agenda for Theology.* Grand Rapids: Zondervan, 1990.

Pinnock, Clark. *Reason Enough.* Wheaton, Ill.: InterVarsity Press, 1980.

Purtill, Richard L. *Reason to Believe.* Grand Rapids: Eerdmans, 1974.

Ramm, Bernard. *Varieties of Christian Apologetics.* Grand Rapids: Baker, 1965.

Trueblood, David Elton. *Philosophy of Religion.* New York: Harper & Row, 1957.

Warfield, Benjamin B. "Apologetics." In *Studies in Theology.* New York: Oxford University Press, 1932.

Wolterstorff, Nicholas. *Reason Within the Bounds of Religion.* Grand Rapids: Eerdmans, 1976.

ABOUT THE AUTHORS

Michael Green, formerly professor of evangelism at Regent College, Vancouver, is advisor in evangelism to the archbishops of Canterbury and York and joint coordinator of the Springboard Initiative for the Decade of Evangelism. He is a popular author, with many well-known books to his credit.

Alister McGrath is research lecturer in theology at Oxford University and research professor of theology at Regent College, Vancouver. He has published extensively on the theme of apologetics.

ABOUT THE CONTRIBUTORS

Linda Christensen is a researcher at the University of British Columbia, with a special interest in the New Age movement.

John Fieldsend, a worker for many years with the Churches' Ministry among the Jews, is the leader of a Messianic congregation in England.

Michael Griffiths, formerly principal of London Bible College, and professor of mission at Regent College, Vancouver, until his recent retirement, is a missionary with extensive experience in Eastern religions.

Patrick Sookdheo is director of the International Institute for the Study of Islam, London.